Geography and Education

THE LONDON EDUCATION STUDIES

A series published by Kogan Page in association with the Institute of Education, University of London.

Titles so far published:

Initial Teacher Education: policies and progress

edited by Norman Graves

Education and the Good Life: beyond the National Curriculum

John White

Post-Sixteen Education: studies in access and achievement

edited by Clyde Chitty

Geography and Education

National and International Perspectives

Edited by Michael Naish

Contributors:

D.S. Biddle
E.H. Brown
Simon Catling
John Fien
Rod Gerber
Hartwig Haubrich
Keith Hilton
Gerry Hones
Ashley Kent
David Lambert
John Lidstone
Lucile Marbeau
W.M. Marsden
W.R. Mead
Michael Naish
Julie Okpala
Frances Slater
Joseph Stoltman
Henriëtte Verduin-Muller
M.J. Wise

INSTITUTE OF EDUCATION
University of London

First published in 1992 by the Institute of Education, University of London, 20 Bedford Way, London WC1H 0AL.

Typeset by Direct Printers (Bournemouth) Ltd.
Printed and bound in Great Britain by Billing & Sons Ltd, Worcester and London.

British Library Cataloguing in Publication Data
Geography and education: national and international
perspectives.
1. Schools, Curriculum subjects: Geography
I. Naish, Michael *1937-* II. University of London;
Institute of Education
910.71

ISBN 0-85473-329-9

for Norman Graves, in recognition of his outstanding contribution to the development of geography and education both within the United Kingdom and across the world

Contents

Part 5 CONCLUSION

List of Figures

Notes on Contributors

Don Biddle is retired Principal of the Sydney Teachers' College, Sydney, New South Wales, Australia.

E.H. Brown is Professor Emeritus of Geography, University College London.

Simon Catling is Senior Lecturer in Primary Education, School of Education, Oxford Polytechnic.

John Fien is Senior Lecturer in the Division of Australian Environmental Studies, Griffith University, Brisbane, Australia.

Rod Gerber is Associate Professor and Head of the School of Social, Business and Environmental Education, Queensland University of Technology, Brisbane, Australia.

Hartwig Haubrich is Professor of Geography and its Didactics and Head of the Research Department at the *Pädagogische Hochschule*, Freiburg, Germany.

Keith Hilton is Head of the Department of Geography at the Chester College of Higher Education.

G.H. Hones is National Co-ordinator, Geography 16-19 and formerly Senior Lecturer, School of Education, University of Bath.

Ashley Kent is Senior Lecturer in Geography Education at the Institute of Education, University of London.

David Lambert is Lecturer in Geography Education at the Institute of Education, University of London.

John Lidstone is Senior Lecturer in the School of Social, Business and Environmental Education, Queensland University of Technology, Brisbane, Australia.

Lucile Marbeau is Senior Researcher and Programme Director for Research on Initial and In-Service Training of Teachers in Didactics Through Research at the *Institut National de Recherche Pédagogique*, Paris.

W.E. Marsden is Reader in Education and Dean of the Faculty of Education and Extension Studies at the University of Liverpool.

W.R. Mead is Professor Emeritus of Geography at University College London.

Michael Naish is Senior Lecturer in Geography Education and Senior Tutor for Initial Courses, Institute of Education, University of London.

Julie Okpala is Lecturer in Geography Education and Measurement and Evaluation, at the Department of Education, University of Nigeria, Nsukka, Nigeria.

Frances Slater is Senior Lecturer in Geography Education, and Chairperson of the Department of Economics, Geography and Business Education, Institute of Education, University of London.

Joseph P. Stoltman is Distinguished University Faculty Scholar and Professor of Geography at Western Michigan University, Kalamazoo, Michigan, USA.

Henriëtte S. Verduin-Muller is Professor Emeritus and retired Head of the Department of Geography for Education and Public Information, Utrecht University, Utrecht, The Netherlands.

Michael Wise is Professor Emeritus of Geography at the London School of Economics and Political Science and was President of the International Geographical Union, 1976-80.

Acknowledgements

The editor wishes to thank his colleagues, Frances Slater, Ashley Kent and David Lambert, for advice and support in planning the volume. He is grateful to Denis Baylis for his skill and efficiency in seeing the book through to publication.

The editor also wishes to thank the following for permission to include copyright material: the Geographical Association for the table 'Assessment targets for geography in the National Curriculum' (Daugherty, 1989); New Internationalist Publications for the table 'Three views on race' (*New Internationalist*, March 1985); *Shared Experiences: Significant Issues* for the figure 'Key questions in a framework for a teaching unit on "The Geography of Defence" prepared for Australian students' (Studdert, 1985); P.J. Taylor and the publishers Longman for the tables 'The "nature" and politics of human ecology' and 'A rationale for the use of different spatial scales' (Taylor, 1985); the *Journal of Geography* for the figure 'Exploitation of labour through the extraction of surplus value' (originally reprinted by permission of Fred Wright, United Electrical, Radio and Machine Workers of America); C. Griffin, Mirror Group Newspapers, for the figure 'Go on ... please. One more won't make any difference' (*Daily Mirror*, 31 August 1988); the National Council for Educational Technology for the figure 'The challenge of the micro' (MESU, *Learning Geography with Computers*, 1988); Jacaranda Wiley Limited for the figure 'What do geographers do?' (Gerber, Lidstone and Mead, 1989) and the figures 'Sequential development of mapping elements', 'Developing the concept of a legend with younger learners', 'Sequence for developing effective mapping skills' (Butler et al., 1984); the *ITC Journal*, Netherlands, for the figure 'Scheme for designing cartographic symbols' (Bos, 1984); the Australian Board of Secondary School Studies for the figure 'Geographical concepts and the Jacaranda Kits' (Board of Secondary School Studies, 1977) and for the figure 'Syllabus in Geography 1954 Leaving Certificate' (Board of Secondary School Studies, 1954); Eostat, Lanham (Maryland) for the figure 'International remote sensing systems, 1972-2000' (Eostat, 1988); the Australian Board of Senior School Studies for the tables 'Geography Syllabus in Forms 5 and 6, 1965, First, Second and Third Levels, Higher School Certificate (Board of Senior School Studies, 1965), 'Geography Syllabus in Forms 5 and 6, 1973. 3 Unit Course and 2 Unit Course, Higher School Certificate (Board of Senior School Studies, 1973), and 'Geography Syllabus in Years 11 and 12, 1980, 3 Unit and 2 Unit Courses, Higher School Certificate (Board of Senior School Studies, 1980); the Australian Board of Secondary Education for the figure 'Geography Syllabus, Years 11-12, 1987, 2 Unit and 3 Unit Courses, Higher School Certificate (Board of Secondary Education, 1987); Neil Diamond for the lyrics 'signs that burn like shooting stars'; the West African Examinations Council for examples of questions from the 1988 Senior Secondary Certificate geography examination (WAEC, 1988).

Introduction
Michael Naish

Norman Graves has, at the time of writing, been active in the field of geography in education for very nearly forty years. He started this career as Assistant Master for Geography and Economics at East Ham Grammar School for Boys in 1950. At his retirement at Easter, 1990, he was Robert Ogilvie Buchanan Professor of Geography Education at the Institute of Education, University of London, where he became Pro-Director with special responsibility for Professional Studies.

These forty years saw dramatic developments in the study, teaching and learning of geography. First, there were the rapid and radical developments which took place in approaches to the subject at research level. Then, curricular changes were activated at school level, culminating, in 1988, with the imposition (for want of a better word) of a National Curriculum for all 5 to 16 year-olds in maintained (state) schools in England and Wales.

Norman Graves played an important part in these developments where they were pertinent to his interests and to the welfare of geographical education in general. His work was not confined to Britain, but was influential in geographical education on a world scale through his links with Unesco and the International Geographical Union (IGU).

This book has been written by some of the friends and colleagues of Norman Graves. Of course, it proved impossible to involve more than a small number of them and those who were not directly involved, including his erstwhile colleagues at the Institute of Education, Molly Long and Bertie Roberson, wish also to be associated with this tribute to his work.

The best possible tribute, in respect of his own approach to and attitude towards geography education, is that, far from being a totally retrospective volume, this book sets out to offer teachers of geography and teacher educators, a stimulating source for the future development of their work. This is, indeed, very much in the spirit of Norman Graves' work. Furthermore, again in order to reflect the breadth of his interests, the book has international dimensions, drawing its authorship from many parts of the world.

It sets out with two main purposes. The first is to provide a critical analysis of the position of geography in schools and universities in the last decade of the twentieth century and to look beyond this into the century ahead. The second purpose is to provide practical advice on the management and teaching of new developments related to the subject, such as peace education, international understanding, values education, new technology, textbooks, maps and remote sensing. The implications of research for the teaching, learning and evaluation of geography are also considered.

The book is divided into main sections dealing with curriculum, the values dimension, resources and learning, and international issues.

Curriculum matters

Simon Catling opens this section with a chapter on the primary curriculum, mainly referring to England and Wales, but with important principles for geographical education for young children anywhere in the world. He argues that geography has played a somewhat marginal role in the primary curriculum and that this raises a number of key issues about the future of the subject in primary schools (5 to 11 years), since, in England and Wales, geography is now specified as compulsory for all children as a foundation subject in the National Curriculum. The issues are discussed in some detail, and this leads to the conclusion that all those involved in promoting primary education should recognize and foster the value and role of geography within it.

In Chapter 2, I take similar arguments forward with respect to secondary education, again, largely with a focus on England and Wales. Some basic curriculum principles are discussed and contrasted with the model based on a simple syllabus-assessment link. Developments through the 1970s and early 1980s took forward work based on curriculum principles to good effect, but there may be a danger that, under the auspices of the National Curriculum, some of these benefits could be lost. The situation in England and Wales is considered in the light of evidence based on a small scale research study of the impact of centralization upon geography curricula in several other states and countries.

Turning to curriculum matters in the university sphere, Eric Brown and Bill Mead note the impact of rapid changes in the character and content of geography upon curricula at this level. In broad terms, teaching programmes have become more flexible and assessment more complex. Consideration is then given to details of curriculum changes in recent years, and an examination of the pressures and influences which have brought about these changes is undertaken.

Gerry Hones has always been interested in the links between teacher education and classroom reality. In his chapter, he examines the role of the curriculum tutor, focusing on university departments of education in the United Kingdom. This demonstrates the breadth of the concerns of these tutors, not least of which is to establish and develop professional links with colleagues across a wide spectrum, including colleagues in schools, thus helping to create a constructive level of credibility with all concerned with the teaching of geography.

The importance of effective communication in geographical education is a major interest of Henriëtte Verduin-Muller, working at the University of Utrecht. In her chapter, she develops the idea of promoting communications facilities in order to enhance geographical education. At the same time, she argues, learning geography should help open students' eyes to the phenomenon of the communications revolution in meaningful ways.

Working at the *Institut National de Recherche Pédagogique* in Paris, Lucile Marbeau has developed research into the pedagogy of geographical education. Her particular interests include the kinds of pedagogic and scientific reasons for choices made and decisions taken in the setting up of geography curricula. Her findings are applied to curriculum design in France and offer teachers and curriculum decision makers opportunities for rational curriculum planning and effective implementation of curricula.

Ideology and change: the values dimension

In recent years there has developed a considerable interest in ideology and geography as well as ideology and education. Putting the two together is a fruitful enterprise which opens up the potential of geography as a medium for education.

In exploring ideas about ideologies and their influences on geographical education, Frances Slater traces recent developments in the subject and the range of paradigms available. This leads to consideration of how society is represented in geography, particularly with regard to issues connected with race, gender and class. She raises the basic question, do we travel with different views in our work as geographers and educators? To do so may help us in maintaining opportunities for our development rather than closing doors.

John Fien is involved in national initiatives for peace education in Australia. He argues that geographical education has a significant role to develop through its alignment with questions concerning human rights, development and political and environmental education; all falling within a broad definition of peace education. A reconsideration of the objectives, content and pedagogy of geography education is called for to take account of this role and it is, he claims, important for such reconsideration to be based on cross-curricular initiatives.

Through his involvement as current chairperson of the Commission for Geography Education of the International Geographical Union, Hartwig Haubrich has the opportunity to emphasize once more the significance of geography in education for international understanding. In his chapter he reports his study of the writing of teenage children in various countries about their own countries as they see them. Profiles of the cognitive and affective structures of the students' perceptions of their countries suggest that they, the students, demonstrate potential for the development of their international understanding.

In his review of the value of Radical Geography in the discipline and in geographical education, David Lambert traces the development of Marxist analysis and the more recent focus on the relationship of structure to agency and place. He argues that such perspectives are important in the realm of 'real human geography' and that a radical stance forces us to examine ideologies. This may be very important for the development of the potential of geography in education.

Resources and learning

This section reviews some recent developments in resource provision for learning geography.

Ashley Kent takes a realistic view of the significance of new technology, particularly microcomputers, in geographical education at school level in Britain. Reviews of the uses of computers in the classroom, the role of outside agencies such as the Geographical Association and the National Council for Educational Technology, a major new pack for in-service education and a project linking history and geography, lead to consideration of research into the take-up and application of these vital developments. Finally, he looks ahead to the year 2000.

Having completed valuable research into the use of textbooks in geography education, John Lidstone considers criticisms commonly levelled at textbooks and argues that in fact they offer considerable support in taking forward new ideas in the subject and the teaching and learning of it. In this way, textbooks can make an important contribution to students' understanding of issues of social and environmental concern, but their use by teachers would probably benefit from careful analysis and development.

Again working from his own research experience, Rod Gerber develops ideas about the value of maps as resources for learning. He notes the complexity of processes involved in their effective production and use and suggests that current practice in teaching mapping skills has not kept pace with developments in cartography and geography. Geographers need to understand the nature of these developments, he argues, in order to make optimum use of maps in teaching and learning. A radical and wide ranging programme of development is recommended.

Images from remote sensing offer tremendous potential in geographical education, but as yet such potential is far from realized. Keith Hilton outlines the history of remote sensing, from air photography to satellite systems and explores the educational implications of the developments. He reviews two particular products in order to raise general issues about the learning implications. Looking to the future, he anticipates improvements in the quality and quantity of environmental data from satellite remote sensing and analyses the implications of this for geographical education.

International perspectives

Norman Graves' continuing interest in the international dimension is reflected in this section, which begins with an overview of the international scene and then draws in viewpoints from Australia, USA and Nigeria.

The history of education and educators is an important and often neglected area of study, yet it is now fashionable in research to invite important personalities in various fields to talk and write about their experiences and to record recent events in the development of the subject and its pedagogy. Michael Wise presents here a review of the work of the International Geographical Union's Commission for Geography Education, with which Norman Graves has been associated for many years. This valuable history provides an important record of a productive group in the field of education and raises the issues concerned with developing international co-operation.

As a researcher in the field of geography curriculum and an active curriculum developer in his own right, Don Biddle is uniquely placed to review the development of changes in curricula in New South Wales. He traces the construction and implementation of three senior secondary syllabuses between 1955 and 1988. This history is used to illustrate changes in the decision-making process with regard to curriculum development over a period of dramatic development in the subject and the teaching of it.

Exciting developments are under way in the United States, where, it is claimed, geographical education is experiencing a renaissance. Joseph Stoltman traces the development of the important initiatives which have emerged since 1983. He regards these as somewhat spontaneous in their origins, but subject to certain underlying circumstances. He selects ten developments that have contributed to the dramatic resurgence of the subject in America and explores their origins and significance.

For Julie Okpala, working in Nigeria, there are real problems about developing the potential of geography in education in that country. A new curriculum was introduced in 1986 for Nigerian secondary schools, and it was hoped that this would improve the teaching and learning of the subject. In a careful analysis, Julie Okpala demonstrates that such improvements will be difficult to achieve and she recommends that an effective national association for geography teachers should play a key role in developing improved geography teaching and, through this, improved perceptions of the subject.

Conclusion

In the concluding chapter, Bill Marsden analyses the contribution of Norman Graves' writing in the field of geography and education over the last thirty years. In doing so, he is able to review changes in this field as well as in curriculum study and educational policy making over this period. The chapter forms a fitting tribute to the man and the subject over a period of great significance for education in Britain and internationally.

Part One
Curriculum Matters

Chapter One
Issues for the Future of Primary Geography
Simon Catling

Geography has existed largely in parochial and marginalized terms in the primary curriculum. Since geography is now a foundation subject in the National Curriculum, this raises a number of key issues about its future in primary schools. These issues relate to continuing arguments supporting geography as well as to what sort of geography is most appropriate in the primary school: the perceptions of geography held by primary teachers and views on how it may be best taught; concerns over the assessment of children's geographical understanding; and the need to consider both in-service education and curriculum development in primary geography. Alongside the debate and action on these issues remains the requirement for all those involved in promoting the breadth and quality of, as well as specific initiatives in, primary education to recognize, support and foster the value and role of geography in the primary curriculum.

Geography has *not* been out of the primary classroom but in many classes it has been in disguise, in some so well disguised that it has not been noticed. The following example observed in one primary school illustrates a relatively common context and perception of geography in primary education.

> It had been windy, and the class of 6 and 7 year olds had been attempting to describe their experiences. To encourage them their teacher had been reading stories and poems to them, they had been outside to find windy and sheltered places around the school grounds, and they discussed what wind is, where it comes from and where it goes and how it can affect people and places.
>
> In the class of 10 and 11 year olds a *topic* on canals had been in progress for most of the first half of term. Visits had been made, studies of the development of canals undertaken, consideration given to current potential

uses of canals, the lives and work of those connected with canals examined, and the canal network of Britain explored through photographs, maps, reference books, computer programmes, original sources and stories.

In both classes the work was lively, thoughtful, well resourced, stimulating, challenging, well matched to the children's understanding and clearly planned by the teachers in relation to the school's general aims and *environmental studies* guidelines.

However, neither the head nor the teachers saw these studies as having much to do with geography. Yes, there had been some mapwork and the older children had looked at some places in the UK and were aware of the location of 'famous' canals elsewhere in the world. These studies, the teachers stated, had really been to do with *language* and *science* work, through an *environmental* focus, and with a *historical* dimension for the older children.

The Education Reform Act of 1988 requires that the veil of disguise be drawn aside. The introduction of a *National Curriculum* of core and foundation subjects for all 5 to 16 year olds is guaranteed to push the staff of this school together with all other primary schools, into recognizing more clearly the existence of geography, as well as into becoming clearer about the value, focus, content and teaching methods appropriate to primary geography. Why? Because *geography* is one of the foundation subjects for all primary age children. This seems radical, but is in reality not so, because it is quite clear from the *practice* of the school in the example, as it is of so many others, that geography *is* a dimension of their curriculum; indeed, it is potentially a very strong area of their curricular expertise.

Geography's place in the National Curriculum has not been taken for granted. The 1980s saw a determined promotion of geography as a key subject in the curriculum for all children by, among others, the Geographical Association, the Royal Geographical Society and the geography members of HM Inspectorate. This was given impetus by the lack of any direct reference to geography in the ministerial publication *The School Curriculum* (Department of Education and Science, 1981). Further initiatives were taken when the inclusion of geography still seemed more tentative than whole-hearted in *Better Schools* (Department of Education and Science, 1985b). Now that geography would *seem* to have a more secure future (for it should not be forgotten that the Secretary of State can alter the list of core and foundation subjects) consideration needs to turn to what this might mean for primary schools. Indeed, it raises a number of issues for the future of primary geography; it does *not* diminish the challenge facing geographical education.

The focus of the remainder of this chapter will be upon a number of the issues facing the development of geography in the primary curriculum. They can be posed as a series of questions:

1. Why should geography be an element of the curriculum of 5 to 11 year olds?
2. What understanding of geography do primary teachers have?
3. What should geography in primary education be like?
4. How should geography be taught in primary schools?
5. How will children's geographical achievement be assessed and monitored?
6. What in-service education will be needed for primary teachers in geography?
7. How will the primary geography curriculum be developed in schools?

These are not particularly new questions, nor are there necessarily unequivocal responses to them. In considering them, the purpose is to offer some direction to the development of effective geographical work for primary age children.

Examining the issues

Geography in the primary curriculum

Geography may be a named subject in the National Curriculum, but the nagging question remains: *why*? What is it that geography has to offer young children? This question raises an issue which the promotion of the National Curriculum fails to address, namely: what is the rationale for including a subject in the compulsory curriculum of all primary-age children? Inevitably the failure to explain the value of subject contributions to children's education raises concerns about their validity. Unless a compelling justification can be argued, the case to review geography as a foundation subject will arise and will not readily go away. Geographers cannot be complacent about the tenure of geography as a curriculum subject. On what basis, then, might an argument for geography's contribution be made? There are a number of justifications which can be offered.

The first lies in the view that children's interest in and interaction with people and places – their experience of social and natural environment – is a fundamental dimension of their early years development. This is particularly so in the context of their growing understanding of such key elements of environmental understanding as their senses of locational and territorial awareness which provide a framework upon which to build an understanding of their spatial relationships with other people and places in the world around them (Bailey, 1987; Catling, 1987, 1988, 1989). Equally, children develop a sensitive awareness of their surroundings, not just of their home locality, but also, through travel and television, of distant places. These elements of experience are not trivial but have been central both to human survival and to the capacity to maximize (or exploit) the potential of environments (Mays, 1985). On this basis, geography must play a curricular role since *children arrive at school developing as geographers.*

The second set of reasons lies in the role of geography as an intellectual pursuit. Geography, as the study of places and of the interactions of people and the environment, does itself provide a framework which enables children to develop a deeper and broader understanding of the nature and variety of natural and human environments and conditions (Department of Educational Science, 1986). The value of geographical study is that it *can* extend children's awareness, introduce them to a wider range of resources through which to examine the world near and far, and provide them with the tools to observe, investigate, describe, analyse and evaluate the dynamics of places.

Thirdly, a justification for geographical study at school lies in the contribution it makes to the impact that people have on the environment. Places are not static but constantly respond to the pressures of change, some for the better, others for the worse. Both in the locality and on the world stage people *act* upon the environment. Such actions are based not simply on knowledge, understanding and skills but also on *values*. Primary school age children have views about and developing values in relation to the environment, which include such interests as good play places, the provision of local services, the management of resources, ways to respond to people affected by disasters, and attractive and unattractive places. Geographical study provides a framework for children, even in the earliest years, for them to explore their own and others' values and the impact of these, particularly in terms of the conflicts of different interests (Huckle, 1982), and to understand the potential outcomes of their actions in the environment as adults.

Finally, the narrowest reason, but one that cannot be set aside, lies in being informed about where places are. As with the understandings referred to above, such information can develop haphazardly and be ill informed and inaccurate. There is a need for children to be able to recognize a globe, to know the locations of places and areas of importance in the world, locally and globally. There is no shame in knowing where places are; the shame lies in an education which denies, or seemingly does not care, that one element of the armoury of being well-informed enough to make effective judgements is being able to locate places mentioned on the news or in a report, a discussion or a photograph, within a *mental map of 'the world'* (Storm, 1987). Geography in the primary school has a role in initiating and fostering the development of children's locational awareness and knowledge (Daugherty, 1989).

We come full circle. These justifications are not isolated and separate but interrelated, as Figure 1.1 illustrates. Geography's role as a subject is to build upon, extend and develop the interest, emerging understanding and developing values the child already has in relation to places and the environment on coming to school. Its justification as a National Curriculum subject lies in its contribution to the development of a key area of all children's experience in a world *within which they exist* and increasingly *upon which they will act.*

Primary teachers' perceptions of geography

It is one thing to set out a case for geography in the curriculum (Bailey and Binns, 1987); it is another to expect it to happen. A second issue arises from this new found role for geography in the primary curriculum. It lies in the question: what understanding of geography do primary teachers have?

There is limited evidence to consider how primary teachers view geography in their curriculum. Research studies in this topic have been few and are dated (e.g. Conner 1974; Cracknell 1976; William and Richards, 1980). Drawing broadly on inspections of schools, the national sample surveys of primary, first and middle schools by HMI provide some insight into geography in primary classrooms (Department of Education and Science, 1978, 1982a, 1983, 1985a). But these studies do not provide a picture of current practice. This can most effectively be drawn from the HMI reports dating from the mid 1980s on individual schools catering for children aged between 5 and 11; even so it is *practice* that is observed and reported, not the attitudes or levels of understanding of teachers in a subject area. Comparisons with earlier reports indicate that, sadly, there appears to have been little

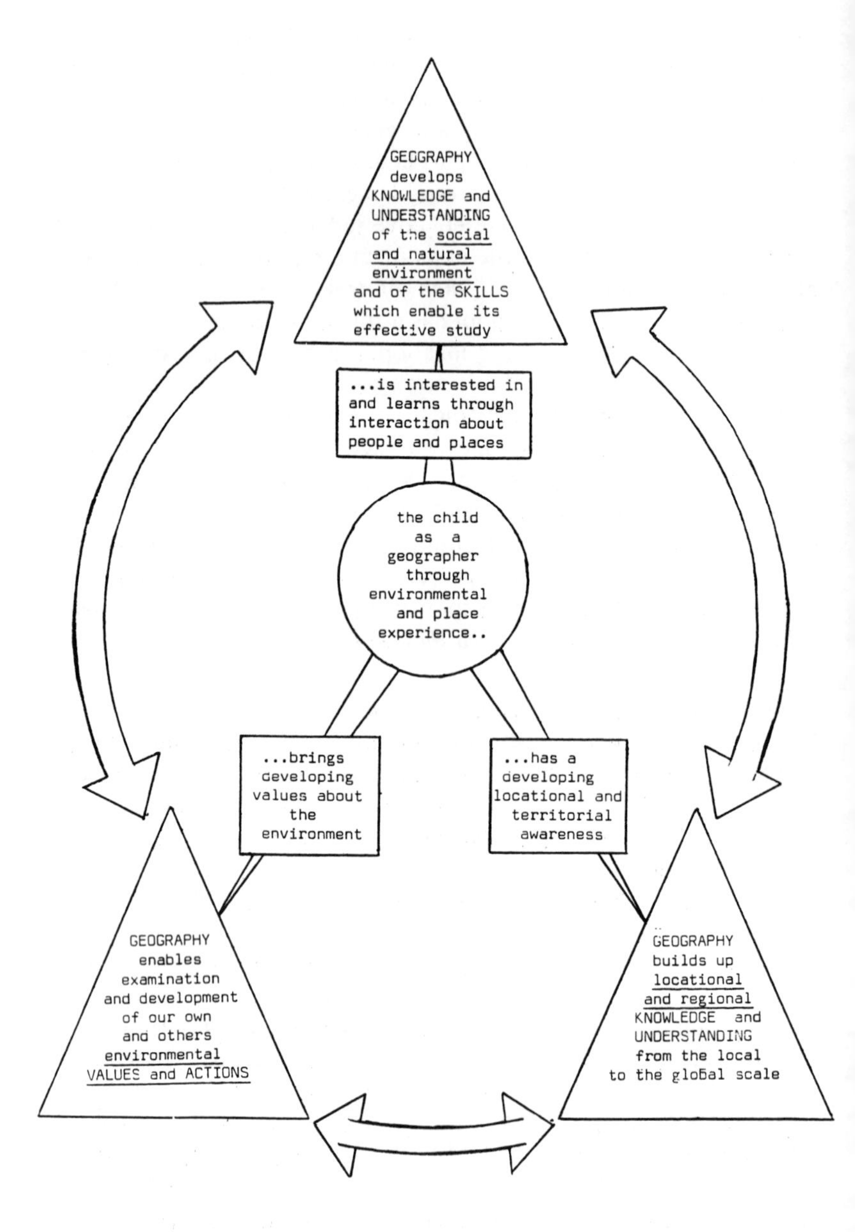

Figure 1.1 The basis for geography's contribution to the primary curriculum. (source: Catling)

improvement in the nature and quality of geographical work during the 1980s; the disguise has held (Department of Educational Science, 1989b).

Extrapolating from HMI reports, a number of conclusions can be drawn about attitudes to and the nature of geographical work in primary schools in the period leading up to the implementation of the National Curriculum.

1. A wide variety of practice exists. There is by no means a shared view of the value and contribution of geography. This conclusion is drawn from evidence which indicates, at one end of the scale, no consideration of geography in some schools, to examples of well-developed policy and practice within a whole-school approach in a handful of cases. Many schools lack guidelines for geography. A minority of schools have a teacher who takes responsibility for encouraging or resourcing specifically geographical studies or strands in topic work.

2. Where geographical work does occur in schools, not only does it lack consistency and coherence, but there is also little evidence of progression. Pockets of good and excellent geographical study exist, but at times younger children can be found to be doing more challenging and better matched work than older children in the same school. Frequently, the work of older children is no more stretching than that given to younger children.

3. Often geographical studies are limited to mapwork and local studies. There is little evidence for the study of other places in the United Kingdom, Europe, or the rest of the world. Where studies of more distant places do occur they are rarely well resourced, often they are at too large a scale to be of much meaning to the child, and there is a tendency not to challenge stereotypical images.

4. Even where the basis for good work in geography throughout a school exists with well constructed guidelines and good resources, in a number of cases not all teachers put them into effect. Most often work that is good is found in only one or two classes.

5. Yet the picture is not entirely gloomy. In a large majority of schools there is evidence of geographical work, albeit in most cases ill-defined and patchy. There are effective schools whose geographical work is well developed, even if in some cases it is not in fact recognized as geography by the teachers and children learning through it.

Can any reasons be identified for the current state of geography in primary schools? Several seem to be involved. In many cases teachers have limited experience of geography. For many it has been a fairly insignificant part, often in an integrated context, of their initial teacher education; by no means all have recognized the geographical element (if any) in their professional studies courses. In essence, geography has been given low status and this is reflected in the low value attaching to it in the primary curriculum. This trend is not changing significantly according to evidence about the preparation of new teachers in primary and middle schools (DES, 1982b, 1988a). This is further exacerbated by very limited geographical background in many primary teachers, for example no qualification in geography even at 16-plus. Although it is a popular GCSE subject, geography is still not taken by a majority of school children to that level. Indeed, the view teachers have of geography from their own schooling varies from a subject much enjoyed to one loathed, from tedious and dry note-taking to stimulating and illuminating experientally based courses: from narrow statistically oriented abstractions through the study of widely diverse communities and regions to investigative and evaluative courses examining environmental issues. There is a diversity of experience in school that makes the sharing of experience problematic.

Other reasons also exist, but drawn not from experience of geography so much as from a perspective on the appropriateness of geography to primary children. The concern here is that geography remains seen as a dry body of locational information, essentially to do with a world well away from the experience of children. Here we have the persistence of a dated conception of geographical study. As a substitute, all too often *environmental studies*, interpreted and undertaken locally and parochially, are justified as far more relevant to younger children, while geography, encompassing much more than this, is ignored.

Thus, despite the range of resources, including many textbook series and books offering advice on teaching geography, available to primary teachers (Blyth, 1985; Mays, 1985; Bale, 1987; Mills, 1988; Marsden, 1989), the view persisted through the 1980s that geography was not wholly appropriate for primary work. This leads to the conclusion that geography, as geographers see it, is not clearly understood by many primary teachers. Yet, in the late 1980s change was in the air, prompted by the development of the National Curriculum. Increasingly, teachers wanted to find out what geography they should be teaching.

The focus of primary geography

To tackle the question, 'what should geography in primary education be

like?' there is a need to draw on the rationale for primary geography noted earlier. The work of HMI and the Geographical Association has emphasised several key dimensions of geographical experience for primary children (HM Inspectorate, 1986; Wiegand, 1987; Mills, 1988; Daugherty, 1989). These are:

1. investigating the local environment;
2. investigating people, places and environments beyond their immediate experience, including both the UK and abroad;
3. developing an awareness and appreciation of diversity in physical conditions and in communities and societies;
4. developing an understanding of the interaction of people and environments, of their interdependence, and of the impact each has on the other;
5. developing understanding of the spatial context and dynamics of natural and human features and activities;
6. developing an understanding of change in the environment and of the role of decision-making in change;
7. developing an understanding of maps and globes;
8. developing enquiry skills in fieldwork, the use of information systems, and the capability to communicate findings and ideas through a variety of media;
9. contributing to the development of language and mathematical skills;
10. building an appreciation of the role of values and attitudes in issues related to people, places and the environment;
11. studying a variety of aspects of the environment, including settlements and communities, economic aspects such as farming and industry, weather and atmosphere, physical environments and the movement of people and goods;
12. stimulating interest and curiosity in the world around them, as a basis for fostering an increasing knowledge of the world from the local to the global.

The National Curriculum requires the identification of attainment targets, programmes of study and assessment arrangements in geography. In essence, attainment targets specify the aspects of geographical study to be covered in the primary curriculum; the programmes of study outline the essential experiences that will enable children to progress in achieving understanding in the attainment targets, and the assessment arrangements will track children's progression (Department of Educational Science, 1989a). Reviewing the nature and impact of this curriculum model, the Geographical Association's own National Curriculum Working Party identified fourteen attainment targets for geography, ten of which it was felt should be assessed in the primary years (Daugherty, 1989). These are listed in Figure 1.2.

Profile Components and Attainment Targets	Primary levels at which assessment reported Key Stage 1 7 years	 Key Stage 2 11 years
PC1 *Understanding Environments*		
1. The Local region	*	*
2. The Wider World		*
3. Landscapes and their formation		
4. Weather and Atmosphere	*	*
5. Ecosystems and Resource Management		
6. People and Settlements	*	*
7. Movement of People, Goods and Information		
8. The Location and Organization of Economic Activities	*	*
PC2 *Investigating Environments*		
9. Fieldwork Investigations	*	*
10. Understanding Maps		*
11. Sources of Geographical Information		*
PC3 *Evaluating Environments*		
12. Environmental Issues		*
13. The Potential of Places		
14. Environmental Appreciation		

Figure 1.2 Attainment targets for geography in the National Curriculum, (Daugherty, 1989).

The development of geography within the National Curriculum was set in motion in mid-1989, with the setting up by the Department of Education and Science of the National Curriculum Geography Working Group. One of the papers tabled at its first meeting was the Geographical Association's proposals (Daugherty, 1989). Another was its *Terms of Reference* (DES, 1989d), which set out, among other things, the brief regarding the *knowledge*, *understanding* and *skills* which five to sixteen year olds should be required to develop during their compulsory years of schooling and which were amenable to assessment. This brief is summarised in Figure 1.3. In late 1989 the Working Group's draft proposals for *attainment targets in geography* were published (DES, 1989c). In mid-1990 their Final Report, *Geography for Ages 5 to 16*, appeared (DES, 1990a).

The Geography Working Group proposed programmes of study and attainment targets constructed around three core elements of geographical study, with *thematic* and *skill* aspects supporting place or *area studies*. It was argued that this provided a particular focus for geography in the school curriculum. No distinction was made within the proposals, nor were there supportive arguments for a different focus for primary geography than for geography in the secondary curriculum. Thus, the Working Group saw the *distinctive contribution of geography* to younger children's learning as stressing these features:

1. the study of people's interactions with and in places,
2. the study of the processes creating and sustaining environments and places,
3. the study of people's use of and care for environments,
4. the development of children's knowledge about environments and places, and
5. the use of particular skills to study places and environments, including enquiry, fieldwork and mapping skills.

Children's geographical knowledge, understanding and skills were to be developed through their study of areas at a range of scales, from the locality of the school and home to the planet as a whole, and through a variety of case studies, including the local area, places that could be visited for fieldwork and distant places studied through secondary sources. This is not uncontentious (Catling, 1989, 1990a, 1990b, 1990c; Chambers, 1990), but such a view strongly supports the proposals made over many years about what primary geography should examine;

THE STUDY OF GEOGRAPHY FROM THE AGES OF 5 TO 16 SHOULD ENABLE PUPILS TO DEVELOP:

1. an informed appreciation and understanding of the world in which we live;
2. the ability to put information and experience in a geographical context;
3. an interest in, a sense of excitement about and an enjoyment of geography;
4. awareness of the direct application of geography to their daily lives;
5. a sense of place;
6. an understanding of the relationships between places;
7. a framework of knowledge and understanding about
    - their locality
    - other places in Great Britain
    - Europe
    - the world as a whole;
8. knowledge, understanding and appreciation of the similarities and differences in ways of life and cultures other than their own;
9. understanding of physical, economic, political and cultural relationships linking people in places throughout the world;
10. understanding of and respect for natural environments;
11. understanding about how physical conditions influence and are affected by human activity;
12. understanding of how physical processes and human actions bring about change on the Earth's surface and how these changes affect people's lives;
13. understanding of the ways people use the Earth and its resources in making a living and in seeking to improve the quality of their lives;
14. understanding of the impact of human activities on environments, and of the costs and benefits of different activities;
15. their abilities in the skills and processes of geographical enquiry, including
    - collecting, analysing, interpreting, reporting evidence
    - at first hand through field study, including in the local area
    - from secondary sources, such as maps, books, photos, satellite images, diagrams, statistics;
16. an appreciation of maps.

Figure 1.3 The knowledge, skills and understandings to be developed in school geography, 5-16 (from the Terms of Reference of the Geography Working Group, Department of Education and Science, 1989c).

indeed, the purpose was to broaden and deepen the foundation of geographical study for children in Key Stage 1 (5-7 year olds) and Key Stage 2 (7-11 year olds).

During the latter part of 1990, the National Curriculum Council consulted on the Geography Working Group's report, which modified the original proposals following comments from local education authorities, the Geographical Association and many other organizations (NCC, 1990). These proposals formed the basis for the draft *Statutory Orders for Geography in the National Curriculum* (DES, 1990b), and the Final Orders (DES, 1991) which were legally required to be taught from September 1991.

The key elements of the programmes of study and the five attainment targets for geography are set out in Figure 1.4. They retain the original structure and focus intended by the Geography Working Group and will act as a *framework* for outlining and structuring geographical studies for younger children. The attainment targets and programmes of study provide a *core set of criteria* or *objectives* that form the basis for schools and teachers to identify and decide upon their own approaches to geographical work.

The question, 'what should primary geography be?', is circumscribed and, for the forseeable future, no longer an open question; but the framework must be seen as *enabling* rather than limiting teachers' decisions. What primary teachers will need to consider is the specific content in terms of case studies and resources, as well as the structure which will support and develop geographical study within their own practice. This leads us to the next issue.

Approaching the teaching of primary geography

The consultation paper on the National Curriculum (Department of Educational Science, 1987a) stressed that the *delivery* of the curriculum remained with teachers; the structure of, resources for and approaches to teaching geography are matters for individual schools. The question faced by primary teachers now is: how should geography be taught?

Two approaches to geographical work in primary schools seem to predominate. There are those schools which follow a more *subject-centred* approach, based not uncommonly on either a television series such as *Going Places* (for 7-9 year olds) or *Landmarks* (for 9-11 year olds) or a textbook series (of which some sixteen are currently available for the junior age range); a few schools follow their own geographical syllabus drawing on a variety of resources. The alternative and most

KEY ELEMENTS IN GEOGRAPHY PROGRAMMES OF STUDY	THE FOCUS OF STUDIES IN GEOGRAPHY	ATTAINMENT TARGETS FOR GEOGRAPHY	KEY COMPONENTS IN THE GEOGRAPHY PROFILE
Geographical Skills and Investigations	• the use of maps • fieldwork techniques • enquiry and investigation skills • the use of secondary sources	*1* Geographical Skills	Geographical Skills
Places and Themes	• a knowledge of specific places, including: – the locality of the school – a contrasting UK locality – a locality in an economically developing country – a locality in a European Community country outside the UK – the home region – a core of locational knowledge at UK, European and global scales • an understanding of the distinctive features that give a place its identity • an understanding of the similarities and differences between places • an understanding of the relationships between themes and issues within particular locations	*2* Knowledge and Understanding of Places	Places
	• weather and climate • rivers, river basins and seas • landforms • soils, plants and animals	*3* Physical Geography	People and Environments
	• population • settlements • communications and movements • economic activities (primary, secondary and tertiary)	*4* Human Geography	
	• use and misuse of resources • quality and vulnerability of different environments • possibilities of protecting and managing environments	*5* Environmental Geography	

Figure 1.4 The strands of geography in the National Curriculum in Key Stages 1 and 2 (sources: DES 1990, 1991; NCC 1990)

common approach is the *topic-work* approach, in which schools examine themes often employing a limited number of disciplinary perspectives. HMI identify these as usually being environmental studies, geography, history and social studies. Science, language and art are also, but less often, involved. It is not unusual in topic work for a geographical strand to remain unstated by the teacher, though it may well in fact be an important dimension of the nature of the studies undertaken; indeed 'environmental studies' can often be the familiar 'carrier' of geography in disguise (Kerry and Eggleston, 1988, Tann, 1988).

This raises the central concerns in the discussion about approaches to geographical teaching. Will the naming of subjects mean a strengthening of or, indeed, a total return to a subject-centred approach? Will it be possible to continue working in or, even, to move towards structuring the curriculum in a topic-work approach? There is no particular answer to this dilemma. Inevitably it is a matter of judgement for schools; and here lies the crux of this issue. *It will be vital for a school policy on teaching approaches to be developed.* It can no longer remain a case of varied practice and quality from class to class. The basis of a school policy will lie in a variety of criteria:

1. Is what is to be taught as geography clear to all staff?
2. Does the teaching approach foster progression and achievement for the child?
3. Does it take into account the varied needs of differing individual children?
4. Does it ensure variety, breadth, coherence and balance in the experience of the children?
5. Is continuity ensured as the child progresses through each year from 5 to 11?
6. Are records maintained which identify the experiences and achievements of children, and which facilitate evaluation of the approach to teaching?
7. Is there appraisal of the nature and appropriateness of resources, particularly in terms of 'readability' of language and graphics as well as of the stereotypical images of people and places portrayed?
8. Does the approach to teaching geography reflect the aims of the school?

(source: Catling)

Whichever approach to teaching geography is adopted in a school, what is clearly vital is that teachers will be confident in their understanding of the subject. It is one thing to have an agreed school policy; it is another to be able to plan, structure, sequence and record effectively the activities and achievements of children in geographical studies where a teacher is less than certain about her or his ability to respond to and exploit children's geographical interest and experience, whether it is in a subject or topic-centred approach.

There is a further issue in the teaching of primary geography which must be addressed at this point. In deciding on approaches to teaching, the *focus* of that teaching will be central. Figure 1.5 summarizes three distinct approaches to geographical work. In considering the focus of their geographical work, primary teachers must ask themselves what they see the gains for the children being. Through an *information-centred* approach children will tend to build up an encyclopaedic knowledge of the world. This may be of value in answering quiz questions but it provides little insight into the patterns discerned and the processes at work in the natural and human environment and of the interactions, impacts and interdependence of these. This is the focus of the *analysis-centred* approach. Here information is an aid to

	Finding out about places	Study concerned with explanation about places	Enquiry focused on evaluation and action in relation to places
Structural focus	*information-centred*	*analysis-centred*	*issue-centred*
Focus for under-standing	building up locational knowledge about the locality and the rest of the world	exploring pattern and process in physical and human phenomena	examining environmental values and potential for change from local to global scales
Learning focus	information RECALL	information concepts, skills UNDERSTANDING	information concepts, skills, values DECISION-MAKING

Figure 1.5 The focus of approaches to teaching primary geography: a continuum (source: Catling)

understanding, not an end in itself. The *issue-centred* approach sees an understanding of environmental processes as a basis for the exploration of people's environmental feelings and values which affect the way people might make decisions and act within the environment. The stance teachers take as the focus of their geographical curriculum will depend on whether they view primary education simply as developing information-saturated children or as concerned not just with children being well informed but also with their being able to relate that understanding to their own and others' lives. Such judgements may be influenced also by the requirements of National Curriculum geography, but these do *not* limit the focus of primary geography: they merely indicate what will be assessed.

Assessing and recording learning in primary geography

Probably the most challenging issue to face the development of effective geographical work in the primary school is identified in the question: how will children's progress and achievement in geography be assessed? Assessment is not a new topic for the primary teacher, but the formality of assessing and reporting achievement, which the National Curriculum requires, will be new for many in the context of geography. Certainly, informal approaches to the assessment of environmental learning have been part of teachers' practice, though the quality and effectiveness of these approaches have been open to question, particularly because there has been a lack of clarity about what should be assessed. The stating of attainment targets and levels of achievement within them will, to some extent, tackle the latter problem. Nonetheless, the issue about the styles of assessment remains; as also does a further issue, that of recording the progress and achievements of children. Simply reporting achievement at ages seven and eleven is inadequate for the teacher; effective teaching builds progression for each child on diagnostic and formative assessment as part of a continuous activity.

The nature of diagnostic assessment tasks will need to be considered carefully by primary teachers in relation to geographical work. These should not be seen as separate from the activities children undertake in the ordinary way as part of their geographical work. In planning or sanctioning activities primary teachers will have to be quite clear about the principal geographical learning involved (SEAC, 1990). In a subject-centred approach this may be relatively easier to achieve than in a topic work approach. It will be possible, in planning geographical activities, to identify the central idea(s), skill(s), value(s) and information, and through the child's response to the activity to assess the quality of that child's understanding, perhaps on a scale ranging from initial experience through competence to mastery and application. In topic work which integrates geographical dimensions with other subject strands, the same principle applies; but the demand on the teacher is greater in that not only does s/he need to be able to identify the geographical contribution in planning; s/he also needs to be able to spot the geographical needs and achievements which the child adds unplanned to the topic.

The method and structure of recording children's geographical experience will be crucial in this. Again the attainment targets for primary geography may well form a basic framework for recording progress, but will such a 'tick-list' be the most appropriate or valuable method of recording? Monitoring that is of value to the teacher identifies interests, stimuli, experiences and responses as well as particular achievements and areas of need. It will be necesary to develop records which provide a guide to the particular progress of each child in geography. How this might be done for this subject, as well as for each of the others, without creating an enormous recording work-load has yet to be resolved. One way forward may well be to give more status to the child's own work through building a *portfolio* of experiences, tasks and achievements, which involves the child in structuring the record of her or his progress. Linked to the development of a *profiling approach to recording achievement* in geographical work, this could be operated on a selective, not cumulative, basis, and could travel with the child through schooling from five to sixteen. Such an approach would not only provide a statement of experience and progression but would also present the pattern of that development, enabling both teacher and pupil to gain insight into individual rather than group needs when planning the way forward in teaching.

INSET in primary geography

It will be clear from the focus taken thus far that the issues in primary geographical education relate particularly to the needs of teachers: why should they teach geography? What will they be expected to do and how will they work? Will this match their perceptions of the subject, their level of understanding and their preferences in teaching styles? How should and can they assess and record children's progression effectively? These are and will continue to be very real questions about geographical work for many primary teachers. Some may feel there is a simple solution and hope to work from a textbook series that 'does the job' for them; the large majority will wish to have greater ownership of the geography dimension of their classroom curriculum. In all cases help will be needed, and in most requested. The need for in-service teacher education (INSET) is already growing in primary geography. Demand will continue to increase.

The issues that arise here are fourfold: first, the identification of real needs and starting points, for teachers have individual needs as learners; second, the nature of such in-service education; third, the availability of provision and how it may be supplied most effectively; and fourth, the priorities of schools. The first and last of these issues are closely intertwined, for the priorities a school sets itself may well be related to perceived needs within the school.

There are pressures that interfere in the most appropriate resolution of these issues. One such pressure is the demands placed on INSET priorities for the school by the core subjects in the National Curriculum, partly because of their implied greater importance and consequence, but also on account of some muddying of the water in the areas of experience each of them cover. For example, a school may perceive that geographical INSET work is a lower priority because there is a view that several aspects of geography are adequately covered by science and mathematics INSET, particularly in relation to environmental and spatial aspects of geography. Another pressure may be the structure of curriculum consultancy in the school, in which geography may find itself as one of two or three areas covered by the same staff member, perhaps for more than one school.

Even so, where these pressures may not influence decisions unduly, important questions will need to be considered by a school in identifying its INSET needs in geography, including:

1. What is our current level of understanding about geographical requirements in the curriculum? What are our strengths and our weaknesses?
2. To what extent can we share the range of potential competence in teaching primary geography through the school to help each other?
3. What do we identify as particular priorities for INSET study? Are these priorities for all of us, or some only?
4. Who do we need or wish to involve in our geography INSET development? What would be the value of someone from outside identifying our needs?

5. What do we intend to do once we have completed initial and later phases of INSET? How shall we monitor our progress?

Considering what the in-service needs are for a school also means identifying appropriate approaches and foci for INSET activity.

Different requirements and topics, or the current level of teacher awareness may well require INSET to take different forms. Some examples illustrate this issue:

1. Teachers may feel that their awareness of both appropriate content and teaching methods are so limited that an 'experiential' approach will be most fruitful, resulting in working in ways themselves that they might use with children before considering the merits, limitations and contexts of the particular content and methods.

2. It may be that a school is concerned about its resources and spends time examining the quality and variety of these, drawing up criteria upon which to base the potential and acceptability of new resources, and creating a priority list of those resources it wishes to obtain.

3. A school may lack or need to redraft its guidelines or teaching syllabus for geographical work, perhaps in the context of topic work or environmental studies. To do this it may set about examining and evaluating its current practice, identifying the direction of change and drawing up a draft document to implement and evaluate over more than one school year.

4. Having identified priorities, a school may send one or two of its staff only, or go as a team, to an INSET course with the specific purpose of taking up a particular focus, for example mapwork or developing a 'distant place' dimension, during a term or year to evaluate the impact of the work on classes and the school.

The availability of INSET provision in primary geography depends on more than finance; it also requires the availability of course leaders. Neither of these is in plentiful supply, and nor are they likely to be for geography in the forseeable future. Therefore, schools need to be imaginative in their initiation of INSET. The development of school consortia has been one approach to enabling whole school INSET to take place, though often this has required outside contributors who provide ideas for developing primary geography. Local education authority courses in primary geography offer the opportunity for curriculum consultants to bring inputs back to individual schools and to consortia. As experience in geographical work in the classroom develops teachers will be able to share their growing confidence and expertise with others in their own and other local schools, which offers perhaps the most effective long-term opportunity for INSET; that is, an approach which involves teachers being given time to work alongside others in schools, whether for a day or at intervals over a term or year. This last approach would not only have the benefit of being INSET that draws on working with children, but as INSET which provides greater opportunities for the children involved. To achieve it, as with other approaches, the commitment of the school to developing geographical work is fundamental, which raises the final issue to be considered.

Developing geography in the primary school

The National Curriculum will require primary schools to develop a commitment to geographical education. It is, after all each child's entitlement. It will provide both the framework of the curriculum through attainment targets and guidance through programmes of study. Several of the aspects of this issue in the future of primary geography have been touched upon already: what geography might be considered to be like; teachers' confidence in teaching geography; the introduction of a school policy; consideration of teaching approaches; assessment of learning; and INSET development. What has been implied through the foregoing discussion is the need for clarity of purpose and understanding to underpin the importance of consistency and coherence in geographical experience, which enables progression in learning for children.

If the development of the geography curriculum throughout the primary school is to be successful, several criteria will need to be fulfilled. These draw together a number of the points raised above.

1. The broad aims of the school need to be clear and to inform its view of the curriculum and of approaches to teaching. Not only will this provide a context for developing a view on the *aims, nature and role of geographical experience* for the children, but it will also enable a rationale for and approach to teaching geography to develop which fulfils the aims of the school. In this way geography is seen as an appropriate 'subject' building on an area of children's experience, contributing to the whole education of the child. Geography is a medium for learning as much as an element of experience.

2. Bearing in mind the requirements of National Curriculum geography, the school will then be able to develop *guidelines for the geographical dimension* of the curriculum. These should be constructed around the need to facilitate progression for each child. This implies continuity of geographical experience, which is underpinned by coherence across experience. Building on the views of HMI (1986), the key elements of primary school geography guidelines can be summarized as:

(a) aims and objectives of primary geography;
(b) identifying teaching and learning methods that will provide experience built around the aims and objectives;
(c) a framework to provide for progression through the primary years;
(d) guidance on the balance of content, on the choice of themes and places for study, and on the emphasis given to local and global studies;
(e) guidelines on approaches to selected topics and activities;
(f) critieria for selecting appropriate resources;
(g) means of assessing and recording progressive achievement;
(h) identification of cross-curricular links between geography and other subjects in the primary curriculum, both as a basis for integrated studies or topic work and to encourage the recognition of opportunities to illustrate the value of geographical understanding, such as in stories.

3. It will need to be recognized that continuous *evaluation of the geography curriculum* will be central to the success of children during their primary years. Clearly it should be the responsibility of a member of the school staff to monitor the geographical work in the school, a process which will involve all staff in recording of and reflection on their own geography teaching. The geography curriculum consultant, perhaps for a group of schools, will have the role of maintaining an awareness of developments in primary geography, of bringing these to colleagues' notice for discussion and consideration in relation to their current practice, and for modifying school guidelines in the light of agreed development in teaching method or content focus, for example. Thus, the evaluation of practice is a two-way affair interlocking current teaching with potential approaches. The primary geography curriculum cannot be seen as die-cast but as evolving.

Developing geography in the primary school not only involves recognizing, clarifying, nurturing and extending children's geographical experience and understanding; it also requires the understanding that neither children's experience nor what is conceived and agreed to be 'geography' is static but clearly subject to development. Not only at school level, but also at national level, this must be realized and acted upon.

The National Curriculum Council has a principal role to play in developing geography in the primary school. One of its required tasks is to keep the curriculum under review (Education Reform Act, 1988). In relation to primary geography, this will demand several important activities.

1. Monitoring the appropriateness of profile components, attainment targets and levels of attainment in primary geography. The focus, initially, must be in terms of over- or under-expectation in relation both to the breadth of the geography curriculum and to children's understanding leading to achievement.

2. Monitoring the value primary schools find in the programmes of study when interpreting these through their own guidelines and practices in teaching, which may or may not be influenced by external forces such as resource allocation or safety requirements for outdoor activities.

3. Maintaining awareness of developments in geography both as a discipline and what might be considered to be best practice in primary schools. It may be that changes in one or initiatives in the other identify a need to change the emphasis or even the structure of National Curriculum geography.

4. Monitoring the role and place of geography in the primary curriculum as such, in terms of its connections with other curriculum subjects, the broader framework within which it occurs, and views on the development of effective approaches to the primary curriculum.

In pursuing these activities, in relation to primary geography the National Curriculum Council will clearly need to work closely with both the Schools Examination and Assessment Council and HMI, whose reports on achievement in school geography and on geographical work in primary schools will be important. In this way a clear commitment to the development of primary geography will be demonstrated.

Conclusion

This chapter began by recognizing that geographical work in primary classrooms is undervalued, and that we can no longer afford to allow this to remain the case. Yet not only will the current hiding and disguising of geography need to be addressed in schools. It will have to be considered much more thoughtfully by many who write about the nature and quality of primary education as well as about aspects of primary practice. Apart from those few who promote the value, potential and development of primary geography (e.g. Mays, 1985; Bale, 1987; Mills, 1988), there are many whose work fails to recognize either the geography in children's experience or the importance of helping teachers be clear as to what are the qualities of effective geographical enquiries.

One of the limitations to the development of geographical work, in whatever form, in the primary curriculum lies in the work of respected writers who fail to consider geography, or who even dismiss it (e.g. Blenkin and Kelly, 1983, 1987; Cohen and Cohen, 1986; Kelly, 1986), though they give clear support to other curriculum areas. A second limitation lies in writers who refer in passing to geographical work, usually in a cursory or barely tolerant style, and who give little space to discussion of geographical perspectives (e.g. Pinder, 1987; Soper, 1987). A third group of authors on the primary curriculum tend to write implicitly rather than explicitly on geography. The limitation here is that though they often illustrate effective geographical approaches through their arguments about good primary practice, the disguise tends to inhibit the recognition of geography by the reader (e.g. Pluckrose, 1979; Blyth, 1984). Often this is because geography is hidden within a social studies or environmental context, or at other times in a project or topic work setting. These latter approaches as particular dimensions of the primary curriculum are frequently criticized by HMI in inspection reports on individual schools. In books explicitly on environmental and topic work approaches (e.g. Dowling, 1980; Gunning, Gunning and Wilson, 1980; Prosser, 1982; Waters, 1982; Kerry and Eggleston, 1988; Mares, Blanchard, Stephenson and Redhead, 1988; Ross, 1988), teachers are often not helped in their understanding of the nature, focus and contribution of geography because of a limited interpretation of the subject or because good geographical enquiry is not clearly identified though present. This limitation can also be recognized in the approach to presenting World

Studies, another strong dimension of geographical study (Fisher and Hicks, 1985).

The final set of limitations can be illustrated from two directions. In both contexts excellent examples of geographical work are extolled but not identified or even related to geographical study. Microcomputer work in primary schools has provided much readily taken opportunity for geographical study, but too often this has gone unrecognized, unstated or is passed by (e.g. Kelly, 1984; Ross, 1984, Fairbrother, 1985; Holmes, Whittington and Fletcher, 1985). Similarly, primary industry projects illustrate good practice in geography that has remained disguised (e.g. Benfield, 1987; Jamieson 1984; Smith, 1986, 1988). All this goes to reinforce the message of HM Inspectorate that clearly focused, well developed, and broadly based geographical work in primary schools is hard to detect and promote (Department of Education and Science, 1987b; 1989b).

The future of primary school geography lies not only in the interest and efforts of those who have a particular concern for it; it also depends on the credence and value given to its contribution to the primary curriculum and to the lives of primary children by those who seek to promote the best primary education for all young children. To some extent the Education Reform Act has forced the hand of primary educators; the future will show whether in broadening the primary curriculum, the potential of geography is developed in children's interests through its recognition, promotion and development by *all* concerned with primary education.

Chapter Two
Geography in the Secondary Curriculum

Michael Naish

Significant developments in curriculum thinking are reviewed and a model of a curriculum system is compared with assessment led geography programmes. With this context in mind, the process of centralization of the education system of England and Wales is traced and the implications for geography curricula considered. The nature of geography in the National Curriculum for England and Wales is discussed and some generalizations about the impacts of centralized curricula upon children's learning suggest some key issues for the future of school geography.

> My father used to say to me, rightly, that I 'knew the name of every one of the Sandwich Islands, the Moluccas, the Philippines, and was thoroughly familiar with the Torres Strait, with Timor, Java and Borneo, yet could not so much as tell you how many départmements there are in France.' And in the bac certificate, under 'Geography', he is awarded a 'médiocre' for 'Rivers of France, course of the Loire and the Rhone'.
> David Cairns (1989), *Berlioz, Volume One: The Making of an Artist*. London: André Deutsch.

The geography curriculum enjoyed by Hector Berlioz, hinted at in the extract above, seems very different from the modern concept of a geography curriculum designed to enhance the learning of the young person through development of her or his knowledge, understanding, skills and values. It is certainly true that the career of Norman Graves as a geographer in education began long after capes and bays geography had been discredited, but he worked through a dramatic and formative period in the development of the geography curriculum both in the United Kingdom and overseas. He was chairperson of the Geography Committee of the Schools Council during the years when three major curriculum projects were set up. His activities on behalf of UNESCO in promoting thinking and action for geography as a medium for education on a world scale is well known through his editing of key texts (Graves, 1975b; Graves et al. 1975c; Graves 1982e; 1984a and b) and his work in setting up a range of international meetings and conferences. His chairing of the Commission for Geography Education of the International Geographical Union also gave him the opportunity to aid the development of thinking and action about the role of geography in the curriculum which was and is influential in many countries throughout the world. His central interest in curriculum is well illustrated in his book, *Curriculum Planning in Geography* (1979a).

The purpose of this chapter is, first, to examine some principles for the development and implementation of the geography curriculum that have emerged through the period of Norman Graves' activities in this field, that is the nineteen sixties, seventies and eighties. Events in England and Wales are then traced from the mid-Sixties in order to provide a case study of dramatic curriculum change. Finally, some consideration of general issues about centralized curricula is offered.

Syllabus versus curriculum

Perhaps the most significant change in thinking about school geography in the second half of the twentieth century has been the recognition of the need to consider the teaching and learning of the subject within the framework of a curriculum system rather than simply from a syllabus statement. Early ideas about curriculum planning developed through the work of, for example, Tyler (1949), Taba (1962), Wheeler (1967), Kerr (1968) and Biddle and Shortle (1969), among others.

A key concept deriving from such work is that the curriculum may be viewed as a system made up of several components linked by feedback loops. A simplified illustration of such a system is given in Figure 2.1, below.

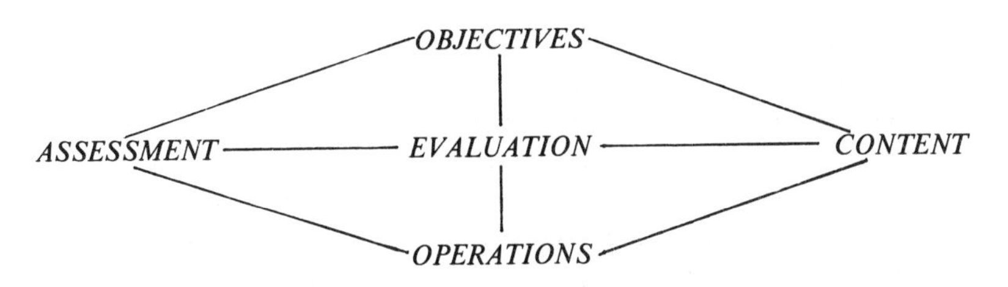

Figure 2.1: A simple curriculum model (source: Naish)

Each of the components warrants careful consideration. For example, it is part of the movement for curriculum renewal, that objectives should be carefully considered and that thinking about this should begin with very basic questions about the needs of the students, the nature of the subject and what it has to offer to the education of young people. Consideration of more specific objectives should come at a later stage and it is at this stage that the debate about the nature and value of an objectives approach becomes more important. This debate is mainly concerned with the level of detail at which objectives are specified.

In this model, factual content is placed into perspective, as operations have equal status with the content. Thus it is possible to consider constructively the relationship between content and process rather than allowing one to dominate at the expense of the other. It is also significant to note that assessment takes its place as part of the system and is developed in response to decisions taken about all other elements of the system. It does not dominate and lead the system, but follows on naturally from the objectives, content and operations. It can play an important part in evaluation, the central element. All elements should be susceptible to evaluation and consideration of evaluative findings may affect any element of the system, thus causing implications for all other elements.

Such a dynamic, inter-linked curriculum system has many contrasts with the more linear idea of syllabus which it challenged from the early Sixties. In caricature, syllabus thinking was based on reaction to pressure from higher education about the nature of the subject and the manner in which it was researched. Course outlines tended to be dominated by syllabus statements specifying content and assessment. Little attention was given to consideration of aims and objectives, which were rarely if ever specifically stated, and, in content dominated syllabuses, scant attention was given to operations or the processes of learning.

As a result, it could be said that syllabus-led programmes were restrictive in their contribution to the education of the students. Programmes based on the full curriculum system, on the other hand, might well provide opportunities for the development of skills and abilities and open up the affective domain of learning as well as enhance the knowledge and understanding of the students. An important influence here was the work of Bloom et al. (1956) and Krathwohl (1964) in discussing the cognitive, affective and psycho-motor domains of educational objectives and demonstrating that attention should be balanced between the three domains.

The context for change

It is very important for the development of the potential of geography as a medium for education that these advances in thinking about the nature of curriculum were accompanied by other fundamental changes in education, and by dramatic changes in the nature of the subject itself. The result was overpowering pressure for change during the Sixties, with reaction to such pressure in the form of changing curricula developing through the Seventies.

Examples of the developments in educational thinking included the opening up of the affective dimension signalled by Bloom and his colleagues (Bloom et al, 1956). There was recognition of the significance of conceptual learning and the understanding of principles (Bruner, 1960) and, following on from this, greater emphasis on the encouragement of skill development and of ideas about transfer of learning. There was also recognition that curricula should be relevant to certain recognised needs. The response to the opening up of the affective domain led not only to consideration of the sensitivities and feelings of children, but also to the development of a range of approaches to values education (Fien and Slater, 1981). Such approaches are designed to enable children to investigate value-laden situations, to analyse the range of attitudes and values held by various factions, groups or individuals, and to clarify their own stance with regard to such issues. With the development of radical and welfare geography at the academic level, the relevance of such approaches was quickly recognized and developed.

The opportunity for a geography of greater relevance to issues in the real world was also provided by these developments at the research level. If such issues are to be investigated by the pupils and students themselves, then the need for skill development is obvious and, through skill development, the potential for transfer of learning is enhanced. The basic idea of this is that students are enabled to transfer what is learned in one situation to a completely different situation. It is a case of encouraging added realism in learning, so that it is not narrowly constrained within a subject structure and so that general principles, concepts and skills can be applied appropriately to any situation. In this scenario, conceptual understanding and understanding of basic principles becomes more important than factual learning for its own sake, and the work of Piaget (1926, 1962), Vygotsky (1962), Bruner (1967) and their critics and commentators took on a new significance, for it demonstrated that school learning should be concerned with helping children to acquire accurate and meaningful concepts.

These developments were going on at a time, through the late nineteen fifties and sixties, when geography itself was experiencing what was described as a 'conceptual revolution' (Davies, 1972).

The dramatic and widespread changes in approaches to the subject at the research level which were heralded by this dramatic drive for a more thoroughly theoretical approach are well known and thoroughly documented elsewhere (see, for exmaple, Johnson, 1983 and 1986, and Holt Jensen, 1980). The changes are encapsulated in key words such as 'quantification', 'logical positivism', 'behaviouralism', 'radicalism', 'Marxism', 'welfare approaches', 'humanism', 'structuralism' and 'post-modernism'.

Under the syllabus model of renewal, there was a tendency for pressure for change exerted by such developments in the subject to build up until, too late, attempts at wholesale revision of syllabuses would rather uncritically take on the changes and attempt to mediate them for school work. The result was likely to be further overloading with factual content of already overcrowded syllabuses, thus further militating against the development of skills and abilities and the consideration of questions of values and attitudes. In the curriculum model, developments in the subject are critically assessed for their potential effectiveness in fulfilling the needs of the students and the objectives of the curriculum. Thus changes of approach in the subject may play a constructive role in the education of the students.

A medium for change

In such a situation, where pressures for change in the geography curriculum in the UK were making themselves felt, the setting up of the Schools Council for Curriculum and Examinations in 1964 presented an opportunity for action. The Schools Council provided the means for initiatives to be taken forward by funding curriculum development projects for schools and colleges in England and Wales.

Between 1967, when the Environmental Studies 5 to 13 Project was established, and 1984, when the Schools Council was abolished, continuous curriculum development work in geography took place through the auspices of the Council. In addition to the Environmental Studies project, the Council funded History, Geography and Social

Sciences in the Middle Years of Schooling from 1971 to 1975 (Blyth et al, 1976), Geography for the Young School Leaver (known as GYSL or the Avery Hill Project) (Boardman, 1988) and Geography 14-18 (The Bristol Project) (Tolley and Reynolds, 1977), which both began in 1970 and focused on 14 to 16 year-olds. The Geography 16-19 Project, which began in 1976 was originally funded by the Schools Council and continued to be funded centrally (by the Secondary Curriculum Development Committee after the closure of the Schools Council) until June, 1985 (Naish et al., 1987).

The geography projects, and in particular GYSL and Geography 16-19, have enjoyed widespread take-up of courses, GYSL being described as 'the jewel in the crown of the Schools Council' because of its introduction into every local authority in England and Wales (see Boardman, 1988) and have been a key influence in decision making with regard to the geography curriculum in recent years, particularly in the establishment of new GCSE (General Certificate of Secondary Education) examination courses for 14 to 16 year olds which were first taught in 1986. The projects shared common features such as their adherence to a curriculum system model such as that illustrated in Figure 2.1. and their emphasis on balanced objectives ranging across the areas of knowledge, understanding, skills and values. All three secondary projects were concerned with issues about the use of space, and this was developed by the Geography 16-19 Projeect into an approach based on investigation of the questions, issues and problems which arise from the interaction of people and their varied environments. This became popularized as the 'people-environment' approach. All three embraced the notion of active enquiry learning as offering the most appropriate ways of developing students' skills, abilities and values as well as enhancing their knowledge and understanding.

The drive for centralization

The scenario described thus far was developed in a laissez-faire situation so far as control of the curriculum in England and Wales was concerned. The position in Scotland and Northern Ireland was somewhat different as the schools in those areas were already subject to more centralized control. The situation was succinctly described by the Department of Education and Science (DES 1985c).

In law, the curriculum in all maintained primary and secondary schools, with

> the exception of voluntary aided secondary schools, is the responsibility of the LEAs (local education authorities), unless the articles of government of the school state otherwise. However, the articles of government of most maintained schools specify that the general direction of the conduct and curriculum of the particular school shall be the responsibility of the governing body; and, in practice, decisions about curriculum content, teaching methods, timetabling and the selection of textbooks are usually left to headteachers and their staffs. There is no national statutory requirement for the inclusion of any subject in the curriculum of maintained schools, with the exception of religious education.

It ought to be said that this freedom and responsibility to make curriculum decisions was welcomed by teachers and regarded as a privilege to be jealously guarded since it enabled them to plan and revise their curricula as they deemed appropriate for their school location, their own interests as professional subject teachers (dominantly with degrees in the subject) and the needs of their pupils. It also meant that constraints on curriculum renewal were, in theory, reduced. It gave teachers a high level of responsibility.

Already, by 1985, it was clear that this situation would be changed by legislation by the Conservative government which would ultimately complete a process of centralization of control of the curriculum. The process was clearly recognized and described by Lawton in his paper entitled *The Tightening Grip* (1984). It had been heralded as early as 1976, when James Callaghan, the then Socialist Prime Minister, called for a 'Great Debate' on education. Landmarks in the process were the axing of the Schools Council in 1984 and the generation of national criteria, both general and subject specific, for the main school leaving examination, the GCSE, at 16 years plus. In 1983 the Government revolutionized the style and process of curriculum change with an unprecedented injection of funding from the Manpower Services Commission for TVEI (The Technical and Vocational Education Initiative) (See Davidson, 1984). Work was begun on grade related criteria for assessment in public examinations in the early Eighties and core statements on the content of Advanced level courses in the General Certificate of Education (mainly for 18-19 year-olds) were developed (GCE Boards, 1983). It became clear through the Eighties that legislation would be brought in to establish a national curriculum for England and Wales for the first time since universal schooling was required through the Education Act of 1870.

During this period, geographers in education in Britain, spearheaded publicly by the Geographical Association (GA) and supported, less publicly, by other bodies, individuals and geography HMI (Her Majesty's Inspectorate of Schools), ensured that the value of geography as a key subject in the school curriculum would not be ignored. Early experiences following the initiation of 'the Great Debate' had led geographers to fear that the subject might be marginalized in any national curriculum (Naish, 1985b), but the action of the GA appears to have been most effective in drawing attention to the nature of the subject, its recent developments and its educative value. Sir Keith Joseph, then Secretary of State for Education, was invited to address the Association in 1985. He threw down a challenge for geographers in seven famous questions, concerned with selection of content, teaching through direct experience, the handling of controversial issues, the balance between people and environment, the impact of political and economic influences, the organization of the teaching of geography as a single subject or as part of broader courses and the question of continuity and finally, the key elements of geography for 14 to 16 year olds and how these might be included in a curriculum under pressure for this age range.

The GA response took the form of a booklet entitled *A Case for Geography* (Bailey and Binns, 1987), and this was discussed with the new Secretary of State, Kenneth Baker in 1987. It soon became clear that geography would be included as part of the national curriculum and when the Education Reform Bill became law in July 1988, geography was indeed included as a foundation subject.

The National Curriculum, to be implemented for all 5 to 16 year-olds in all maintained schools in England and Wales with effect from 1st September 1989, is made up of ten foundation subjects, including three core subjects: mathematics, English and science and seven other foundation subjects: technology (including design), history, geography, music, art, physical education and, for 11 to 16 year olds, a modern foreign language. Religious education is also to be provided for all pupils. Working groups were to be set up to produce programmes of study specifying essential teaching within each subject and attainment targets at up to ten levels of attainment at each of the ages 7, 11, 14 and 16. Assessment arrangements, consisting of standard attainment tasks (SATS) for each key stage (the ages 7, 11, 14 and 16) were to be developed following the statutory orders which would derive from the final report of each working group (DES, 1989a).

The Geographical Association again responded quickly and with helpful effect through the publication of *Geography in the National*

Curriculum. A Viewpoint from the Geographical Association (Daugherty, 1989). This was produced by the Association's own Working Group on the curriculum, which worked on a similar exercise to that which a National Curriculum Working Group would have to undertake. The Group first considered the contribution of geography to a general education and then proceeded to outline three key components of the geography curriculum called, after the terminology adopted in the National Curriculum, profile components. These are clusters, or sets of attainment targets. The profile components and attainment targets suggested by the Geographical Association are set out in Figure 2.2 below.

PROFILE COMPONENT I: UNDERSTANDING ENVIRONMENTS

Attainment targets

1. The local region
2. The wider world
3. Landscapes and their formation
4. Weather and atmosphere
5. Ecosystems and resource management
6. People and settlements
7. Movement of people, goods and information
8. Location and organisation of economic activities

PROFILE COMPONENT II: INVESTIGATING ENVIRONMENTS

Attainment targets

9. Fieldwork investigations
10. Understanding maps
11. Sources of geographical information

PROFILE COMPONENT III: EVALUATING ENVIRONMENTS

Attainment targets

12. Environmental issues
13. The potential of places
14. Environmental appreciation

Figure 2.2: Profile components and attainment targets for geography for 5 to 16 year olds as suggested by the Geographical Association Working Group on the Curriculum (source: Daugherty, 1989)

Ten levels of attainment for each attainment target were then specified, programmes of study set out and assessment arrangements considered. The Group also considered the contribution of geography across the curriculum, links between subjects and cross-curricular themes, thus continuing to parallel the kind of task the official Working Group would have to complete. In addition, the Geographical Association group also made a particular point of discussing more general issues about the learning and teaching of the subject, claiming that 'we have given as much attention to those apsects of a national curriculum which will be for teachers to determine as to those which will be for Government and we have tried to relate those different perspectives to each other.' Thus the Geographical Association document tends to follow the kind of curriculum model discussed earlier (Figure 2.1) and rejects the idea of an assessment-led approach leading to a syllabus statement imposed externally.

In producing this valuable discussion paper, the Geographical Association was able to draw on work appearing from those Working Groups that had been set up at an early stage. Those for the core subjects were the first to be established. Working Groups for design and technology, and then history, followed fairly quickly, and a Geography Working Group was announced on 5 May, 1989. The first interim report of the group was expected on 31 October 1989. For this the Working Group was required to indicate, with examples, as far as possible, 'the contribution which geography should make to the overall school curriculum', since this should inform thinking about attainment targets and programmes of study. Secondly, the interim report should indicate 'provisional thinking' on levels of attainment and the profile components into which attainment targets should be grouped. This would involve thinking about the knowledge, skills and understanding to be expected across the range of ability and maturity. Thirdly, the group was expected to report on its thinking about programmes of study. In all this, the Group was to take account of the work so far undertaken in the core subjects and in design and technology and history; the broad framework for assessment already announced; the contribution of geography to learning about other subjects; cross-curricular themes, particularly environmental education; good practice; research findings and 'the issues covered in the supplementary guidance to the Group's Chairman' (DES, 1989d).

These supplementary notes of guidance to the chairman placed a very demanding agenda before the Group. If we omit the guidance on assessment, ages and stages, GCSE and so on, and focus mainly on the guidance on programmes of study, it is apparent that the Group would have to work a conceptual miracle to make sense of geography in a way that would be meaningful to children, relevant to their needs and capable of engendering a committed level of enthusiasm in teachers. According to the guidance, the study of geography should:

- enable pupils to develop a sense of place
- enable them to develop an understanding of the relationships between places
- develop an appreciation of the value of maps
- create a framework of knowledge and understanding about the pupils' home areas and other places in the UK
- be related to wider perspectives of the world, the continents and oceans, the place of Britain and Europe within the world
- enable pupils to put information and experience in a geographical context
- enable pupils to develop 'an informed appreciation and understanding of the world in which they live.'
- foster their 'understanding of and respect for natural environments'
- help them learn 'how physical conditions such as climate and natural resources both influence human activities and are affected by them.'
- help them gain knowledge of 'ways of life and cultures' other than their own and 'appreciate the similarities and differences.'
- help them understand 'the physical, economic, political and cultural relationships that link peoples living in different places throughout the world.'
- 'give due weight to the physical processes and human actions that bring about changes on the earth's surface and the ways in which these changes many affect peoples' lives.'
- enable pupils to investigate and understand 'the ways in which people use the Earth and its resources in making their living and seeking to improve the quality of their lives.'
- give 'particular attention to the impact of human activities on environments and the real costs and benefits of different activities.'
- 'lay the foundation for the progressive development of the skills and processes of geographical enquiry' (defined here as collecting, analysing, interpreting and reporting evidence obtained both at first hand and through use of secondary sources, including maps, books, photographs, satellite images, diagrams and statistics)
- make appropriate use of material drawn from the local area
- make use of field study in providing experience
- link with other subjects across the curriculum so as to contribute to learning in other subjects and be 'promoted by' work in other fields. In particular, links with science, mathematics, design and technology (including information technology), economic and political understanding are mentioned.

- 'bear a heavy responsibility for environmental education and the European dimension in education'
- 'promote the development of good written English and numeracy'
- 'have clear attainment targets and programmes of study so as to ensure progression and coherence in what is taught.' (Ibid.)

'Above all', the notes for guidance state, 'the programmes of study should reveal to pupils that geography is interesting, exciting and enjoyable as well as having direct application to their daily lives.'

The Reports of the Geography Working Group

In the light of that last comment, the Interim Report of the Geography Working Group, published on 31 October, 1989, was a considerable disappointment (DES, 1989c). It portrayed an image of geography that was some twenty years out of date and showed little hope that children would find it 'interesting and enjoyable', while the expectation that it would have 'direct application to their daily lives' rested squarely in the hands of teachers implementing the Orders that would follow from the Final Report. Furthermore, the Interim Report appeared to ignore most of the very constructive curriculum development work in geography that had taken place in many countries since about 1965. Perhaps because of this, it bore little relationship to the curriculum system discussed above. Indeed, it promised to provide a good example of an assessment-led curriculum.

The main reasons for this derived from the constraints placed upon the Working Group by the framework of the National Curriculum, which, as noted earlier, requires that subject reports be based on attainment targets, programmes of study and assessment arrangements. The Working Group seemed to fall into the trap of concentrating on attainment targets (ATs) in their work for the Interim Report.

The Group proposed eight ATs:

AT1: The home area and region
AT2: The United Kingdom
AT3: World geography: Part 1
AT4: World geography: Part 2
AT5: Physical geography
AT6: Human geography
AT7: Environmental geography
AT8: Geographical skills

The ATs contained 'statements of attainment' which were posed on a range of ten levels so as to suggest a progression of attainment, with levels 1 to 3 referring to attainment tests for 7 year-olds, Lèvels 2 to 5 to tests for 11 year-olds, Levels 3 to 7 for 14 year-olds and Levels 4 to 10 for 16 year-olds.

Examples of the statements of attainment are:-

AT1, Level 1, Statement 1: 'to be able to say their own address'.

AT1/L6/S3: 'know and understand the reasons for the distribution of settlements in the home region and the relationship that exist between settlements of different sizes'.

AT4/L3/S1: 'know that one of the following islands is a small territory and be able to locate it on a world map or globe: Barbados, Bahrain, the Falkland Islands, Fiji, or Mauritius'.

The question is, 'Why those particular islands?' and, of course, this illustrates one of the major problems with the proposed scheme: the selection of examples is dictated in the scheme and it is a partial selection. Children studying within this framework are likely to end up with a very biased view of the world.

But this is only one of the problems with the model set out in the Interim Report. In brief, the other problems are, as I see them:

- the dated model of geography which it portrays, i.e. mainly regional and with an emphasis on spatial analysis

- the lack of commitment to enquiry, which should have been absolutely central to the proposals rather than partitioned off as a separate AT

- the narrow view of what constitutes enquiry, being mainly concerned here with a positivistic stance and ignoring more humanistic approaches and the methods of the social sciences. Whatever happened to empathy or decision-making skills, for example?

- lack of a clear commitment to environmental education, exemplified, again, by proposing a separate AT on 'Environmental Geography', whatever that may be, rather than having the environmental perspective pervade the curriculum. Either you are committed to an environmental approach or you are not. Half hearted commitment is no good!

- lack of attention to values education and political literacy, despite the fact that these are mentioned in the aims
- lack of attention to assessment issues, which should have been integrated into the consideration of the ATs and programmes of study rather than left until later
- overemphasis on knowledge and understanding through the weighting given to 'to know' and 'to understand' in the statements of attainment
- lack of clarity about the notion of what exactly it means to 'understand'.

Possibly the main weakness of the Interim Report was, in my view, the failure to propose an imaginative overview of the subject, a clear, energizing and motivating directional focus which would set it on the road to achieving its undoubted potential as an essential part of every child's education. A major opportunity appeared to have been missed. Much would depend on the mounting of a rescue operation between the publication of the Interim Report and the production of the Final Report which was due to be completed by the end of April 1990.

The Final Report of the Geography Working Group appeared on schedule and was published in June 1990 (DES, 1990a). It was clear that an attempt had been made to meet the criticisms which were made of the Interim Report. There was, for example, considerable improvement in the treatment of ideas about enquiry. The statements of attainment targets were improved by the inclusion of a far greater range of command terms such as 'identify', 'locate', 'describe', 'compare', 'classify', 'demonstrate', 'explain', 'analyse', 'examine critically', and 'evaluate'. Most of the statements were now accompanied by an example or some examples.

The Attainment Targets were restructured and reordered as follows:

AT1: Geographical skills
AT2: The home area and region
AT3: The United Kingdom within the European Community
AT4: The wider world
AT5: Physical geography
AT6: Human geography
AT7: Environmental geography

There was some rationalization of the divisive ATs 3 and 4 of the Interim Report list and the geographical skills AT had been brought to the top of the list. Unfortunately, the AT on environmental geography had been left at the bottom!

Despite these attempts at improvement, there remained some major concerns. These may be summarized from the responses returned to the author from eleven experts in geographical education in English universities. The main issues of concern raised were:

- The ATs remained content based rather than process based. This was seen as a fundamental flaw in the proposals, which could lead to an emphasis on rote learning and factual recall in a subject which had demonstrated its value as a medium for the development of a range of skills and abilities through the study of content of genuine significance for continuing life on our small planet.

- The proposed curriculum was overloaded in terms of the sheer amount that had to be covered.

- There was prescription of examples to be studied and what was prescribed suggested a biased selection. It was felt that it would have been much more preferable to have set up clear criteria for selection for teachers to put into practice.

- There were inherent problems in achieving and evaluating progression.

- The way in which assessment would work was still far from clear.

- The report was seen as backward looking rather than forward looking in terms of the development of the geography curriculum and it was felt that this would alienate many highly professional teachers of the subject.

(Simon Catling summarizes the final stages of the production of the geography curriculum on page 21 and in Figure 1.4.)

Prospects

The imposition of a centralized system for control of the curriculum is the most radical development in the education system of England and Wales since the Education Act of 1944. The transition from a laissez-faire system of curriculum management to one where Statutory Orders set out what must be done by law, raises many important questions about the nature of the curriculum which will actually result.

In a study of the impact of centralization upon the geography curricula of 22 states and countries including China, Denmark, France, Hong Kong, Japan, Netherlands, New Zealand, Nigeria, Poland, South Africa, Sweden, USSR and some states in West Germany, USA and Australia (Naish, 1990), a common view to emerge what that a centralized curriculum has several potential advantages.

If there is sufficient flexibility to allow teachers in schools to contribute towards the process of curriculum development, a centralized curriculum can encourage a common body of knowledge, ideas and skills without stultifying teacher creativity. In Queensland, for example, it was felt that the curriculum framework involving school-based curriculum development through a system of co-operative procedures gave all parties ample opportunity to participate. In Michigan, geography teaching had been strengthened, it was claimed, through the publication of State Guidelines, while in New Zealand, a centralized system had helped to enhance the image of geography. In Nordrhein-Westfalen, guidelines provided a distinctive framework of objectives, but allowed teachers to select content. This framework was seen as facilitating the transfer of pupils between schools without interrupting progression in their geographical education.

Advantages mentioned by others included the provision of common aims so that teachers know what is expected of them and making it easier to monitor the curriculum. A range of textbooks on common themes may give teachers a wide choice of resources, while in developing countries, a centralized curriculum may result in more economical use of learning resources. The involvement of competent professional geographers in curriculum design was also recognized as a potential advantage.

There was a greater level of agreement about the possible constraints of a centralized curriculum. In particular there was concern that teachers' creativity may be limited, with less likelihood of innovation. Curricula, it was thought, tend to become too assessment orientated and those in control of the curriculum may assume too much power. The system of centralized control may become more important than the needs of the pupils. Confrontation may develop if the views of the centre are opposed to those of the periphery. If a decision taken at the centre is wrong, it is wrong for all pupils.

In general, respondents would like to see a flexible approach based on some kind of balance between centralization and decentralization, which will give teachers freedom of choice in terms of content and teaching approaches within a common framework. The correspondent from Nordrhein-Westfalen considered teachers' commitment, philosophy and skills as key elements of an enabling curriculum and felt that even within a highly centralized and inappropriate curriculum, good teachers will ensure that the experiences of their students are educationally worthwhile.

Conclusion

This chapter began with an examination of the benefits of curriculum development based on a view of the curriculum as a system. The development of the geography curriculum of England and Wales was then traced from the mid-1960s. While the Schools Council geography projects worked within the framework of a curriculum system, the Working Group for the National Curriculum reverted to a somewhat more assessment-led approach. The Group paid less attention to fundamental curriculum questions about the nature of the pupils and the potential of the subject as a medium for education and placed more emphasis on content than on process. It must be recognized that the Working Group was bound by the constraints of the 1988 Education Reform Act, and the centralized structures which followed from this.

In the immediate future, then, in England and Wales, the quality of experience enjoyed by pupils in their studies of geography will depend on the interpretations which teachers are able to make of the Statutory Orders which will follow from the Final Report of the Working Group. Experience suggests that teachers will make an effective job of it, given appropriate support in terms of resources and in-service enhancement.

Chapter Three
Curriculum Development in Universities
E.H. Brown and W.R. Mead

The speed of change in the character and content of geography has led to a nearly total transformation of the university curriculum in the space of a generation. Teaching programmes have become more flexible: examining procedures more complex. There is a general consensus about the first year curriculum. Thereafter a wide range of options confronts students who are required to make their own selection. The range is inseparable from the research interests and staffing levels of individual departments. Written communication remains the paramount skill, but all curricula allocate generous time to the acquisition by students of rapidly evolving new techniques. Field work and project work have a central place in all syllabuses, looking to the problems of present-day societies and economies as well as to those of the physical environment.

A generation of change

Curriculum development is a response to the changing character and content of geography set against the background of changing educational values and practices. The speed of change has resulted in a near total transformation of the university curriculum in the space of a generation. Naturally, change in the content of curricula has not been uniform throughout the country: the differentiation between departments is greater now than in the past. Departmental stamps of individuality are inseparable from the personalities of their members. It is good to have gurus, as well as radicals and conservatives around, creating, hastening or retarding the acceptance or promotion of new ideas and procedures. Whatever individual attitudes, the speed with which change has been and continues to be absorbed must be accounted a positive characteristic of those engaged in the discipline.

Curriculum development has been inseparable from the growth in student numbers and the expansion of university departments. Development has also been inseparable from the opportunities for increasing specialization in research, with staff anxious to incorporate their findings and experiences into their teaching programmes. Indeed, the pace of change (to a greater or lesser extent it is almost annual in most departments) is frequently such as to suggest that the subject is in a continuous state of experiment. It is as though the rigid curriculum that existed until a generation ago, especially in the University of London, has induced by way of reaction a system that is almost excessively flexible.

Curriculum change has impinged directly upon examining procedures, which have experienced parallel transformation. The introduction of the course unit system and a wide variety of methods of continuous assessment are in some respects attempts to offset the pressures of increased work load experienced at the undergraduate level from the tempo of change.

Independently of changes in the school syllabus and examination structures, the tendency for syllabuses in the university to draw away from those in the schools is heightened. Because school examination syllbuses change more slowly, the gap between information imparted in the schoolroom and that expected of a student arriving at a university department tends to widen.

During the course of the last generation, those responsible for planning undergraduate syllabuses have had to resolve the tensions between divergence and convergence in a developing subject, to accommodate that which is new within revised frameworks and to retain something of the art of geography in a technologically transformed milieu. The syllabus has always been an expression of a consensus, but increasingly democratic procedures have replaced oligarchical ones in its achievement. Partly as a result, procedures have tended to become more complicated and certainly more time-consuming.

Divergence and convergence

The institutionalization of geography (as with other disciplines) was initially accompanied by a certain straight-jacketing of teaching programmes which, with minor variations, acquired much the same features in most departments of geography. Courses, often of a bread-

and-butter character, were given by members of staff whose research interests (in so far as they had time and energy for such pursuits after completing their heavy teaching loads) lay for the most part elsewhere. A legacy of this feature tends to remain in the virtual core curriculum that persists for first year students. It retains a measure of allegiance to the old-established trinity of physical geography, human geography and techniques. Inevitably, it makes assumptions — often erroneous — as to what has been covered in the school syllabus. For example, such fundamental knowledge as the content of the geological column cannot be assumed. The prospective situation, with the possibility of a leaner syllabus in a changed 'A' level structure, is likely to reduce further the basic knowledge of geography acquired at school — and to stress the need for a 'traditional' first year (with even a measure of rote learning). In a way, it calls for a national school syllabus, with a body of information sufficiently clearly defined as to distinguish it from the content of the university syllabus. This could economize on time in first year university teaching and (as is not infrequently the case at present) reduce the need for 'unlearning' such topics as location theory which are commonly misunderstood. Concern with literacy, numeracy and graphicacy remains, though what is covered by the three words may differ somewhat from that which they embraced when W.G.V. Balchin first strung them together (Balchin, 1965).

The full consequence of the near exponential growth in the content of the subject only strikes undergraduates as they emerge from the more tightly controlled first year. Thereafter, the loosening of the structure of the curriculum confronts them with the responsibility of making choices (which repeats the experience suffered after GCSE/O level). The range and variety of courses incorporated within most university curricula can be both a stimulus and incubus to students. The divergences within the subject become more apparent, the more so because of the frequently narrowly circumscribed fields of research of teaching staff.

Depending upon the point of view, the curriculum is seen as offering either a wide range of options within a flexible framework or a seeming fragmentation of the subject with inherent problems of integration. As a result, at first sight, much of the contemporary curriculum appears to be far removed from what has been traditionally acknowledged as geography. This is certainly the case in some third-year options where undergraduates can be operating near the frontiers of research. Given this situation, it would seem wise at intervals to explain to all undergraduates the integrative forces in the subject and to underline the prevailing convergences. It is at this stage that the dichotomy between physical geographers and human geographers becomes more pronounced, with student reactions heightened because of the relative order presented by physical geography and the more anarchical array of courses in human geography. Because of its inherent character, geography cannot escape from the complexities that confront the social sciences as distinct from the apparent simplicities that favour the physical sciences. The situation is exaggerated because human geography has asserted itself forcefully in recent syllabuses.

On the organizational side, multiplication of options raises its own problems. It may lead to demand for courses in excess of the facilities available and to inadequate demand for others to justify the effort being expended on them. And since fashions in this respect may change within a matter of several years Pelion is piled on Ossa. The problem is compounded by the multiplication of joint degrees and course unit-based degrees in which geography is a component. It is not always easy to tailor a single honours course to meet the needs of joint and unit degree courses.

The accommodation of the new

The accommodation of the new calls for a continuing compromise in syllabus planning. In respect of content, it cannot imply the total rejection of the old. Often the new is a replacement of the old at a different level of understanding: sometimes it is the old approached from a different angle. The globe, the ultimate symbol of geography, has suffered neglect, save perhaps as a universal logo. The atlas, its cartographic complement and once familiar to every student, is less consulted than formerly; the 1:1 million world map, hardly ever. Yet increasing concern with global strategies and the ability to view the earth from space have restored macro-geographical considerations to favour — the very phrase 'one world' underlining the ultimate unity of geography itself. Global features of the syllabus range from plate tectonics (drifting continents *redivivus*) to desertification, from environmental pollution to famine. At this macro-level, globally-wide data bases have become the order of the day. No less important is the fact that there are now available technical means for handling them. One result is that the draughtsmen and women who for a generation drew highly professional illustrations for publication are frequently replaced by the technicians who are required to service the equipment that is increasingly employed for even undergraduate courses.

Appreciation of the world view has been reinforced by the development of satellite photography. Together with computergraphics, satellite imagery has given new meaning to those twin features of earlier syllabuses — maps and diagrams. Computer mapping and modelling call for different skills from those needed by the field surveying that was an integral part of geography syllabuses until not much more than a generation ago. The vocabulary associated with instruments central to survey and navigation seems arcane today. Astrolabe and sextant, theodolite and plane table appear to belong to a handmade age. Ever increasing refinement of machine-made equipment — from photogrammetric and remote sensing apparatus to electro-scanning microscopes — calls for new skills (and additional finance). Simultaneously the teaching sets of maps that were an integral part of many courses a generation ago have been consigned to the bottom drawers of map chests. Map projections, formerly a compulsory part of almost every university syllabus, have been eliminated (to the relief of teacher and taught alike)... And yet, their construction underlined two points of considerable consequence. First, they made plain the historic link between geography and mathematics. Secondly, their study had direct relevance in that it exposed the inherent dangers in the employment of the map as a political tool. Mercator 'thou shouldst be living at this hour' so that you could realize the errors that need to be expunged! Knowledge of those errors should still be part of every undergraduate syllabus.

It is interesting to see the old-time features of the syllabus appearing in a different guise or with a different emphasis. Two examples must suffice. First an essential feature of earlier syllabuses was a concern with the home region, the home country — the home continent too. The succession of volumes published for the meetings of the British Association confirm the place occupied in earlier syllabuses by the city region. In the same way that so-called regional geography (even when it assumed the form of area studies) has been reduced in the syllabus, so also the study of territory tributary to most university departments has tended to suffer an eclipse. Nevertheless, within the span of several university intakes, it became manifest that to be resident in a university city calls for at least a measure of attention to its character and problems, especially those of the inner areas of the capital and the older provincial cities. Thus, in the inter-war years, London's river claimed its own place in the university syllabus: London re-asserted its position with the work on the *Atlas of London* (Jones and Sinclair, 1968-9). The dramatic changes in its urban geography have demanded its re-instatement in the syllabuses of the London colleges.

The re-instatement is inseparable from the leap forward in the status of urban geography. The British are a nation of urban inhabitants, a characteristic slow to be accepted by geographers. The volume and variety of publications in the area of urban geography is witness to the changing attitude: so, too, the demand of students for urban courses in the syllabus. In the urban syllabus, the old can also appear in a new guise. Fieldwork, traditionally associated with the countryside and with the accent on physical geography, has been in part shifted to urban areas. Urban studies generally have the advantage that they raise no serious financial problems for participating students and they offer challenges in social geography no less valuable than those in physical geography. For example, they expose students to the problems of generalization that tax all social scientists. To come face to face with the issues of classification and imprecision on the ground are useful exercises in their own right. The fieldwork notebook, an integral feature of earlier examining procedures, is no more: but the reports required from urban studies are no less valuable as training exercises.

On the physical side of geography, one of the most distinctive of the changes in emphasis has been the increasing attention paid to physical processes, especially the role of water. Hydrology is a branch of physical geography which has immediate consequences for human geography in water management. At the same time, it is an admirable means of introducing the systems approach.

It is perhaps in the so-called quantitative revolution that the accommodation to the new has been most impressive. The quantitative approach has come to be regarded as a positive feature, not least because of its potential as a unifying force in the subject, being applicable with equal effect to both human and physical geography. It is significant because it brought statistical methods to the fore on the threshold of computerization. In the process, it gave rise to another new element in the syllabus — regional science (which at one time tended to become a major sub-branch of the subject). In a way, the introduction of quantitative methods has restored the historic link between geography and mathematics.

Across the entire curriculum — above and beyond the Marxist geography or the feminine geography that enter some teaching programmes — a new system of values has to be taken into account. In the past, physical geography — even in certain respects human geography — was regarded as an objective scientific study and therefore value-free. Today, it is accepted that value judgements affect scientific enquiry simply because scientists are human. The focus on processes — especially human processes — has automatically introduced value judgements of a social, political and economic character. And the values in themselves are changing. 'A curriculum is a grand time-bound surrealism,' wrote Hugh Kenner in a lively classroom essay in *A Handmade World* (1975). Small wonder that perception studies have become a critical feature of the contemporary syllabus.

The cultivation of skills

All across the syllabus, too, there has been a growing emphasis on the cultivation of an increasing number of skills — skills which frequently give to geographers the edge over those who study many other disciplines when they enter the labour market. The very language of the contemporary curriculum bears witness, with its data evaluation and hypothesis testing, its computer manipulation and simulation, its modelling programmes, its remote sensing and image analysis.

At the same time, to keep matters in perspective, it is never forgotten that for most geographers the art of communication remains the most important skill developed and refined at the university. The ability to produce reports from personally conducted investigations has become an integral part of most syllabuses. The cultivation of the skill is also implicit in tutorial essays — a part of most syllabuses which has been subject to less change than most, save that the handwritten essay has yielded successively to typescripts and to the product of the word processor.

The continuing refinement of concepts and the multiplication of specialisms has called for a new vocabulary. This introduces a problem calling for tutorial consideration which was not manifest a generation ago. It implies that undergraduates need to learn a new language — which the multiplication of geographical dictionaries reflects. But dictionaries of this kind are what George Steiner would call private thesauruses as distinct from those that embrace the current vulgate. It is interesting that at the top scientific level a simple language is encouraged, 'Royal Society prose, low-keyed, unmetaphoric, crammed with nouns,' as Hugh Kenner has described it in *The Mechanic Muse* (1987). The employment of everyday discourse needs to be a continuing part of the taught syllabus, for it is only a minority of geographers who are likely to enter the professional circle after graduation and to enjoy the luxury of using their own language. It is all very well (as Jacques Ellul puts it) to be possessed by the machine: to be possessed by words is likely to be more important for the majority (Ellul, 1981). Possession by words (and ideas) is still an examined part of most university courses and it has its fullest expression in the still quite widely favoured essay paper — necessarily hand-written.

The art of reading is taken for granted. Syllabuses are crammed with recommended readings and with reading lists ranging over hundreds of books and journals. The literature covered by individual students is common to an ever diminishing number. The textbook has a diminishing role: while increasing attention is paid to the proliferating specialist journals. The reading party disappeared with the Mackinderian phase of geographical evolution: the reading week still lingered to the middle of the century (certainly in other subjects if not in geography). Never was more geographical literature published than today: proportionately less is probably read than a generation ago. Nor can the occasional tutorials afford to neglect extra-curricular reading.

An accent on participation

The accent on participation is inseparable from the educational philosophy of the day. The approach has been partly by way of the emphasis placed upon 'problem' issues. Indeed, for a while, the word 'problem' seemed to find its way with almost disarming frequency into the course title. The problem approach has manifested itself in a number of different ways. It appeared first in the traditional courses, which were given a new twist. Thus, area studies (regional geography) focused its attention on the problems of the areas concerned. Simultaneously, a new fillip was given to political geography. Environmental problems sprang to the foreground — pollution leading them, almost every aspect of it being of geographical significance.

Participation has been especially significant in project work — which brings the student body into direct contact with the community and with what A.N. Whitehead called 'the stubborn facts of life'. Project work is favoured because it may spring from hypothetical assumptions and call for testing by direct observation. It generally assumes data collection, the construction of data bases and the computer handling and processing of material. It provides the basis for the widely (but not universally) favoured undergraduate dissertations. In an ideal situation, there may be collaborative endeavour, with different students undertaking different parts of a larger project. The roots of such project work are probably to be found in the Land Utilization Survey of the 1930s. Project work also gathers together the employment of a variety of skills, again underlining the unity of the subject.

In some respects, it is paradoxical that at the same time as participation in project activity demands objectivity, a parallel change in the syllabus reflects a new concern with subjectivity. This springs from perception studies, with mental reactions to geographical phenomena, which have become an integral part of the contemporary syllabus.

A temporary consensus

Syllabuses in universities are increasingly likely to be no more than the product of short-term consensus. Those who ultimately prepare undergraduate syllabuses are faced with a task in didactics which has become anything but easy. They must recognize the reality of what can be expected of students. They must realize that syllabus change rarely leads to rationalization — at best perhaps it makes for a redistribution of effort. In pursuit of their objectives, most departments tend to agree upon an infinity of compromises which offer the students the greatest possible choice coincident with the minimum of constraints demanded in the name of a respectable geographical training. There will be continuous lamentation as the old is discarded: equal lamentation as the new fails to live up to its ideal.

Within this framework of compromises, there remain certain guiding principles. First, it may not be the task of syllabus planners to adjust their courses to the career needs of students (the diversity of careers chosen is in any case too wide for this to be possible). Nevertheless, the syllabus cannot fail to be influenced by what is fashionably defined as 'relevant'. Certainly, the current stress placed upon the vocational aspects of geography and the concern with participation are closely related. The old Le Play formula 'place, people, work' is not very far away from current thinking, though it has experienced something of a sea change in definition.

Next, adjustment to the new age of prescription, which heralded the passing of the age of description, has brought in train major changes to teaching programmes. Models with predictive values, ideally capable of testing, have entered the arena. They imply the broadening of the theoretical base of the subject and a new emphasis upon methodology and technology. Models tend to enter severally and separately in individual courses. At least it is to be hoped that students are aware of the published compendia in which models are brought together and the integrative features between them are shown. The same applies to the unavoidable concern over the teaching of the philosophy behind geography and the ideologies that affect its appraisal.

All around the periphery of the syllabus, geography advances into the territories of other disciplines. In parallel, others advance into the accepted domain of geography. Time was, for example, when the word 'environment' was the virtual prerogative of geographers — to be succeeded by a time when they nearly lost control of it to others. Future syllabus-makers must heed this inter-disciplinary development and find a slot in which the links that exist between geography and other disciplines can be explained and discussed. Joint degrees have all too often lacked a bridging course and have tended to consist of two unrelated parts (with a correspondingly heavier load for their students to bear).

Finally, the syllabus must make plain the purpose of geography without sacrificing its spirit. If its content does not result in a heightened awareness of the landscape (be it rural or urban) and stir up an element of passion about the human condition associated with it, something has failed along the line. The exciting can easily be made dull: the ordinary, extraordinarily exciting. But perhaps this is a subjective matter which ultimately springs out of the infectious enthusiasm of those who proclaim the gospel.

Chapter Four
Teacher Education and Classroom Reality
Gerry Hones

The strength of the links between 'teacher education' (seen all too frequently as being too concerned with 'theory') and 'classroom reality' depends very largely on the work of those people generally known as the 'subject method tutors'.

This chapter seeks to examine the role and functions of these key individuals, suggesting that the breadth of their work requires a title, such as 'curriculum tutors', which reflects their wide ranging commitments. The need to develop and maintain strong professional contact with different groups of colleagues in higher education as well as teachers in schools is included among these commitments.

Teaching to teach

Many teachers may see the phrasing of the title to this chapter as reinforcing their view that a dichotomy does exist between 'teacher education' and 'classroom reality'. Teachers working in the schools have often felt that those concerned in teacher education were too far removed from the real world, able to be unrealistic in their consideration of educational issues as they remain secure in the knowledge that they would rarely (sometimes in the past even never!) face the need to put their ideas into actual practice. This view has often been expressed in the aphorism

> If you can, do it!
> If you cannot do it, teach about it!
> If you cannot teach, teach teachers ...

even to continue by suggesting that researchers are further down the line! In a confusion of metaphors, overworked teachers at 'the chalk face' have seen their counterparts as too comfortably ensconced in the 'ivory tower' of higher education and only willing to make the occasional foray into the real world outside.

Clearly, the basic problem is how to link theory with practice, how to match ideals with reality, in ways which can be accepted by everyone involved in the process. Key individuals in what is an extremely complex pattern of relationships have generally been the subject method tutors in the departments of education and this chapter will focus on their work in order to illustrate some of the issues involved. Although the term 'subject method tutor' is still generally in use, being a modification of the earlier title 'master (*sic*) of method', in fact these tutors play a much broader role and are concerned with the curriculum in a wider and more constructive way than would be possible were they to concentrate on 'method' alone. As the next section attempts to illustrate, this role could better be represented by the term 'curriculum tutor'.

An attempt will be made to see how the role and function of method tutors has changed over recent decades and what their contribution could be in future.

The subject method tutor

Unlike most of the rest of the lecturing staff in higher education, the method tutor has always had the difficult task of developing close working links in at least *three* major specialist areas. This has meant there has been a need to maintain strong professional relationships with three different groups of people, all expecting a different type of background experience and competence, seeking a different style of credibility.

The *first* of these major working relationships links the tutor with other lecturers in higher education whose responsibility is to teach the (academic) subject concerned at degree level while also being involved in research, both as a supervisor at postgraduate level and in an active personal capacity. As far as these other tutors are concened, education lecturers have long been seen as 'different' for a number of reasons such as: *1.* their regular work in and with schools; *2.* their having less time available for research; and *3.* the fundamentally different perspective from which they view the subject.

It is not difficult to see that the method tutors need this regular contact in order to keep abreast of developments in the subject so that they may, in turn, be in a position to use such knowledge in their work

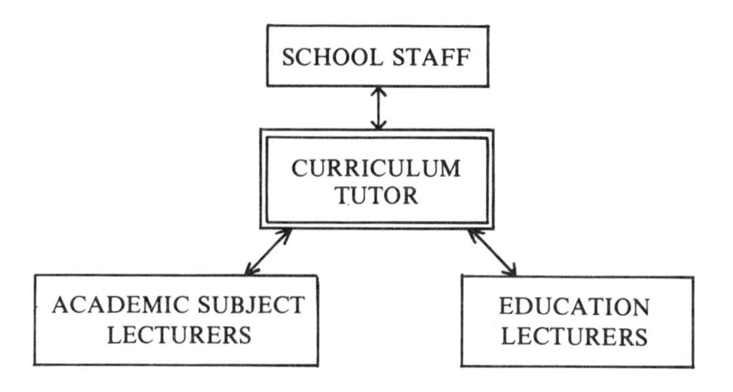

Figure 4.1: Professional links: secondary and higher education (source: Hones)

with student-teachers and teachers in schools, probably acting as a filter through which new ideas are passed after modification. Method tutors will often be in a position to facilitate curriculum development in this way through their work in such professional bodies as the Geographical Association, in-service education and the external examination system.

Difficult decisions

It is often, however, difficult for the method tutor in the role of 'facilitator' to be sure how much the changing philosophy of a subject, how many new concepts or techniques, should be transferred into the preparation of student-teachers and thus into the school scene. It is also difficult to decide on the speed of change, particularly before the innovations have been given the official status they so often need through inclusion in an external examination syllabus. Some of the student teachers will feel frustrated and inhibited if they are not encouraged to take recently acquired knowledge, culled partly from their undergraduate courses, into the school system. Others will believe that the problems associated with this introduction will provide an extra burden to add to the already formidable task of coping with classroom management. Many will thus be likely to prefer a more traditional line of action, temporarily at least, whatever their real feelings are towards the innovations. Such developments in the teaching of a subject need to take place in a way, and at a pace, which is conducive to their being tried out carefully and sympathetically by all concerned. This will often mean that the method tutor is in the critical and sensitive central role of influence. It is not surprising, therefore, that many of these tutors have been very involved in the work of the Schools Council Projects. Some have been assisting these important examples of curriculum development through initial training courses and in-service work, and now continue to support teachers working on project-based courses.

Method tutors and education

In addition to developments in the actual subject being taught, there may well also be major related changes occurring in the broader educational sense. It is generally through working with colleagues in education departments that the tutor will be kept informed about such events. This is a *second* broad band of communication, with the method tutor needing to maintain credibility with colleagues by demonstrating a professional awareness of advances in a wide sphere of educational areas. Once again the task is basically to be able to evaluate such changes and seek to help translate them into the school situation where appropriate. Whether it is the need to understand a different style of learning theory or the potential for computer assisted learning in the classroom, the method tutor must first be able to communicate effectively with specialist colleagues and then, through the system and methodology of 'teacher education', provide the link with 'classroom reality'.

The student teachers concerned will once again be looking to their method tutor for expert knowledge in a broad spectrum of education in order to have the confidence to co-operate in the work of translation into the classroom context. The very breadth of knowledge expected could lead to some loss in credibility but the tutor's general experience of marrying theory with practice should compensate for this, especially when the tutor is seen to act as 'organizer' rather than 'expert', referring the student to other specialist tutors and/or relevant literature. The students will also be expecting (even demanding) that the tutor should be a competent practitioner in the school situation, able to demonstrate expertise in practice.

Tutors and teachers

This, then, leads to the *third* and crucial connection, that between the tutor and all the staff involved in the school. Although the various staff – head teacher, faculty or department head, teacher responsible for teaching practice organization, classroom teacher – will all see the tutor from different perspectives according to their own specific role, they will all expect the tutor to be an experienced classroom teacher who is familiar with the contemporary school scene and all the practical issues involved. Building on this foundation, they will search for a positive working relationship which is a partnership between teachers, student and tutors. Naturally it is the student who is the raison d'être for this work, and it is the student whom one would expect to be gaining most benefit, but the interaction and the growing relationship between teacher and tutor is of major importance, both in meeting the needs of the present and providing the basis for future action.

It is clear that the teacher of today has long been working in a very complex situation which is comprised of many components. Most of these are interrelated in ways which further complicate the issues involved.

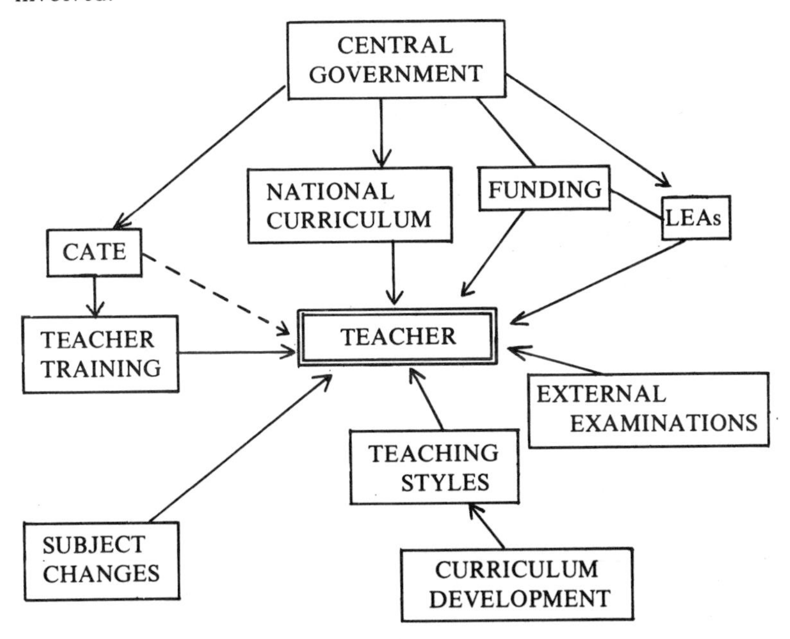

CATE = Council for the Accreditation of Teacher Education
LEA = local education authority

Figure 4.2: Changing influences on the teacher (source: Hones)

The diagram portrays a situation which includes many of these factors, none of which remains static for long and most of which have been undergoing major changes vary rapidly. Some are on such a scale that the teachers will feel far removed from the actual decision-making process (for example, the creation of the National Curriculum) but others can place teachers in a more active role by giving them the opportunity (or burden in some eyes!) to decide on how the 'classroom reality' will actually operate. The diagram does not, however, attempt to reflect the complexity of the network within which different topics impinge on each other. The pressures are such that it is essential to consider ways in which teachers can be helped to handle this dynamic situation and a genuine partnership with those concerned with teacher education could offer support in many different ways.

Probably the most obvious method is through in-service education. The tutor is in an excellent position to work with teachers in identifying their needs, in conjunction with the LEA advisers, initiating the most appropriate programme for INSET. The method tutor is likely to know who could best provide the needed input, how the work can be structured and what outcomes could reasonably be expected. Less immediately apparent than the formal in-service work, however, is the equally important informal support given on a more regular basis. While the teachers provide the 'local' support and opportunity for the classroom experience, the tutor and students bring into the situation different viewpoints which could provide the basis for comparative studies.

Partnerships

An example of the type of partnership that is possible took place recently when a research group at Bath University School of Education (comprised of a teacher and the geography and mathematics method tutors) undertook a co-operative venture with three local education authorities. Given support by the Microelectronics Education Programme to develop a new type of computer software for use in the geography classroom, the development team involved the LEA advisers and local teachers from the outset. As ideas were turned into a new program, trials were arranged at every stage possible with the teachers providing a crucial evaluation of the system's value in the classroom. A range of in-service courses helped in a number of ways. Short courses (mainly one or two day workshops) provided introductory experience and longer courses (DES funded) were able to build on these. In the latter instances, teachers were actively involved in the production of databases which were specifically designed to meet some of their own particular curriculum needs. They carried out their own classroom trials and, over several months, provided invaluable assistance in evaluating the materials (Hones, 1987).

Believing that this work with schools must be at the core of a method tutor's overall activities, it has been most encouraging to note the growing strength of the relationship over the last two decades. The previous pattern of the sporadic, infrequent, Olympian visit to the school by the tutor is now rarely found. The general picture now is a form of partnership with the basic purpose of bringing 'teacher education' and 'classroom reality' together. In many instances, method tutors undertake a regular teaching responsibility in schools, with and without their students, so that mutual trust and confidence can be built up. There are also examples (as operated at Bath University) where the university tutor has taught a sufficiently large block of time in the school in order to release the school teacher to spend the equivalent time acting as method tutor in the university. In other universities (for example, Oxford), much of the initial training course is firmly school-based with teachers thus playing the leading role. Such arrangements as these can be of great value but it must be remembered that differences do exist between the two roles as each, teacher and tutor, face different pressures. Whereas the teacher (Figure 4.2) encounters one set of demands, which are basically external to but bound to influence the work of the partnership, the university tutor is also having to cope with another separate group of pressures, some of which are well removed from the school scene. As well as the demands of advanced courses and departmental administration, there are also the requirements concerned in the supervision of research students.

The impact of the criteria for initial training as defined by the Council for the Accreditation of Teacher Education (following the recommendations of the Elton Committee) has been considerable. The particular importance attached to an increase in the degree of partnership between teacher training institutions and schools is evidenced, for example, in the request that institutions should ensure that experienced teachers should be more involved in the planning of courses and selection of students, as well as supervision and assessment of students' practical work. Such requirements will be welcomed by most teachers who will also recognize the extra demands on tutors in gaining more classroom experience. They will also appreciate some of the effects of appraisal schemes as they appear in higher education institutions because they will be able to draw a parallel with their own situation. Teachers are less likely, however, to realize the importance of some of the other pressures.

Research

One such is the ever-present demand on the tutor to operate research, preferably by attracting the necessary funding from outside the institution itself, and to contribute to the existing literature in a subject area. Evidence of this work is needed on a number of scales: *1. the personal* – to demonstrate academic quality, assist the appraisal scheme and thus influence future progress in the system; *2. the departmental* – for use in the increasingly sharp competition for resources between departments; *3. the institutional* – when the 'battle' moves into the national scale!

The importance of this research by tutors is less likely to be accepted in school when the topic is seen as esoteric and remote from their viewpoint. Such research can, on occasions, reinforce the stereotype of theoretical isolation, being seen as the producer of a type of academic self indulgence! On the other hand many method tutors have seen such research and its publication strengthen their reputation in the schools. Examples abound of where method tutors have been instrumental in forms of curriculum development which have proved to be extremely well received in schools. The three major Schools Council Geography Projects all had tutors from colleges and universities leading the teams – Geography for the Young School Leaver (Avery Hill College), Geography 14-18 (Bristol University), Geography 16-19 (Institute of Education, University of London) – and sought to marry the strengths of higher education with expertise in the schools. A more recent example is the Geography, Schools and Industry Project established by the Geographical Association in 1984 and based in the Department of Educational Studies at Oxford with Graham Corney as Director.

Involvement

It should be noted that there is a long tradition of involvement by tutors in the work of the Geographical Association, at all levels of operation – acting in many instances as local branch officers, as members of central committees, undertaking such key roles as chairpersons of Working

Groups, editors and authors, publicity officer, chairman of the Education Standing Committee, Assistant Hon. Secretary and on several occasions, as President of the Association. Norman Graves himself comes into this last category.

This work is given high priority by tutors and on such occasions as the publication of the booklet *Geography in the National Curriculum – A Viewpoint from The Geographical Association* (Daugherty, 1989) one can see the critical importance of the co-operation between the tutors and teachers strongly represented in the Working Group that prepared this response. Another example was the work of a group concerned with the use of language in geography teaching and learning. Set up by the Education Standing Committee of the Geographical Association, the Working Group included two tutors, Bryan Stephenson and Michael Williams, as well as four teachers. In addition to their co-operative work under the auspices of their professional subject association, teachers and tutors have also become increasingly involved in the external examination system, with the changing assessment structure requiring more 'face-to-face' moderation in the examining process.

Books written by tutors on more 'theoretical' topics have become important additions to the teacher's library (Bailey, 1974; Boardman, 1983, 1985; Graves, 1975a, 1979a; Hall, 1976; Jay, 1981; Marsden, 1976; Naish, Rawling and Hart, 1987; Slater, 1982; Walford, 1973, 1981a and b; Wiegand and Orrell, 1982; Williams, 1976.) Textbooks for school use have also proved to be an excellent bridge in many ways (Bale, 1976; Robinson, 1975; Slater, 1986; Tidswell, 1973), particularly at such times of major change as when geography became 'new'! The tutor is strengthening the relationship by showing a willingness to contribute in a very practical way designed to help the classroom teacher. At times the combination results in joint authorship, tutor and teacher (Cole and Beynon, 1968-72; Graves, Lidstone and Naish, 1987a; Marsden and Marsden, 1987; Riley and Spolton, 1974; Robinson and Jackson, 1984).

It is thus suggested that the method tutor's role is complex but by no means impossible to fulfil and certainly full of rewarding opportunities. In many situations the tutor is in the best possible position to provide the link between teachers in training and the realities of the actual classroom. There may well be occasions when these professional activities potentially conflict with such other needs as the pursuit of research but the hope is that even then the conflict can often be resolved by relating the research to the professional needs in the classroom.

A case study

As has already been suggested, such co-operation is most needed at times of major curriculum development. As a case study, to illustrate and emphasize some of the encouraging ways in which co-operative action can occur, this concluding section considers the work of the 'Geography 16-19' Project.

Based in the Institute of Education at the University of London and with a method tutor as Director (Michael Naish), geography teachers were strongly involved from the outset as members of the project team, in the supporting Consultative Committee, and in work which was school-based. After a major survey to gather opinions on the contribution of geography to the education of the 16-19 year-old, a strong regional network was set up in order to ensure that practising teachers should be directly involved. After assisting the team to develop the basic ideas for the new curriculum framework, teachers' groups helped by producing new resource units, trialling the materials and the courses, and regularly providing the feedback needed by the project team. The story of this early partnership is well documented (Naish, Rawling and Hart, 1987) and there was also a booklet illustrating a case study of how teacher education was involved (Corney, 1981).

Now that the project's curricular ideas are well established in geographic education, the links between 'teacher education' and 'classroom reality' continue strongly. Of the 20 regional co-ordinators operating the national support system set up to assist teachers working with '16-19' courses, nearly half are classroom teachers, others are method tutors, and the rest are mainly LEA advisers. This formal network is also well supported by the work of a number of method tutors as they involve their PGCE student teachers in their curriculum development work, assisting them to understand the implications for the classroom of undertaking the type of teaching required by the 'Geography 16-19' curricular structure and preparing them to cope with the demands in practice.

Although a great deal has already been achieved, much remains to be done in linking 'teacher education' with 'classroom reality'. Joint workshops involving tutors, students and teachers are already operating in order to help with course design and resource materials but there is a need for careful research into a number of aspects of Geography 16-19 courses. The strong emphasis on enquiry learning, for example, has required many teachers to face up to a radical change in their teaching style and attitude so that much more needs to be known about the effects on both teacher and student. Another topic in need of active research stems from the project's focus on the examination of environmental issues and the different demands on both teacher and student that result. Although the handling of controversial issues has long been recognized as needing sensitive treatment, more still needs to be understood if teachers are to gain the right type of supportive framework. A third example of necessary research lies in the study of the potential value of different aspects of information technology in the classroom, for example in relation to enquiry learning and accessibility to databanks of information, (Kent, 1983; Kent and Lewis, 1987).

Conclusion

'Teacher education' and 'classroom reality' are increasingly being seen as interdependent with the 'curriculum tutors' acting as catalysts, continually strengthening the links between different elements of the system. As a geography teacher who became a 'geography method tutor' at 'the Institute', Norman Graves has throughout his career always shown himself to be a true 'curriculum tutor'. Not surprisingly, the depth and breadth of his work were deservedly recognized in his appointment as Professor of Geography Education. The present strong state of geography education, with all the exciting prospects of future development, owes much to his unique contribution over the years.

Chapter Five
Geography and Communication: a new challenge for the geography curriculum

Henriëtte S. Verduin-Muller

The world in its unity and diversity is studied in geography. Thus it seems to go without saying that the extension of communication facilities should promote geographic education. Does it indeed? Not per se, but the potential is there. Unfortunately the geographic knowledge produced often lacks coherence of content and effective means of communication. The geography teacher, educated and trained to formulate and to design lessons, is the one to open the student's eyes to the phenomena of the communications revolution in intelligible ways.

Geography always has been an important field in education, a field becoming more important in respect of the development and improvement of communication facilities. Attention will be paid in this chapter to the interaction between geographic education and the communications revolution, and the inherent consequences of this interaction for the geography curriculum.

Awareness of space in the sense of environment has a long tradition. We could suggest that human awareness of and for the environment is as old as the concern for existence. In building a shelter, in making a living, through hunting, fishing or agriculture, environmental awareness and adequate reaction are simply essential. In other words without reacting intelligently to the environment humans cannot survive. In addition to immediate environmental awareness people began to wonder, for reasons of safety and curiosity, about what was beyond the direct environment.

The development of geography

In his *Geography in Education*, Graves has excellently described and explained the coming into existence of geography as a school subject (Graves, 1975a). The study of place and its liveable and less liveable aspects has for long been the aim of geography. In the course of time geographers began to sharpen their questions to consider the character and use of the environment.

Next to the 'where' and 'what-is-there' questions, the crucial and analytical 'why' and 'how' questions were posed. In asking the 'why' and 'how' questions the discipline, so to speak, hooked on to the human being, *the* user of space. Nowadays, perhaps especially in the more developed work, the decision to make specific use of the environment is of course a very complex one.

The 'why' question leads to interpretation and explanation of such specific use. Distribution of goods and services and interrelationships between physical, social-economic and cultural phenomena are studied. Geographers may now be concerned with future planning and prospective views may be stated. From a more or less descriptive discipline, geography developed into an analytical and prospective one.

Things always happen somewhere in space. The fact of spatial location is, especially in an educational respect, attractive, because it represents something realistic and is perceptible. The 'where' and consequently the 'what' can be described in words or expressed in visual images. But describing and explaining differ considerably. Often, there is a world in between the two processes.

'Why' questions can never be answered once and for all. An explanation given holds at best for the present moment. New facts may always turn up, refined arguments be brought in, interdependence might become clearer or a supposed interdependence may not exist at all. We owe such new perspectives to more research and better technology, as well as to more precise information and communication.

Paying attention first to the 'where' and 'what' questions and then to the 'why' and 'how' questions is fundamental in geographic education. It not only does justice to geography and aspects of its interdisciplinary context, but also can be related to the student's maturation. The human, it might be the young or the adult student, in asking questions concerning the 'where', 'what', 'why' and 'how' of the environment and its use, on the local, the regional or supra-regional level, has the right to get clear and in-depth answers. In consequence the content has to be of high quality as well as user-friendly. This means that information should be highly structured, optimally expressed and well-considered with regard to the medium used.

Communication

Communication as such is inherent to human life, even in the most primitive living situations. Without communication, or more precisely information supply, humans simply cannot survive. But it is its world-wide potential that makes communication so important at this time (Verduin-Muller, 1982, 1-30). The increase in communication facilities is indeed impressive. We will briefly go into this phenomenon.

The diversity of print and non-print media has grown spectacularly since the mid-1970s and travel has also expanded enormously. The business of printing books, including textbooks, is flourishing. A comparison between the supply of books, including the appearance and outfitting of bookshops between the mid-1960s and the mid-1980s is really striking. Main European newspapers can be bought all over Western Europe the same day a few hours after appearance and, depending on time difference, one day later in other parts of the world. The content of typical world-wide papers is transmitted by satellite and printed close to the market, eventually completed by (macro-) regional news. A good example is the *Wall Street Journal*, which has a USA, a European and an Asian edition. All three have the world news, transmitted by satellite, in common, but are flexible with respect to more specific regional news. This is added at the printing/publishing location. The editions all have a similar appearance.

Radio and television disseminate by satellite, messages and information about the immediate location, region or on a more world-wide scale, thus bringing places straight into the living rooms. The most recent and diverse information is available from data-bases and can be retrieved at a moment's notice. Documents can be made accessible from a distance and studied via a screen. Private persons have direct personal access to friends and relatives all over the world through clear-sound telephone contact. To make the consequences of the revolution in communication facilities still more impressive, there is the enormously enlarged possibility of travel by train, boat, car and plane. As never before in history humans, young and old, are moving around for business and vacation purposes.

We could continue for several pages about the penetration of communication (and information) facilities into everyday life. But it was our aim, for the purpose of this chapter, only to signal the phenomenon. All ideas, all events, need, when communicable, a medium to transmit the content. Moreover the (supposed) target group must be reached. Therefore the message, the information, or whatever the content of the communication act may be called, must be offered in an orderly way. After all it is the communicator's aim that the message will be picked up and processed by the receiver. First it will be necessary to present the message clearly and in a straightforward manner in every respect.

A presentation has two main aspects: an expressive and a technological one. In general the purely technological side of the communication act is well covered. In the last decade communication has not only expanded spatially but also gained in technical efficiency. Now the presentation is solved technologically, it seems high time to pay attention to the expression of the content in relation to the potentialities of the related medium. And indeed this is just what is happening: interest in expression is growing. The concept of 'design', so popular for industrial products, urban planning and housing is gradually also becoming an issue in the context of knowledge products.

Reasons for this trend are complex. In my opinion the world-wide extension of communication together with its high technological quality and the demand for products which inform, invite this shift. In other words it makes sense to study the theory and practice of the expression of content. Picked up by geography educators, awareness of the expression trend could influence teaching positively.

A new challenge for the geography curriculum

What then will be the new challenge for the geography curriculum when thinking of geography plus communication? The question is easily posed, but the answer is complicated. Full explanation and reflection would fill many pages. An essay, however, does not give that much space, neither literally nor figuratively, but it is clear that geography communication activities can be integrated into the curriculum and so into normal classwork: no new or specific learning/teaching situations have to be set up. Let us consider some of the actual activities.

The increase in communication facilities together with easy accessibility has brought us more and more diverse information in the sense of data and messages. This has the potential to lead to openness and understanding. Has the improvement of communication facilities brought us closer to reality? By closer we not ony mean nearer as to space and time, but, in particular, in terms of understanding. As far as understanding is concerned we have good reasons for doubt. Facts and actions as aspects of the 'where' and 'what' can be located, described and shown, but do not include automatically the 'why' and 'how'. Explaining the 'why' and 'how' in such a way that understanding takes place is, as argued above, of a different order. And it is just the understanding of the nearby and far-away world which is so much needed.

Unfortunately there are people, among them geographers, often those having a wide knowledge of the subject, who think that to name and show events leads to automatic understanding. This is a misconception well known to teachers. The problem is, moreover, that so often during acts of communication, especially in television and radio broadcasting and in low quality newspapers, presentation of messages suggests an explanation at the same time: the setting of the tone and text are convincing and serious, the content in words and/or visual images customarily short and penetrating. Apart from the aim of the act of communication, each medium also has its own potentialities. A medium should not be used for content it is not suited for. The content might be, roughly speaking, too much or too little for the medium chosen or available.

Textbooks, newspaper articles, a-v series, radio programmes or television programmes differ principally as media for communication. One is not necessarily better than the other, but only different in achieving the posed aim. It does not make sense to compare a helicopter and a jumbo jet as means of transportation, since each has its own merits. Over the years a medium can evolve. The medium might undergo a refinement in a technical sense; the function become multipurpose. Parallel with improvement and enlargement, the medium is normally gaining efficiency as a means of communication. In recent times television and computers are vivid examples of such a development and further back in history the evolution of the textbook may be mentioned.

To transform ideas or instances, in our case geographic content, for communication, words and images can be produced. To attain maximum communication of the content, both forms of expression, the verbal and the visual, must be used complementarily and not substitutionally. Awareness of the complementarity between word and image is essential, but unfortunately not always recognized and experienced. Moreover, things can be 'said' in different ways. Putting content as expressed via any medium is and ought to be a point of discussion. The coherence of content and medium indeed is at the heart of the matter. Optimally there should be a feeling of shared responsibility between the designer in the sense of devising the conceptualization and composition of the content and the designer as an actual materializer. The content-designer and the medium designer should know about each other's discipline, so they become real partners in the making of the knowledge product under consideration.

We think that school education, as far as geography and its connection with communication is concerned, has a very special task today and will be even more important in the near future. Communication facilities will continue to increase and with that the number of knowledge products. Communication facilities, though, need to be *used.*

A challenge needs action! What kind of action could be undertaken to fit communication into geography curriculum activities? We will give some examples adopted from educational practice in which students have been involved. The teacher aware of the importance of geography plus communication as an educational issue and willing to meet the challenge will easily find opportunities to experiment and put ideas into practice.

A good start is to focus the student's attention on communications in everyday use, that is to say well-known, geography-based knowledge products (e.g., textbooks, articles in newspapers, certain radio and television programmes, as well as computer software) with the intention to 'see' the geographical content as expressed by the medium.

Proposals to examine geographic aspects of current events in newspapers and articles in magazines, specific themes dealt with in geographic textbooks and geographic documentary films, often together with the educational use, certainly are not new (Robbins, 1933, 561-565; Thralls, 1958, 161-189; Verduin-Muller, 1964, 77-111; Monk, 1983, 271-273; Massey, 1986, 116-119). Frances Slater, for example, has made use of articles in newspapers, magazines and books in her textbook *People and Environments*, (Slater ed., 1986). In relation to the geographic theme under consideration the student is invited to reflect on and to analyse the text extracts printed in this book. Diagnosing the content of the knoweldge product in relation to the medium used, is obviously a gain for the student's education.

The teacher should carefully organize discussion, which can effectively be done by putting questions and asking students to reflect on the given answers. The questions refer directly to the 'where', 'what', 'why' and 'how' of the content and to the communication means used. Clearly the medium must be considered in relation to the content and not seen for its own sake. The analysis should be marked and taken up as normal behaviour in respect to the use of a knowledge product. Students must realize that in daily life it is quite normal to 'investigate' consumer goods, to weigh a purchase. The way of doing this depends upon the 'form' of the knowledge product: a book, an article, a television programme show differences in access. However, this does not affect the essence of the proposed 'rules'.

Many omnipresent knowledge products could serve the purpose. As a first example, the geography textbook may be cited as a product in which the author communicates geographic knowledge important enough to be learnt and to meet the examination requirements at the same time. The book can be introduced as a whole, then one chapter can be reviewed as a geographic communication product, followed eventually by a comparison of the whole with the chapter as an element. Geography-based knowledge products are, like most knowledge products, easy to come by and to be made available. An interesting newspaper article, fitting into the geography curriculum, can be photocopied and analysed as a knowledge product. Also a magazine article, together with its visual images, may serve the proposed aim. And of course the widely used video-recorder makes it attractive to use a geography programme as a knowledge product. The same is true for computer programs. At the moment they are still taken too much for granted within the geography curriculum as they are.

The question now arises as to whether the geography teacher could meet the challenge. I am convinced that such is the case, because the type of expertise needed is in principle that acquired by a well-educated and trained geography teacher. The well-educated and trained teacher has a good knowledge of the discipline and a thorough training in educational theory and practice, and thus in educational communication.

Such training has gradually come into being since the early 1960s in many countries. One of the first examples was that developed at the Institute of Education, in the University of London, and continued and extended by Norman Graves. I well remember the first of many talks with Norman in which we discussed the requirements for a functional education and training programme for geography teachers. This happened in July 1964, during the 20th IGU Conference in London, when both of us had just been appointed to posts in geography education. The training of geography teachers as developed by Norman Graves and his colleagues in London, prospered over the years, and his entrepreneurial activities in the field of geographic education influenced many generations of geography teachers for the good, world wide.

So, teacher trainees nowadays explicitly learn to conceptualize and to structure geographic content in respect of optimal educational communication. In doing so, different types of aids are used: books, texts, audio-visual materials, etc. The next step then is to take the prepared lesson into the classroom to communicate effectively, an activity determined by many and variable factors.

Teachers do not always realize that, as part of their profession, they have at their disposal such essential skills and values. And no wonder, because they are focusing upon good geography teaching, that is the 'where', 'what', 'why', and 'how' questions and not on the communicative setting and aspects of the knowledge products they use during the actual teaching.

My point is that instead of being busy giving a geography lesson in which use is made of knowledge products such as texts, visual aids, computer software, etc., it is also possible to work the other way round, i.e. analyzing the content of the knowledge products from the point of view of their function of communicating geographic information. This is particularly important where the geographical 'why" and 'how' questions are concerned, because, as suggested earlier in this chapter, explanation is often suggested in knowledge products when it is not there at all. Thus the user is misled.

The well educated and well trained geography teacher should have an affinity with the expertise needed to meet the challenge posed by geography plus communication in the information age. Confident of a positive outcome, analysis of geographical knowledge products from which communication aspects are inseparable, can be undertaken. And once on the way, the teacher may obtain pleasure from some supplementary reading in the media. Keeping up with developments is fundamental to good teaching!

Chapter Six
The Need for Curriculum Research in Geography: the case of France

Lucile Marbeau

When one observes the development of school syllabuses in geography since the end of the nineteenth century, it is difficult to find the pedagogic and scientific reasons for the choices made and changes carried out.

Only the results of didactic research in geography (which integrates sociopolitical aims of the Establishment, the pupils' real situation and, in a general way, the total existing parameters) enable coherent, rigorous and flexible syllabuses to be established, taking into account the psycho-cognitive potential of the pupils involved and the development of scientific knowledge. Putting the syllabuses into practice depends on the training of teachers in didactics.

In order to clarify how school syllabuses, in this case in geography, are formulated and retained, research is useful. What kind of Geography? For which pupils? What are the aims and objectives? These are important questions for the curriculum researcher. So as not to fall into the trap of superficial generalizations, it would be better, in the case of France, to refer to the development of syllabuses in the national context, since all the parameters which led to this or that decision have, at least since the second half of the nineteenth century, always been linked to the sociopolitical situation of the time and to the aims imposed on teaching at all levels and for the whole country by the Establishment.

Such research, which would go back and look at the development of syllabuses since the beginning of the Third Republic, implies the need not only to have a good knowledge of geography and its development as a science, but also to have access to historical research. For example, why did the French State (during the Second World War) replace, in 1941, general geography which had been on the syllabus for the *classe de seconde* of the *lycée*[1] since 1902, by 'the two Americas'? Is it easier for pupils of 15-16 years old? Is it better adapted to the aims? After 1944-45, general geography was, in fact, introduced again without any perceptible change for the 2nd form until 1980.

But, it is one thing to carry out research on syllabuses which were used in the past, quite another to direct curriculum research with the aim of making changes in the syllabus, or even producing completely new syllabuses in line with explicit aims and objectives laid out at the beginning and based on the existing situation in schools. This is what the INRP (*Institut National de Recherche Pédagogique*) teams did from 1969-1981 for primary schools on the education minister's request. For secondary schools similar work was carried out on the initiative of INRP researchers, but in close contact with and in agreement with heads of government departments and the general inspectorate.

What were all the different kinds of projects carried out in order to formulate, experiment with and evaluate new syllabuses? What will be the future impacts of the results of INRP's research?

Organization of research

Action research was organized (Marbeau, 1983, 9; Hugon and Seibel, 1988, 1) to include teams of volunteers who were teachers associated with the researchers from the INRP. Lecturers from teacher training colleges,[2] primary school teachers and Local National Education Inspectors (IDEN) joined in teams for research into '*activités d'éveil*' (i.e. an authentic process of construction of knowledge by each child) in history, geography and the social sciences for children from 6 to 11 in primary school. Secondary school teachers[3] worked to realize a new curriculum, which was mostly adopted by the institutions from 1977 until 1981. The teams of researchers then aimed at perfecting the history and geography syllabuses, integrating an introduction to economics for pupils 11-15/16 in the years of compulsory education, with pupils grouped in mixed-ability classes. Secondary school teachers[4] also worked on history and geography syllabuses for 15-18/19 year old pupils. The teams were engaged in long research programmes extending over a number of years, whereby teams of teachers met each week at school level, and delegates from each team took part once or twice a year in national research meetings organized by the INRP researcher.

History and geography, with an introduction in economics, are compulsory subjects for all pupils from the beginning of primary school up to the *baccalauréat*, and have national syllabuses and timetables.

Having described these general conditions, let us summarize briefly the common characteristics of the syllabus research projects which we carried out between 1969 and 1981.

The duration of the research was delimited by the number of years in each educational cycle (5 for primary school, 4 for *collège*, 3 for *lycée*) plus 2. The first year was reserved for reflection, perfecting common research hypotheses and forecasting their results, putting into effect innovations, pre-experimentation on methods and tables of contents and preparing annual pedagogic itineraries to be coherent for the whole educational cycle.[5]

If we take the example of syllabus research in the first cycle, that is to say the *collège*, the second year of research involved experimentation with an new curriculum plan in the sixth form (with pupils from year group no. 1 and the reorganization of the school system); the third year enabled new experiments to be carried out in the sixth form with a new year group of pupils (no. 2), while taking into account, with feedback, everything that was observed and evaluated the previous year, development of theory from practice, whilst pre-experimentation was pursued with the fifth form with year group no. 1 and so on. The sixth year of research was the one which led to experimentation and evaluation with the 3rd form, with year group no. 2 and also to the preparation of the final research reports and to the improvement of the tools and aids designed and used.

From the beginning, there was a continuous exchange between theory and practice in the group's reflection led by the INRP researcher. This also occurred in each group in conjunction with systematic, formative evaluation and with the help of a report written up at the end of each academic year, using the same questionnaires for all pupils in the classes involved. Editing the summary of the research conclusions and the scientific report was facilitated during the last year of research.

Our action research was carried out in different places; the experimental *collèges*, or those involved in voluntary experiments, were chosen with care; they were spread out over the country in different cities and towns or in rural areas and included children of different abilities from all socio-professional milieux. Although we did not use scientifically formulated samples, our results were reliable because they covered large numbers of pupils who formed a representative body.

There was a significant number (about 4,000-5,000 pupils for each of the four years) of the French population of pupils at each level.

When the preliminary reflection and forming of the teams takes place it is advisable to anticipate as much as possible all elements, means and authorizations involved in the organization of the research, which are essential to the pursuit and completion of the work. This action research was therefore 'planned research', the terms of which were agreed at the beginning by all levels of the hierarchy in the Ministry of National Education and published in the INRP's research programme.

The research was conducted in a collegiate manner, all decisions being taken at national meetings where several teachers from each team worked with the INRP researchers. They worked realistically and democratically, taking maximum account of observations and evaluations made in class: everyone expressed themselves freely in a non-hierarchical research structure. Information bulletins and research reports were published regularly (INRP, 1969-1985, 5, 6, 7 and 8), so that every teacher associated with INRP research could be kept informed of the current situation and could have access to documents and common aids. Aimed at the decision-makers and the inspectors, our publications also made possible the development of ideas on the new syllabuses.

In this way phases of the controlled innovation – pre-experimentation, experimentation and evaluation – took place clearly, creatively and freely in the group. As the years of research passed, the issues and problems encountered were dealt with in greater depth, while at the same time, the competence of the members of the research group increased.

The problems to be solved

We will continue to use the example of the production of new geography syllabuses for the first cycle of secondary education: 1966-1977 and 1977-1980.

In 1967 and 1968, the syllabuses were much debated by history and geography teachers[6] and the inspectors (IRP and IGEN)[7] in France. The meetings, which began in 1967-69, led to new official syllabuses in geography in 1969. They only brought about one major change: general geography, taught in the sixth form since 1902, was abolished. It was considered by teachers and inspectors to be too abstract and difficult for 11 and 12 year old pupils, so it was to be gradually integrated into geography studies from the sixth form until the end of the third form: they would begin with concrete aspects, possibly directly visible, or iconographic, cartographic or graphic documents and then graduate to ideas, concepts and structures of a general kind. The order of teaching was reversed: from then on they began with the concrete and moved on to the abstract.

But the official 1969 geography syllabuses for the *collèges* are still based on the study of continents and countries: the load is lightened by dealing with Africa in the sixth form, Asia, America, and South Seas, Australasia and the North and South Poles in the fifth, Europe in the fourth and France and the former French colonies in the third forms. What is the general issue raised by this? It is above all a very descriptive education and perspective, even though official directives have since 1954 insisted on the necessity of understanding how other people live and creating solidarity with them. Should geography be the only discipline to pursue these objectives and will one succeed better by dividing it up in this way? Discussions on geography and geography studies therefore developed.

Teaching situations had hardly changed: describing and labelling, leading to encyclopaedic knowledge, had been denounced, but continued to take the lead, even if official directives insisted (since 1946) on the necessity of employing active methods, using pictures and various documents as resources for learning. The 'drawer plans' (structure, relief, climate, vegetation) always had priority, with an important place for physical geography, whereas human activities were often dealt with to a lesser extent, and the annual syllabuses were rarely completed.

The research group therefore found itself, in 1969 to 1970, facing a situation and problems that each of its members knew well, and with the willingness to find workable solutions. The research objectives were decided unanimously. They were:

- how can syllabuses be adapted to all children and adolescents (compulsory schooling continued to 16 years), without leaving some of them (the sixth and fifth 'transition classes' and the fourth and third 'practical classes' up to 1977) outside of the basic syllabus? Universal schooling brings together in the sixth form more and more mixed-ability pupils. How can a flexible syllabus be established, suitable for all pupils, with more depth for some and only the essential elements, concepts and basic landmarks for others? How can common aims and objectives be retained?
- how can this new style of a basic syllabus, changing from selective secondary education to comprehensive education, be administered? Should

experiments be undertaken with groups of different levels or with mixed-ability classes?

- how can a non-linear syllabus be offered, a syllabus with objectives, explanations and genuinely workable instructions, which is adapted to the school situation of the 1980s and which enables teachers to make choices and take decisions?
- how can teachers progress from the 'study of places' (even if most of them had already abandoned the 'geography of capes and bays') to social geography and the study of social space?
- how can important problems and topics, such as rural and urban planning, under-development, immigration, protection of the environment, international exchanges, the great powers and their impact on the organization of space, be integrated into geography studies? How can the constraints or the natural advantages of the environment of an area be integrated, whilst avoiding determinism?
- how can geography be made not only an interesting discipline, but also, in class, for the pupils, a specific scientific subject, useful for getting to know the world today and for intellectual as well as civic development?
- how can pupils be initiated into rigorous concepts and mechanisms of economic, social and political aspects, which do not fall strictly within the definition of geography?
- how can geography remain a specific subject, but at the same time, as is desirable, be related to history and other subjects (e.g. the study of ecological systems)?
- how can teachers be taught to establish their didactic objectives and to organize and carry out an annual teaching itinerary covering the essential parts of the syllabus but leaving room for choice? How can an annual syllabus be achieved in geography for the whole cycle, retaining some coherence, rigour and flexibility, so that large gaps are avoided?
- how can instruction be focused on the pupils and their learning difficulties? Our curriculum research has led us to reflect upon and work on the necessity of developing a differentiated teaching style.
- how is it possible to progress from empirical notation to formative and summative evaluation?
- how can pupils of different abilities be assessed when they follow the same basic syllabus?
- how can some coherence be maintained between the syllabus taught in the *collège*, primary school and the *lycée*? How can some continuity be established in the conceptual and structural learning process without resorting to boring repetition?
- which hypothesis of the learning process should be given priority? How can the course and the teaching aids, all the documentation and documents to be used by the pupils, be organized?
- how can both documentation essential for the teachers involved in

research and the pupils (no textbooks were available for experimental syllabuses), the creation of working tools and research tools be made available at once?

The 139 teachers and the national researchers involved in this research from 1969 to 1977 were not too numerous to bring this long task to a successful conclusion.

In 1977, the reform of the education system for the first year of primary school and secondary school took place. The syllabuses which the INRP tried out had a considerable impact on the decision-makers, particularly in geography. From 1977 to 1981, teams of researchers associated with the INRP's research work experimented with the idea of integrating a social, political and economic introduction into the new syllabuses of history and geography. This was done in particular for geography-related studies corresponding to the 1977 new official syllabus which was put into practice year after year and which was not to be modified before 1985.

Curriculum research in geography at the INRP

It is important to remember that in France, the same teacher is responsible for teaching history and geography up to the *baccalauréat*. It would therefore seem somewhat artificial only to mention research relating to geography, when, in fact, we have at the same time done research relating to history. Nothing of the kind; the two fields remain separate in class: each syllabus has its own content and coherence, even if certain interdisciplinary links are sought.

In the secondary school, geography has the advantage of two strange situations. For various reasons, 70 per cent of qualified teachers who teach history and geography are actually mainly historians: only about 25 per cent of their university course is in geography and the reverse is true for geographers. On the other hand, the same amount of time per week on the timetable is allocated to geography and history; it is compulsory for pupils for 12 years. With one hour at primary school, 1¼ hours at the *collège* and two hours at the *lycée*, geography holds an important place in the curriculum in France, more than in most other education systems in the world.

Let us look at some examples of curriculum research carried out at the INRP for geography syllabuses at secondary and high schools. Such a report is difficult because most of the research was done simutaneously at the different school levels (primary school, first and second secondary cycles): all problems were to be pinpointed and solved at the same time, as soon as the experimental plans were applied (autumn 1970 in the sixth form).

In the methodological framework of the action research, activities, that is carefully prepared, learning and teaching procedures, took place in classes followed by reflection and the drawing of conclusions amongst the teachers involved in research (to and fro between theory and practice). As for experimental grouping, approaches, methods and content have continually been questioned with a view to continued improvement.

The following points were ascertained by research. The aims and objectives of geography in the first cycle (*collèges*) could be:

- to give pupils in the first cycle of secondary education a genuine introduction to the contemporary world in the framework of the earth
- to work out, by research, a coherent, rigorous and flexible course, a geography syllabus with explicit objectives suitable for all from the sixth to the third form
- to set out the objectives of the cycle in conjunction with those of primary school (to reinforce and complement them) and those of the basic syllabus of the second cycle (to be effective as an introduction for a non-specialized and cultural education).
- Working hypotheses: content and methods should not be disassociated: there are no good methods which will produce positive solutions if the subject matter used is inadequate or incorrect; there is no good content which will enable pupils to progress if the methods, approach and teaching procedure are not adapted to those who are learning. The pupils' learning difficulties are linked to a poor appreciation of the level of content used and the psychocognitive potential of those learning, as well as, possibly, a poor grasp of scientific knowledge.
- Learning hypotheses: this requires good teacher training not only in the subject, but also in cognitive psychology. In addition to the work of Piaget and more generally the Geneva school, well-known amongst teachers in France, we have adopted the learning hypotheses of Bruner, in particular that concerned with the spiral curriculum (Bruner, 1960). Consequently, we decided to begin geography studies in the first year of the *collège*, giving priority for a few sessions, to the local geographical area, the area experienced by the pupils, so that the teacher can estimate what they know already and can try to bring all students to the same level of skills and specific vocabulary; this work, all the faster when the pupils are good, aims to define more concrete references (total population, percentages relating to socio-professional milieux, absolute temperatures, divergences, amplitude,

altitude) which will provide concrete references during the study of distant geographical areas.

- At the same time, i.e. before the end of the school year 1969-70, the research group also carried out an analysis of the content and epistemological thought which occurred throughout the research period. What content should be given priority in order to pursue the objectives? How can they be achieved with analysis of geographical concepts and notions, by putting them in order of importance and assembling the plan in a rigorous disciplinary perspective and bringing them up to date by contact with scientific knowledge?

This is what the research group did around several basic concepts: social space, environment, interrelations, scale, distance, network, polarization, distribution. How can specific concepts, key elements of geography instruction, be integrated with different subjects offered to pupils in a spiral learning perspective? How can pupils be taught to think in terms of space and to acquire geographic reasoning? And for what purpose?

The decision was taken to get rid of content and procedures which after 1969 seemed to be negative or not very fruitful; the experience of studying the environment, which was developed between 1963 and 1969 in transition classes was a response, in principle, to the necessity of involving children with difficulties at school in concrete and inspiring activities, which lead to communication. Subjects chosen from local life were hypothetically considered as positive solutions (remember that at that time other pupils in the sixth form had general geography on their syllabuses). In reality, the teaching and knowledge of geography was scarce and debatable in this pedagogic framework. In several cases, teachers gave priority to current isuses (in reality, not all pupils were motivated by problems, some indeed very little); thus the pedagogic style of the occasional and the informal came into being. It was difficult to defend (the floods in Bangladesh, the earthquake in Turkey, a wedding in Geneva...) since the primary objectives for pupils with difficulties, which was communication, was often not realized.

But the idea of using local geographic features, at least as an introduction in the beginning of the sixth form, was retained by the group, who otherwise opposed establishing the occasional and the informal in the system and were favourable towards getting rid of general geography.

Between these two opposing views we organized a new set of didactics, a pedagogic rehabilitation of geography, and thus decided what kind of content, tools and steps to retain. These were:

- a base of conceptual geographic content and the learning aids, factual and concrete subjects which should correspond both to cultural and educational aims and to the dual necessity of considering the development of scientific knowledge and the pupils' learning abilities;
- a structured plan (a coherent assembly of objectives and complementary factual information) enabling the successive choice of subjects to form an annual pedagogic itinerary and true flexibility (flexibility in practice) in knowing the possibility of choosing coherent and homologous itineraries faced with the same range of objectives. Analysis of content, work on epistemology (Marechal, 1986, II) and use of the facts of cognitive psychology aimed to favour the abilities and needs of the pupils. Planning a pedagogic itinerary for the year appears to be indispensable. This preparation before the beginning of the school year is the basis of the development of new didactics: decide what plans are necessary, test them with the pupils in class, so that all essential elements of the syllabus which are retained are discussed in optimal conditions.
- The thinking of the research groups focused on the whole of the cycle and the global aims assigned to geography in the official syllabuses. Even though an experimental syllabus may have been tried out, the official aims were mainly retained: to enable pupils aged 11-15/16 to take stock of geographic space in the whole world, to help them to discover the modern world by studying geography on different scales, to understand the different organization of space by different societies with simple and clear issues; to offer pupils authentic mental activities and to help them develop both socially and intellectually.
- The building of an experimental plan which should lead to new geography syllabuses. As in the official syllabuses, we have kept France for the third form: pupils aged 14-16 discover its spatial organization and problems so that they can place national realities in relation to the geography of the rest of the world. For this reason, we added not only the geography of the European Community, but also the USA and the USSR, the two super powers, with the complex world relations and interrelations in which France finds itself. We emphasized the Continent of Europe in the fourth form, as an indispensable introduction to geography in the third form, but totally reorganized the content. After giving a general presentation of Europe (map of the population, then relief and climate map), we concentrated on:
- case studies focusing on major European problems: a large industrial region (the Ruhr, a big industrial region on communication lines, or the industry of the Midlands, or the industry of the Po Plain, or the industry of the GDR), a large agricultural region (the agriculture of the Northern European Plain, or agriculture in the Pannonian Plain, or agriculture on the Po Plain), a large urban centre (London, or Budapest, or Berlin), an

important dominating activity (Mediterranean tourism in Europe or tourism in the Alps).

- Comparative study of the economy of a captialist country (the economy of Great Britain or of the Federal Republic of Germany) and of a socialist country (Poland or the German Democratic Republic). In fact, we wanted to offer choices and to have varying pedagogic itineraries but at the same time to pursue the same aims and objectives; we excluded the successive study of several countries and states where there would have been repetition (structure, relief, climate, vegetation, soil, hydrography, agriculture, industry, main cities, commerce) and which usually leads to superficial descriptions and nomenclature labelling, to the exclusion of the pupils' active participation in work and issues. We also wanted to reintegrate France (population, general physical features). The structural plan for the fourth form was simple: to enable the pupils to get to know, by studying European geography on different levels (including national), Northern Europe, Southern Europe, capitalist Western Europe and socialist Eastern Europe and the great problems of the organization of European space (European Community, CECA, tourism, energy, pollution). Varying pedagogic itineraries, chosen by the teachers, can help them to achieve these objectives and give them considerable freedom.

Through careful thought, we therefore created pre-experimentation and concrete experimentation in class and a flexible and operational model. We, in fact, perfected it for the geography syllabus for the fifth and sixth forms: if we first presented the curricula plans for the third and fourth forms, it is because the decisions relating to the objectives of those two years were taken first and retained for the whole cycle. Having stopped the content for the fourth and third forms in terms of the level of objectives retained and the complex geographical areas better adapted to the learning needs of adolescents than those of 11-13 years old, the necessity of conducting geography studies in the world outside Europe became the imperative for the first two years of the *collège*. This was no chance decision and was taken after much thought, nevertheless the study of distant areas corresponds to the needs and motivations of young high school students in the sixth and fifth forms. Information in the media, on the other hand, encourages adolescents of 14-16 years to understand national realities better.

In order for young pupils to build their knowledge, we chose two complementary steps for the sixth and fifth forms. The table of objectives for the end of the fifth form includes the geography of societies living in different areas outside Europe. The model, the structural plan, was formulated and operates, chronologically, firstly for these two classes; in the sixth form, certain geography studies were given priority according to their different human bio-climatic environments and in the fifth form, different activities which dominate in huge areas, different from and therefore complementary to those chosen for the sixth form. In a spiral learning context, therefore, there is both methodological (knowing how to put together documentation, progressing from numbers to graphic expression) and conceptual reinforcement, without resorting to factual repetition; and resumption of methodological and conceptual acquisition of knowledge in the framework of other factual studies. Without fear of exhausting the range of topics, it is thus possible, thanks to good analysis of content, to avoid repetition as well as large gaps.

Our project, the reality of the curriculum model created and its operation can be illustrated by a diagram (Marbeau, 1979, 10).

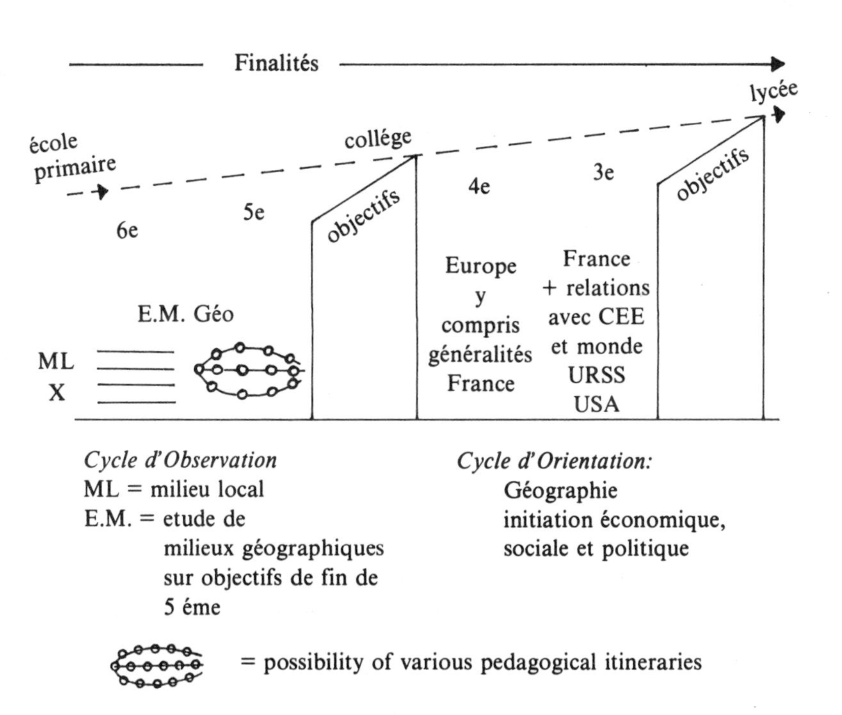

Figure 6.1: Operation of the curriculum model (France)
(source: Marbeau 1979, 10)

In view of the objectives for the end of the fifth form and from concrete geographical references recalled in the local environment at the beginning of the sixth form, several pedagogic itineraries are possible in order to discover human societies living in vast intertropical and equatorial areas, and subtropical and polar deserts (in the sixth form, there is a choice between West Africa or Eastern and Central Africa, the Tuaregs facing the problems of the Sahara or the Aborigines in the Australian sub-desert, the Laplanders and the development of the Great Scandinavian North, or the Inuit in North America). This kind of pedagogic itinerary, comprising only four or five subjects a year (including the local area) is suitable for all children, even for the weaker and slower ones; it can be modulated as far as the objectives are concerned, or can be more ambitious in stronger groups. This method of teaching, *pédagogie differenciée*, enables all children to assemble files and to research documentation; it favours working in small groups. Even with about 45 hours a year of geography in the sixth form, and as many in the fifth, there is time for the work to take place.

In the fifth form, the teacher chooses spatially and conceptually complementary case studies, knowing what was covered in the pedagogic itinerary by pupils in the sixth form: for example, the cultivation of rice in Southwest Asia, the metal industries in North America, the towns of South America, oil in the world and the fishing industry in the world. But if the zones chosen in the sixth form dealt with Latin America, for example, then towns in Africa would be chosen. In brief, the objectives for the end of the fifth form and the teaching and learning procedures are pursued in a logical order for each group of pupils from the beginning of the sixth form to the end of the fifth form.

It would take too long to describe the use of tools or aids with the pupils in order to test their performances, whether it involves formative evaluation, designed to provide the teacher with the means of diagnosis, the means of regulating the didactic plans, or summative evaluation done at the end of the school year in order to check what pupils have learnt (knowledge, ability, attitudes).

In the second case, we systematically conducted comparative evaluations between strong and weak experimental groups in order to check the value of our objectives and our experimental achievements. The results not only underlined existing differences, but also showed that children usually considered to be weak pupils had acquired important knowledge. If the good results from the strong experimental groups were not always significantly different from control groups, the performance of weak pupils in the experimental sector was largely above that of weak pupils at other *collèges*. One important hypothesis was thus verified: it is desirable to offer to all pupils in one year the same topics and to pursue the same objectives in the framework of a basic syllabus. Differentiated pedagogies enable the pupils' learning demands to be modulated (more depth, more stretching for some, more time working on the essentials with others). This implies not only evaluating what was actually put into operation in class, but also having different demands according to the level of acquired knowledge and the group of pupils. This method of teaching is one of encouragement. Many pupils in the sixth and fifth forms are underdeveloped on a cognitive level and unmotivated and unclear about their future education. They can, however, succeed perfectly well later, even at *lycée* and university, if the beginning of secondary school does not lead them into failure and discouragement because of over-demanding and imperative linear syllabuses and over-constraining teaching methods.

Notes

1. In France, secondary school studies are divided into two stages, four years in *collèges*, (6th, 5th, 4th and 3rd forms) and three years in the *lycée* (2nd, 1st and terminal).
2. Lecturers at teacher-training colleges train the teachers; the majority of the trainee teachers are *agrégés*, i.e. they have passed the competitive entrance examination which is open to candidates with a master's degree ... and followed a minimum of six years' university education after the *baccalauréat* (the equivalent of English and Welsh A-level or the German *Abitur*). Primary school teachers have four years of training: 2 years at university leading to the University Diploma of General Studies (DEUG) and then two years at a teacher training college.
3. There are various teachers at secondary schools: *agrégés* and *certifiés*, i.e. they have passed their final teaching examinations (CAPES is a competitive entrance examination open to graduates: these specialist teachers are given one year's professional training after the entrance examination). General Secondary School Teachers (PEGC) receive shorter training (three years after the *bac*) specializing jointly in history, geography and French); since 1987 PEGC-trained teachers are no longer recruited: those qualified (*certifié*) in history and geography become lower secondary school teachers.
4. Secondary school teachers are either *agrégés* or *certifiés* i.e. they have passed one of the teaching examinations.

5. For curriculum research, the National Education Minister and the General Inspectorate authorized the abandonment of the official syllabuses and the use of the experimental plans (content and aims) of the INRP.
6. And their association APHG (Association of History and Geography Teachers in the State System).
7. IPR: Pedagogical Inspectorate at the Regional Level.
   IGEN: General Inspectorate of National Education.

Part Two
Ideology and Change: the values dimension

Chapter Seven
'... to Travel With a Different View'
Frances Slater

'... to be educated is not to have arrived at a destination, it is to travel with a different view'. This chapter takes a quotation from R.S. Peters as its focus. Initially, I trace geography's journeying through the recent past and the development of a plurality of paradigms. These are set alongside the ideologies and values which inform educational thinking. As we know, both paradigms and ideologies use distinctive languages and vocabularies for reflecting their values and views, and we usually choose to travel within *one or another. Paradigms and ideologies provide a choice of terrain in which to travel. In raising questions about how geography represents society in general and deals with issues of race, gender and class, I am suggesting that we need to examine carefully the question, 'Are we travelling with different views?' That question may be answered in the affirmative in relation to research in geographical education, the last area of interest which I briefly address. In conclusion, I claim that in initially acquiring the capacity to travel with a different view, we are also enabled to encounter more views on the way.*

A definition of education

Recently, at the beginning of a new term, I was re-reading R.S. Peters' inaugural lecture, *Education as Initiation* (Peters, 1965). It was, in fact, given its broadly liberal stance, a very salutary exercise in the present political climate for education. I couldn't help recalling at the same time, Norman Graves' introductory lecture in the 1974-75 academic year on the aims of geography in education and how he translated the Peters' points into our specific field (Graves, 1975a). This was my own introduction, too, to the ideas and criteria which Peters spells out as features of the concept, education. Given Norman Graves' own respect for matters philosophical and his penchant in lectures and seminars for undertaking some conceptual and historical analysis, it is not altogether inappropriate, I think, that I choose as title and theme for this contribution to a volume in honour of his contribution to education, a metaphor Peters used near the end of his lecture. Peters in the metaphor is emphasizing that aspect of education concerned with the ongoing development of minds. He writes:

> Education, then, can have no ends beyond itself. Its value derives from principles and standards implicit in it. To be educated is not to have arrived at a destination; it is *to travel with a different view*. (my italic) (Peters, 1965)

'... to travel with a different view'. For many reasons, as a geographer and as a person, this metaphor speaks to me and to many of us, I should think. One of the thoughts it triggers for me is the extent to which those of us concerned with geography in education particularly and broader educational concerns more generally, can say that we do indeed 'travel with a different view' or different views from the ones we held or were surrounded by twenty or thirty years ago. We might say, as doubtless we could say of any time period, that to have worked in education in recent decades has itself been a deeply educative experience. This experience has enlarged our concept of geography and geography in education, as we have lived through change in geography and change in the accepted concerns and aims of education. We have experienced and are experiencing pressures which cause the analyses of philosophers and sociologists in education to come alive.

Geography changes

As I recall it, the first nudge which led to my journeying in geography with a different view came from listening to a lecture by H.H. McCarty at the University of Otago in 1962 (McCarty, 1963). This was my introduction to hypothesis testing and scientific systems of thinking in geography (with apologies to Humboldt). As the impact of these systems of thought developed and particularly when other, different, systems followed on rapidly as challenges, as different views, we realized that our values were being challenged and changed.

Descriptive-rich geography which even now would provide ever growing numbers of tourists with valuable ground plans and images, was considered by the converted, and there were considerable numbers of us, *passé*. Description was intellectually inferior to explanation and prediction. As I see it now, the great god of the western world, 'objective' science, had apparently taken over geography. It all seemed very exciting to examine correlations, to test models, to set up assumptions, to simplify the 'real' world (taken to be an objectively knowable real world). Some of the sense of that excitement stays with me. We were travelling a different path and in an educational sense it was to broaden our perspectives and understandings then and as time went on.

Our language changes

We can say we were valuing the normative, the hypothetical and deductive rather than the observed and the inductive. New terms entered our vocabulary. Our language was changing; our priorities changed. The world became generalizable, not so particular. The methods of scientific geography trained us in different skills and through commentaries like Harvey's *Explanation in Geography* (Harvey, 1969) deepened our perspectives.

Concepts and ideas, knowledge and understanding from scientific geography trickled into schools and made a considerable impact on curriculum planning in geography. At about the same time as the upheavals in geography, notions of curriculum planning were beginning to filter into geography education – interestingly enough from Australian geography educators (Biddle and Shortle, 1969; Cox, 1971).

The language of geography curriculum matters changed from a matter of content to a matter of concepts and 'big ideas'. The value placed on working towards generalizations in scientific geography followed through to geography in schools. Under the impact of scientific geography children were to be taught a geography of spatial distribution and spatial interaction, location, relative location, centrality and accessibility, networks and nodal regions. This was the way it went. Looking back one might suggest that geography-type knowledge was decontextualized, separated to some extent from its 'real' world, expressed in a language which, some argue, misleads children about how societies operate (Gilbert, 1984; Henley, 1986).

'Wait!'

The shift towards science in higher education and schools was not to go unchallenged, however. 'Wait!' said some. They were saying, if I paraphrase them accurately, something like:

'We do not simply exist as scientists observing and modelling our world. We

> are tied to it, to its places and regions and localities. We feel part of its cities and rural areas, its recreational and wilderness spaces. We are tied closely and emotionally, through personal experience and personal meaning – making.'

The subjectivity of personal experiences and places is a dimension humanistic geographers were to draw attention to from about the mid-1970s onwards. They are a small band of people who in their somewhat romantic reaction to scientific geography caused a pause and a halt and, if few in number and overt influence, nevertheless their messages strike a chord in the consciousnesses of many geographers.

We once claimed, and we still do, that geography is a valuable bridge builder between the perspectives of science and arts. Today's gulf between detached analytical observation and the subjective experience of place is, I think, a new version of the science/arts dichotomy in geography. There is the science side of geography and the human side, even the 'poetry' side. Different realms of experience, they both contribute to awareness and understanding, though undoubtedly a version of the science side dominates the school curriculum. How can feelings about places be made to count as solid curriculum content? Teachers of English literature may get away with studying the products of intuitive, feeling-related human expressions but there is not enough substance in this for geography in school. Nevertheless, some have attempted to plan humanistic geography curricula (Briscall, 1980; Brough, 1983; Fien 1983) emphasizing concepts of place, place feeling and sense of place in opposition to the space and spatial relations of scientific geography. To some extent it can be said that these concepts have been added to some school curriculum statements and examination board fare. The language of the personal gets some space, but not a lot.

Who gets what, how and why?

Both scientific and humanistic approaches have been found severely wanting by radical geographers, that is, those who from either liberal or Marxist positions espouse viewpoints which ask 'who gets what, how and why?' or 'who benefits from this observed state of affairs?' or 'how ought things to be?' These are very different questions from scientific or humanistic ones and they link spatial investigations and feelings about places to social, economic, historical and political processes. There are geographers who are, at heart, scientists, geographers at heart humanists, and geographers who are social reformers, which is not to say that some geographers are not all three! The geographer with a social conscience might well say to the others, or the earlier regionalists, 'if you don't ask these further questions then you cut yourself off from "involvement" in the world. You report and you feel but you don't question as I do. You don't raise deeper issues of principle.'

I do not think that the social, welfare and radical perspectives can be ignored or dismissed and indeed their key questions, quoted above, have been incorporated into several of the leading curriculum statements on offer in England and Wales at A-Level and GCSE. These perspectives link geographical studies to power in society and the impact of power and vested interest on spatial patterns and processes. It gives us an opportunity once again 'to travel with a different view'. It's a wonderfully rich world we inhabit (as well as a frighteningly poor one) made richer by a multitude of perspectives.

The welfare and radical geographers are not necessarily to be labelled 'political' in that they can be suddenly accused of bringing politics into geography. The outcomes of politics through the working of human nature in power relationships are there for all to observe and experience. For me, the questions of radical geography raise our consciousness about individual opportunities and individual restraints and society-constructed or structural/organizational constraints and opportunities. We can see something in both determinist and voluntarist positions or views. In the tension between these two we obtain a view on society and societies, how they are organized, what they value, and whom they are organized for. We have additional questions to use in our thinking about spatial problems and processes and relationships. Following on from the social critique paradigm, an historical analysis in relation to places and regions is at present developing, an analysis which seeks to understand patterns through processes of power and social structures particular to a region or economic unit and the social relations characteristic therein.

Enlightenment through geography in the next 25 years will probably come through an increased understanding of society and social processes and culture and cultural processes in relation to spatial patterns. The new paradigm will concentrate not so much on people/environment relationships as on people/people relationships as these exist at individual levels, in groups (e.g. vested interest and pressure groups) and in society at large. Already we see something of this in some school geography topics like the role of multinational decision-makers on working people and their places.

The role of values

The explicit uncovering of the role of value positions, of values and attitudes in our thinking, has enabled us to be more aware of the effect of beliefs and ideologies in social processes. Geography, we might say, is the study of spatial patterns interacting with social processes in a range of environments and at a variety of scales. Environments become less significant in the older conventional senses than people and societies and the processes which they engage in. We recognize social and political decision making to be based on values and ideologies confirming much cultural or mythological bias in our thinking. That is to say that some New Zealanders may carry around as cultural baggage (which they believe to be true and act on) a belief in the equality of people, perhaps defensively and sexistly expressed as 'Jack's as good as his master'. On the other hand, some might hold to the view that some English people live by a belief or myth about knowing one's place, which leads to a great respect for, caution towards, and even fear of, hierarchies. Such diverse beliefs impact on decisions and actions.

Bundles of belief

At this point in the chapter, then, we have begun to approach the notion of ideology and ideologies, those bundles of ideas that people choose to travel within. Ideology is not a term susceptible to easy definition, but generally speaking it has to do with the sets of beliefs and values which we have been inducted into and hold to and operate within to explain ourselves to the world and the world to ourselves. Ideologies might be understood by geographers as environments of thought and beliefs which the mind inhabits. Ideologies inform our attitudes and values and have much to do with forming and informing our reactions and opinions. Ideologies may well be the engines which run society as the sun is the engine which runs the weather. Certainly, in both education generally at the present time and in geography, ideology is a much-used concept.

We are all rather familiar with the main traditions or ideologies of education or curriculum orientations, to use Eisner's (1979) terminology. We are aware of their differing aims and the basic attitude and value positions which they hold to. We travel down their roads fairly self-consciously. Figure 7.1 summarizes the characteristics of the four main ideologies identified in education. This figure can be compared with the next on geography's paradigm positions (Figure

Ideological stance	*Priorities/values emphasis*	*Concepts/language*
Child-centred	• the child • individual development • personal growth • personal relevance • autonomy • the development of the whole person	• experience • discovery • integration (of person and knowledge) • relevance • enjoyment • personal feelings • free expression • personal expression • doing/activity • problem solving • meaning making
Liberal/ humanitarian/ social adaptation	• subjects/disciplines • initiation into the worthwhile • inheriting the culture • a certain conformity	• cultural heritage • forms of knowledge • intellectual growth • thinking skills • cognitive development • excellence • attainment • 'right' answers • received interpretations • education as an end in itself
Utilitarian	• work and the economy • 'getting a job'	• skills • vocational relevance • 'knowing how' • processing information • schooling as a means
Reconstructionist	• changing society	• promoting social and political understanding • questioning the status quo • justice, equity, inequality • social action • concern • vested interest • power • alternative viewpoints • a critical consciousness

Figure 7.1: Language and ideology in education
(source: Slater, based on Eisner, 1979)

7.2). The concepts distinctive to each make explicit what precisely is held in high regard. It is interesting to note that paradigms may be linked to ideologies in a loose way. Some may see a correspondence between, for example, a humanistic viewpoint and a child-centred position, and a social reconstructionist position and a radical geography, for example (Walford, 1981b). To what extent, we may ask, can scientific geography be linked with the utilitarian position?

Paradigm position	*Priorities/values emphasis*	*Concepts/language*
Scientific	• generalizations • deduction • prediction • modelling	• space • pattern • analysis • laws • variables • hypothesis testing • problem solving
Humanistic	• personal understanding • individual meaning • interpretation	• place, people • sense of place • beautiful places • ugly places • feelings • expressions • placelessness
Liberal/radical	• understanding society • critiquing society	• society, structures • organizations • power • vested interest • groups • pressure groups • self interest • equality/inequality

Figure 7.2: Geography's paradigms, post regional (source: Slater)

Various stances

We have become, then, over the past decades, more conscious of our points of view and the various stances we take as geography educators in relation to geography curricula. We might even realize from time to time that ideology, as much or more than theory, informs our views on matters to do with education and teaching. We might ask, for instance, 'Is a curriculum adequate in the breadth and depth given to the range of geographical perspectives and curriculum orientations available?' In asking such a question one is implicitly suggesting that no one ideological perspective or paradigm viewpoint should prevail, but rather a variety should be available in any curriculum. We have in the past used matrices to select our content from a variety of scales or regions. Developments in our awareness in recent decades requires an equal sensitivity to the representation of the range of values given priority in the different paradigms and ideologies we work in. Some curricula incorporate different ideological concerns through key questions and key ideas. It will be important to evaluate the national curriculum in geography for England and Wales in terms of ideology. We cannot take the selection of content and teaching procedures in a curriculum to be non-problematic. Whose interests might it seem to be serving? What views of people in society are being given implicitly and explicitly? What view of society is implied? These questions are worth asking as we participate and as others in our classrooms participate in that process or journey called education.

Do we travel with a different view?

To seek to interpret geography curricula in the light of such questions as posed above may lead us to ask 'To what extent in fact are we travelling with a different view of geography? education? society?' We may well wish to ask of any national curriculum anywhere the questions which arise from Rob Gilbert's work on geography texts. What views of individuals and societies are being given? What images prevail? What content, and concepts, and language dominate? Gilbert's (1984) work causes us to think again and less simplistically, 'to travel with a different view'.

Understanding society

Gilbert argues that in order to understand any society, nothing is more revealing of its values, its central beliefs, and dominant ideologies than the way that society explains itself to its young people. He then examines the social content of the British curriculum through an analysis of textbooks in geography, economics and history. He diagnoses a mismatch between aims and realization by using the idea of an image of society to analyse how subjects represent society and people in society. More often than not, as he sees it, images and analogies of society set up barriers to undertanding society and how it operates. Therein lies the impotent image or the mismatch between aim and realization. We have a set of social science subjects potentially capable of giving us insights which, in fact, are clouded by the accepted ideology to distort understandings of society. Perhaps, indeed, in geography, society is almost totally neglected and environment used as a suitable obfuscating notion.

Gilbert's analysis of geography texts (all pre-1980) reveals an image of people using the resources of the environment to fulfil their needs. This image excludes other aspects of human experience while it purveys a picture of the 'plastic' individual linked into environmental and economic determinism. Further, while the forces of nature and economic laws may be powerful, they are also beneficent and they offer an accommodating society a path to progress, a path along which technology is a benign force. The texts also show a strong faith in planning. Technological achievement and rational planning give those studying geography a certain view of society and the way it works, while avoiding controversial social issues. Where these are touched upon in the selected texts they are analysed in terms of relative viewpoints, and not, for example, in terms of the possession of powers and vested interests. Gilbert believes that geography textbooks disguise the social origins of spatial outcomes of processes and disguise furthermore the political assumptions and implications of their theories. Some may well argue that things are changing, though I think unreflective optimism is misplaced and misguided. The geography lessons my students are asked to prepare are most often in the mould as analysed by Gilbert. And yet, as he says, most geography teachers subscribe to the view that teachers are agents of social change. Here, indeed, is the mismatch between aspiration and actuality. How can we teach new insights with old images and assumptions and misguided beliefs?

We believe we are agents of social change when most likely we are agents of social adaptation. With good reason we need to pose the questions: *Do* we indeed travel with a different view? To what extent is there congruence between belief and practice?

Our opportunities to travel with different views and raise questions have not been limited to developments in geography's paradigm or our raised consciousness in relation to educational ideologies and curriculum orientation. We have also to take account of the progress in thinking about the wider social issues of racism and gender which has taken place. Again we are faced with a number of ideologies and again we are being presented with different value positions and attitudes in these instances towards groups of people and societies rather than ideas about geography in education.

Bias and racism

Generally speaking, three perspectives as summarized in Figure 7.3 are accepted as defining different views and sets of beliefs, opinions, attitudes and values in relation to the fact of the non-acceptance of some human beings by other human beings. It has been demonstrated sufficiently that geography resource materials can be both racist and sexist and this says nothing of other possible biases to do with class and culture, for instance.

Bias, prejudice and stereotyping exist in texts and resources. We also know that bias, prejudice and stereotyping exist in the minds and hearts of people (Robinson 1987; Slater and Spicer, 1980). Robinson has most recently provided evidence of the views children travel with and the majority of sensitive teachers are aware of such views as constituting intervening variables in the process of culture encountering culture in a geography lesson. A recent MA dissertation by Dorothy Haile (1988) raises for me the possibility of what a relatively untouched yet valuable concept we have in the idea of culture shock. Haile used eight photographs of a Zambian village with different groups of people, all of whom were preparing to go there for some period. One comment from one of the discussion groups was:

> ... the first day it'd sort of be a novelty, and then for a while it'd be a bit rough, 'cos if you had to stay there for a long time, but once you got used to it ...

As Haile points out the girl was describing stages in classic culture shock adjustment where a first reaction is one of novelty and interest moving to withdrawal as less attractive aspects of the culture for a person of another culture begin to emerge, and then there is a winning through to a feeling of being comfortable with the new culture.

Perhaps we are often not yet aware enough in our geography teaching that in so many topics we are implicitly and explicitly at second and third remove asking pupils to encounter other cultures and most often presenting this encounter in a supposedly objective, scientific, factual

	ASSIMILATION What most people still believe	MULTICULTURALISM What well-meaning liberals believe	ANTI-RACISM What genuine anti-racists believe
Historical background	Immigrants came to this country because the laws on immigration were not strict enough.	Ethnic minorities came here because they had a right to and because they wanted a better life.	Black people came here, as to other countries, because their labour was required by the economy.
What black people should do	Immigrants should integrate as quickly as possible with our way of life.	Ethnic minorities should be able to maintain their language and cultural heritage.	Black people have to defend themselves against racist laws and practices, and to fight for justice.
The nature of prejudice	There is some racial prejudice in this country. But that's only human nature, and this is a much more tolerant place than most other countries.	There are some misguided individuals and extremist groups in this country but basically our society is just and democratic and provides equality.	This is a racist society, and has been for centuries. Racism is to do with power structures more than with attitudes of individuals.
How to combat prejudice	It is counter-productive to try to remove prejudice – you can't force people to like each other by bringing in laws and regulations	Prejudice is based on ignorance and misunderstanding. It can be removed by personal contacts and the provision of information.	Prejudice is caused by, it is not the cause of, unjust structures and procedures. It can be removed only by dismantling these.
Priorities in education	There should be provision of English as a second language in schools, but otherwise 'children are all children, we should treat all children exactly the same' – it is wrong to notice or emphasise cultural or racial differences. If immigrant children underachieve, this is because of faults in their own families and life-styles.	Schools should recognize and affirm ethnic minority children's background, culture and language ... celebrate festivals, organize international evenings, use and teach mother tongues and community languages, teach about ethnic minority history, art, music religion, literature.	Priorities in education are for there to be more black people in positions of power and influence – as heads, senior teachers, governors, education officers, elected members; to remove discrimination in classroom methods and school organisation; and to teach directly about equality and justice and against racism.

Figure 7.3: Three views on race (*New Internationalist*, March 1985)

and, more seriously, context-deprived way.

The following fragment of a conversation illustrates what I mean. It is a conversation I had with a 14/15 year-old girl at the back of a room when one of my students, developing into a capable geography teacher, was teaching a lesson about population growth, birth rates and death rates with the aid of graphs and statistics.

Girl: Why don't they learn. Why don't they use contraceptives. They're stupid. The women are always worn out and pregnant.
F.S.: They don't see it like that. That's how we see it.
(No effect on girl. I am marked out as equally stupid.)
F.S.: (trying again) They do need children to work as breadwinners and as support in old age.
(The girl still looks sceptical and sure of her own view.)
F.S.: We also have to remember that our own grandmothers and great-grandmothers were in the same position – lots of children.
(Total look of disbelief on pupil's face turning into a food-for-thought look.)

We have a long and hard road to travel to begin to increase our skills in defusing bias, prejudice and racism. There are ideologies in place giving us different perspectives. There is a lot of consciousness raising to be done. We need an enlargement of the concepts and perspectives we now have in geography more humanely to bridge the culture gaps and handle the encountering of cultures more 'effectively' for mutual understanding. At one level a good beginning point is Achebe's *Things Fall Apart* (1958) and, more recently, Okoye's *Men Without Ears* (1984).

Women and geography

The concepts and language which express views about women's position in society like those to do with race also come in different tones and nuances. Do we take a non-sexist or an anti-sexist line for example? Do we ideologically opt for biological, patriarchial or Marxist explanations? A work which gives some insight into what the author claims to be different value positions of men and women may go some way to explaining to us geographers, the different locations of men and women in society.

Carol Gilligan in *In a Different Voice* reports on research which involved listening to and analysing the responses of people to a situation of moral choice and conflict (Gilligan, 1982). In so listening she began to be aware of the differences between the women's responses and other studies and conclusions in the psychology literature. She argues overall that she heard two voices, two ways of speaking about moral problems, two modes of describing the relationship between other and self. Women, it would seem, perceive and construe social reality differently from men. Women's sense of integrity appears to be entwined with an ethic of care. Gilligan is careful to point out that she is highlighting a distinction between modes of thought rather than making generalizations about either sex. She doesn't seem to address the problem of how, very generally speaking, women are socialized into the caring mode and men into a more competitive, less person-orientated mode. Be that as it may, the distinction she hears among voices is an interesting view of 'manly' and 'womanly' attitudes to relationships and society. One might discern a link between such different attitudes and women's position in society generally.

That is to say if people inherently or over time come to hold different values, they will understandably make different choices and inhabit different niches in society. It is probable that there are elements of both choice and non-choice (pressure, subtle coercion) in the process for both men and women. Walden and Walkerdine's (1985) work on girls and mathematics spells out in more detail some of the attitudes and practices I have in mind when I speak of pressure and subtle coercion. Too often research evidence shows we, women included, do not travel with different views.

In some senses, now acknowledged, women are invisible in the niches they inhabit. Closely linked to invisibility is the idea of stereotyping and how women, non-whites, the working class, the middle class, etc., are very often viewed and portrayed in our society in distorted ways. The 'male as norm' and 'white as norm', 'the Western world as norm' are other expressions of the state of things which geographers travelling with a different view have begun to take on board and challenge in a geography curriculum. It seems easier to make progress in developing sensitivity to the latter two norms stated above than the first, however. I am really rather pessimistic as the Western world continues in a period of the strident valuing of competition and a certain kind of enterprise of much lasting progress. In relation to the 'male as norm', I am deeply pessimistic. Much evidence could be cited. Figure 7.4, which displays the programme of an annual conference in which geography teachers working in university departments of education get together, reveals much. The figure may be examined for the position it gives to women and topics women chose to present. A telling conference indeed!

Saturday 30th January
3.30 p.m. - 4.30 p.m. - Conference assembles: cup of tea.
4.30 p.m. - 6.30 p.m. - *Miscellany of Current Issues. Chair:* David Skinner

HMI Reports and aftermath - Norman Graves
CATE Submissions - update of latest position
Which? CATE B.Ed Validation - Nigel Proctor
Consulting work: INSET's new look - Michael Williams
16 - 19 Progress Report - Gerry Hones
Introducing MESU - Andrea Tapsfield
Primary numbers and courses in UDE's
Current Recruitment Pattern
7.15 p.m. DINNER

8.30 p.m. Guest Speaker - Dr. John Pethick
Chair: Vincent Tidswell

Preparing the effective use of T.V. in teaching geography: Granada - a case study

Sunday 31st January
9.30 a.m. - 11.00 a.m. *Geography and the National Curriculum. Chair:* Norman Graves

Political control of the Curriculum - Nigel Porter
The new Baker Initiatives - David Hall
The Politics of sustaining Geography in the Curriculum - Patrick Bailey
COFFEE

11.15 a.m. - 12.45 p.m. *The Way Forward. Chair:* Philip Boden
Recent Activities in Geographical Education in the U.K. - Tony Binns
U.S. School Geography: back from the Brink - Rex Walford
Penetrating the Media and marketing Geography - John Bale, Ashley Kent, Harry Tolley and David Wright.

LUNCH - FREE AFTERNOON

4.00 p.m. Cup of Tea
4.15 p.m. - 6.30 p.m. *Geography and Industry. Chair*
Industry and Teacher Education - Gordon Bloomer
Economic understanding through Geography - Graham Corney (Workshop)
7.15 p.m. DINNER
8.30 p.m. - 9.30 p.m. *Research in Geography. Chair:* Patrick Bailey
David Lambert and Bill Marsden comments on their current research
9.30 p.m. Arrangements for 1989 and beyond.

Monday 1st February
9.00 a.m. - 10.30 a.m. *Working with students in the Classroom.*
Chair: Harry Tolley

Contributions from David Lambert, Frances Slater and Ruth Watts
Preparing students to teach GCSE - Pat Wiley and Mary Robinson

10.45 a.m. - NOON *Innovation - Chair:* Rex Walford

MESU sponsored CAL - Andrea Tapsfield, David Hall and Ashley Kent

Integrated Humanities Course - Ruth Watts.

Figure 7.4: Women and geography (University Department of Education Geography Tutors' Conference 1988 Programme)

A final journey into research

There is, as it were, a final journeying I should not neglect to map in this chapter, albeit now very briefly. Along this journey signposted 'research in geography education', and a substantial part of it flowing from the master's degree course, which Norman Graves began at the Institute in 1968, we can again draw attention to changing preferences, values and viewpoints (Graves et al, 1989).

There is an accepted kind of shorthand often used which polarizes research into two categories, hard and soft. Hard research would be characterized by a scientific approach with perhaps the use of statistical methods, of mathematical models and a set of conclusions drawn from data. The researcher would, as it were, stand outside the research and the findings would be generally agreed to be objective. Such an approach was taken by P.A. Kelly (1978) and his dissertation in geography education stands as a worthy example among many.

Soft research ostensibly adopts different stances and goals and, very obviously, language. The researcher would probably not seek to distance herself or himself from the problem under study. A number of our MA students by the late 1970s were seeking to adopt such a so-called illuminative stance, a more subjective, even humanistic response to data collected. Barrie McElroy (1980), for example, sought to take a 'soft' position as an evaluator. To some extent, interestingly enough, the methods of research seem to have derived from research into evaluation undertaken by the group of people at CARE (Centre for Applied Research in Education). They evolved and adopted what we might call 'soft' stances.

The uniqueness of the situation researched is stressed, the researcher very often is attempting a portrayal, he or she often claims to be taking the stance of an artist rather than a scientist. Sensitivity, a capacity for reflection, for empathy and imagination, are qualities needed by and claimed by the researcher working in and staying within the context of the study. These are their words. Soft research unfolds perceptions and understandings of complex situations. The art of a case study stands in distinction to the experiments of a scientist. Soft approaches create authentic knowledge, hard approaches generalizations, says the language of the soft ideology. Milton's (1984) dissertation may be given as a further example of work taking a 'soft' stance.

Much of our research in geography education, however, cannot probably be classified as purely one or the other. Very often the different views are combined in some way. A recent piece of work by

Stephens (1988) is a good example of research adopting elements of both scientific research and portrayal research. His use of a questionnaire belongs to the scientific side and his use of diaries to the portrayal, subjective side of research methods. On the subjective side, the growing use of diaries as containers of reflection seems to be a significant and worthwhile mode of organizing and contemplating experience. I have found it to yield personal insights which I have reason to believe speak to others, too (Slater, 1988).

Ghaye's work and that of Margaret Roberts are other examples belonging to the growing cluster of 'diary research' in geography education (Ghaye, 1989; Roberts, 1989) while Verduin-Muller's (1967) work is a worthy example from another decade. The evidence that such a mode of working can produce insights and understandings is developing. What I found particularly exciting in the diary exercise I undertook was the capacity it gave me to travel with different views in the very process of writing.

And so along our way we return to Peters:

> To be educated is not to have arrived at a destination; it is to travel with a different view.

We might also extend the metaphor and begin to see that in initially acquiring the capacity to travel with a different view, we are then enabled to encounter yet more views on the journey, to travel in a way which is increasingly worthwhile. Such worthwhileness has, I believe, characterized journeys in geography and geography education over the past decades. Norman Graves has been there during those decades to provide learning experiences and writings for students and colleagues which will continue to be valued by many of us into the future.

Chapter Eight
Education for Peace Through Geography
John Fien

The aim of teaching geography as a contribution to a more peaceful world aligns geographical education with recent renewed emphases on human rights, development, political and environmental education. This chapter argues that a broad definition of peace education encompasses these concerns and gives rise to many opportunities in the geography curriculum to promote the concepts, processes and values of peace through a reconsideration of objectives, content themes and teaching approaches. Effective peace education depends upon more than the efforts of geography teachers and departments. It requires an across-the-curriculum approach in which geography teaching can make an important contribution.

> The geography of the heavenly planet is within reach. It is one in which people will be at peace with each other and with nature; machines will be caged and children free to roam; there will be an explosion of variety and free choice; and there will be a stable population living in great abundance with balanced restraint among people, nature and machines. Yet with all this wonder clearly within our reach, there are many – individuals, groups, whole societies even – apparently dedicated to their own suicide and the murder of everybody else. This collective death-wish has been automated into the hair-triggered computers that control the missiles. They may prevail. We can have heaven; or we may choose hell. In geographical terms, this planet is not too small for peace but it is too small for war. (Bunge, 1986, 291)

A promised land

As geographers, we are often asked to provide maps for friends and colleagues. When David Hicks came to Australia for the 'Teaching geography for a better world' conference in 1986, he came in search of a map as well. He wanted a map of the north-east Queensland coastline around Rockingham Bay between Townsville and Cairns for one of his friends, Bill Lloyd, who had recently inherited one of his grandfather's uncles' diaries. The diary had been written in Australia in the mid-nineteenth century, and on his way to his new property inland from Rockingham Bay, the diarist had called into Brisbane where incidentally, the geography conference was being held 122 years later.

The diary records the party departing Brisbane in April 1864 to sail north to Rockingham Bay where a base camp was established. Over several months, it describes many of the problems of frontier life: the dangerous landing of horses, equipment and sheep, the chopping of trees and burning of clearings for a settlement, the many tropical illnesses, emergency operations, and finally, the cutting of a trail from Rockingham Bay up through the Bellenden Ker Ranges to a place the settlers knew as The Gap. The diary entry for 17 May 1864 reads, 'Went to the top of the Gap to view the promised land'.

It seems that Bill Lloyd's ancestor had a vision of a better world in which he wanted to live with his family, and Bill Lloyd wanted a map of the area to see what the 'promised land' was like. In many ways, the aim of peace education is to help create a vision for the late twentieth century of the 'promised land', that better world which we would like our children and our students to inherit. In fact, I often think of peace education as futures education, that process of helping young people think about the world they want to grow up and live in, of teaching and learning ways of making the visions realistic, and of developing strategies to bring them to pass.

Polarized debate

Remarkably, this education movement which has teaching and working for a better, more peaceful world as its goal is shrouded in controversy. The debate throughout the 1980s over peace education, or education for peace as it has become more commonly known, belies its title as often the debate has been far from peaceful. The polarized public debate, especially as reflected in the media, has generally been quite narrow with the critics of education for peace adopting a narrow definition of peace as nuclear disarmament and peace education as disarmament education. Working from this narrow definition, the critics have sought to jettison all efforts at education for a just and peaceful world on the grounds of political indoctrination, teacher bias and curriculum irrelevance (see, for example, Cox and Scruton, 1985, in the United

Kingdom and Jacobs, 1985, and Partington, 1986, in Australia).

In reply, advocates of peace education claim that this narrow view is only one perception of peace and education for peace. Instead, they point to a broader concept than disarmament, seeing peace as more than just the absence of war. To peace educators, peace is a positive and practical concept, a process, not a condition, that involves action to redress the causes of conflict by practising conflict resolution skills, promoting good community relations, and working to remedy the causes of hunger, distress, violence and inequality both at home and overseas. This perception of peace and its educational task has distinct relationships with multicultural education, human rights education, development education, feminist education, teaching for constructive interpersonal relationships, and education for international understanding. In John Huckle's terms, it means directing our teaching 'to play a significant role in creating fulfilled and happy individuals in a fairer and less troubled world' (Huckle, 1983b, 153).

The same goal was evident in the appeal by geographers from socialist countries at the 1984 IGU Congress for geographers worldwide to work for a peaceful and just world:

> In the struggle for peace it is important to indicate clearly the sources of the threatening catastrophe. Geographers can oppose imperialistic propaganda by telling the truth about the actual lives and peaceful aspirations of people of different countries. At the same time, experts in the field of economic and social geography can help in exposing the actual initiators of arms race – bosses of the military-industrial complex, who pursue super-profits and governmental orders, and with these aims are ready to keep our planet on the brink of war.
>
> We are deeply convinced that it is necessary to put an end to the wasting of productive forces and of natural resources on the arms race, that the use of the contemporary scientific and technological potential of humanity for peaceful co-existence – and not for military conflicts – would open new prospects for satisfaction of material and spiritual needs of people and for a better quality of life, especially in the developing countries. Overall disarmament would improve the international climate, would contribute to scientific and economic collaboration in solving the problems which concern all honest people: those of fighting hunger and maladies, of supplying food products, energy and raw materials, of conserving the environment, of using marine resources and space research for peaceful purposes. (Gerasimov, 1985, 200-201)

A geography of concern

The view of geography and geography teaching reflected in this appeal indicates a remarkable change from the heady days of the spatial paradigm when scientific credibility, objectivity, quantification and theory were the goals. By contrast, today, the goals of geography and geographical education seem to be 'a geography of concern', 'teaching geography for a better world' (Fien and Gerber, 1988), and creating 'the geography of a heavenly planet' (Bunge, 1986). Yet, bringing the two approaches together, Smith (1977) has written that

> the well-being of a society as a spatially variable condition should be the focal point of geographical enquiry ... It simply requires recognition of what is surely the self-evident truth that if human beings are the object of our curiosity ... then the quality of their lives is of paramount importance.

This concern for human welfare represents more than a shift in content emphasis for geography teaching, however. Also involved are major shifts in the world views of teachers and syllabuses, educational goals, the organization of schools, and criteria for the selection of curriculum content and learning experiences as all these are important dimensions of education for peace.

While education for peace has a long history and received a major impetus after World War I with the foundation of groups such as the World Education Fellowship, much of its current impetus is related to genuine fears about the global nuclear threat. The acceptance of the nuclear winter thesis by scientists from both East and West has indicated that even a minor exchange of nuclear weapons could end all life on earth (*Ambio*, 1982, 1989; Ehrlich et al., 1983; Elsom, 1985; Dotto 1986; *Environment* 1988). This realization lead the *Bulletin of Atomic Scientists* to report that:

> No question is more important to all of us than that of safely resolving conflict in our complex and interdependent world. With the fate of the earth itself at stake, the inclusion in our curriculums of courses and readings relating to peace and international security is not only timely, but critical (Simmons, 1984, 35).

At the tertiary geography level, Bunge's (1987) *Nuclear War Atlas*, Openshaw, Steadman and Greene's (1983) *Doomsday: Britain after nuclear attack* and Pepper and Jenkin's (1985) *The Geography of Peace and War* may be seen as appropriate curriculum responses. At the secondary level, note should be taken of the special 1987 issue on 'War and Peace' in *Contemporary Issues in Geography and Education* (Contemporary Issues, 1987) and Stowell and Bentley's (1988) chapter

A GEOGRAPHY OF DEFENCE

1. **What is it? What might the topic embrace?**
   - What is defence?
   - What is the role of the defence forces in Australia compared with their role in other regions, e.g. parts of South America, Africa, Eastern Europe, Middle East, Asia, Western Europe?
   - What are some of the effects of war on the environment?

2. **Where is it?**
   - Where do the super powers locate their bases?
   - Where are the major bases in Australia?
   - Where are the headquarters of the army, navy and air force in Victoria?
   - Where are the major exercises held?
   - Does Australia have bases overseas? If so, where?
   - Which parts of the coastline does the navy patrol?
   - Where do the army reserves meet in the metropolitan area?

3. **Why so located.**
   - Why have the super powers located their bases in Eastern and Western Europe, in S.E. Asia, and in the Pacific and Indian Oceans?
   - Are Australia's bases located in densely or sparsely populated areas?
   - What advantages do the defence forces seek in locating their bases?

N.B. 'Why' type questions can be devised for all the questions posed in the 'where' section.

4. **The inter-relationships between defence and people/the physical environment.**
   - What other things come with the installation of defence facilities? e.g. towns, services, industries, recreation.
   - Does defence create or reduce opportunities for employment?
   - What effects do defence exercises have on the physical environment?
   - What criteria are used to determine colours and types of vehicles, buildings, clothing? Are the colours and materials chosen effective?
   - What was the nature of war damage on the physical and built environment in Vietnam, Beirut, Hiroshima, Persian Gulf?

5. **What will happen if we alter the relationships?**
   - Would the closing of American bases in Australia make Australia more vulnerable to attack?
   - Would the 'balance' between the superpowers be affected if location of their bases was altered?
   - How would Russia's defence capability be affected if its influence was greatly reduced in Ethiopia, Cuba, Czechoslovakia, Vietnam, Afghanistan and South Yemen?
   - How would the defence capability of the United States be affected if its influence was greatly reduced in Canada, the Philippines, West Germany, South Korea, Mexico and Israel?
   - What effect does a change of government in Canberra have on the size, policy and deployment of Australia's defence forces?

6. **What change, if change is needed, should be introduced?**
   - Should we have more/fewer bases, spend more/less on defence, inform people of the implications of modern warfare compared to wars of the past?
   - Should defence forces be permitted in environmentally sensitive areas, for example Portsea, Swan Island, rainforests of Queensland, Central Australia?
   - Would the establishment of an army reserve unit in your local area attract recruits?

7. **What can we do to bring about change, if change is needed?**
   - Should we petition local M.P.'s, the council, rally community support, write to the local paper, prepare a report?
   - Should Australia increase its diplomatic links with countries not usually regarded as Australia's allies?
   - Should Australia take a higher profile in international affairs, for example act as a mediator in areas of conflict?

You will think of many other questions; these are just for starters. If you tackle any of the issues I listed earlier in this article, I'd be delighted to hear how you went about it, and what sort of response you gained from your students.

Figure 8.1: Key questions in a framework for a teaching unit on 'The Geography of Defence' prepared for Australian students (source: Studdert, 1985)

on 'No Nukes' in *New Wave Geography Two*. Also illustrative of such responses are the enquiry questions in Figure 8.1 which Studdert (1985) has prepared as the framework for a geography curriculum unit on the theme of defence for Australian students.

That geography can play a role in helping young people confront the nuclear threat with understanding, hope and commitment to the future is not in dispute, and sound contributions are being made by teachers. As Pepper and Jenkin's (1985, 1-2) argue:

> geography belongs squarely with the central disciplines (of peace studies). This is because so much of the war-peace problematique is inherently highly geographical, all the time requiring us to think about territories, spatial perceptions, geopolitics, potential place annihilation, the developed-underdeveloped world dichotomy, the locational ramifications of military doctrines and the potential spatial effects of nuclear weapons.

While much recent attention has focused on overcoming student concerns about the nuclear threat (see Hicks, 1986), a geography that addressed these issues *only* would be a curriculum response within the 'narrow' definition of education for peace. Such a response would fail to take note of three important issues embedded in the 'broad' view of education for peace outlined in the introductory paragraphs. These three issues are:

1. teaching about the nature of direct and indirect violence and of negative and positive peace;

2. the importance of teaching methods for a peace perspective in the curriculum; and

3. the integration of a peace-centred geography curriculum into a whole school approach to education for peace.

The implications of these three issues for geographical education are explored in the three sections in the balance of this chapter.

Negative and positive peace

The problem of war and violence is only one of at least five problems confronting peace identified by Galtung (1976, 1980) and Hicks (1983, 1988a). The other four barriers to peace are economic inequality, social injustice, environmental destruction and social alienation. Galtung and Hicks argue that, turned around, the 'problems of peace' give rise to five values which underpin a peaceful and just world:

Problems of peace	**Values underlying peace**
Violence and war	Non-violence
Economic inequality	Economic welfare
Social injustice	Social justice
Environmental destruction	Ecological sustainability
Social alientation	Democratic participation

Welcome as arms negotiations and nuclear reduction treaties are, putting an end to war and personal violence would not necessarily stop people going hungry, house and clothe the poor, or put an end to racism or environmental destruction. It would only put an end to *direct violence* providing, quite literally, a *negative peace* with all the historical and structural causes of poverty, racism, prejudice and greed unaddressed. As Figure 8.2 shows, replacing inequality with economic welfare, injustice with social justice, environmental destruction with sustainable development, and alienation with participation are needed to end *indirect* or *structural violence* and provide the conditions for *positive peace.* As Pope Paul VI said, 'If you want peace, work for justice'. The geography of Bunge's 'heavenly planet' (Bunge, 1986) is based upon this view of positive peace and the ending of structural violence.

Many recent trends in geography and geographical education have been conducive to research and teaching on this broad front of education for peace. These developments include welfare and radical geography and the increasing acceptance of world systems theory as a framework for explanation within the discipline. Welfare and radical geography are part of the humanitarian and political response to the dispassionate view of humanity embedded in the positivistic assumptions of spatial analysis.

Welfare geography seeks to describe patterns of inequality in social well-being around the world and to understand the processes that cause them in order to plan fairer patterns of social well-being. In many ways welfare geography was probably the major influence on geographical education during the 1980s, especially through its focus on explaining urban, national and global inequalities and fostering empathy for the Third World's poor (Bale, 1983). The contemporary geography teacher's keen interest in development education is a reflection of the influence of this 'geography of concern' on curriculum development in school geography.

Radical geography approaches the changes needed to bring about a

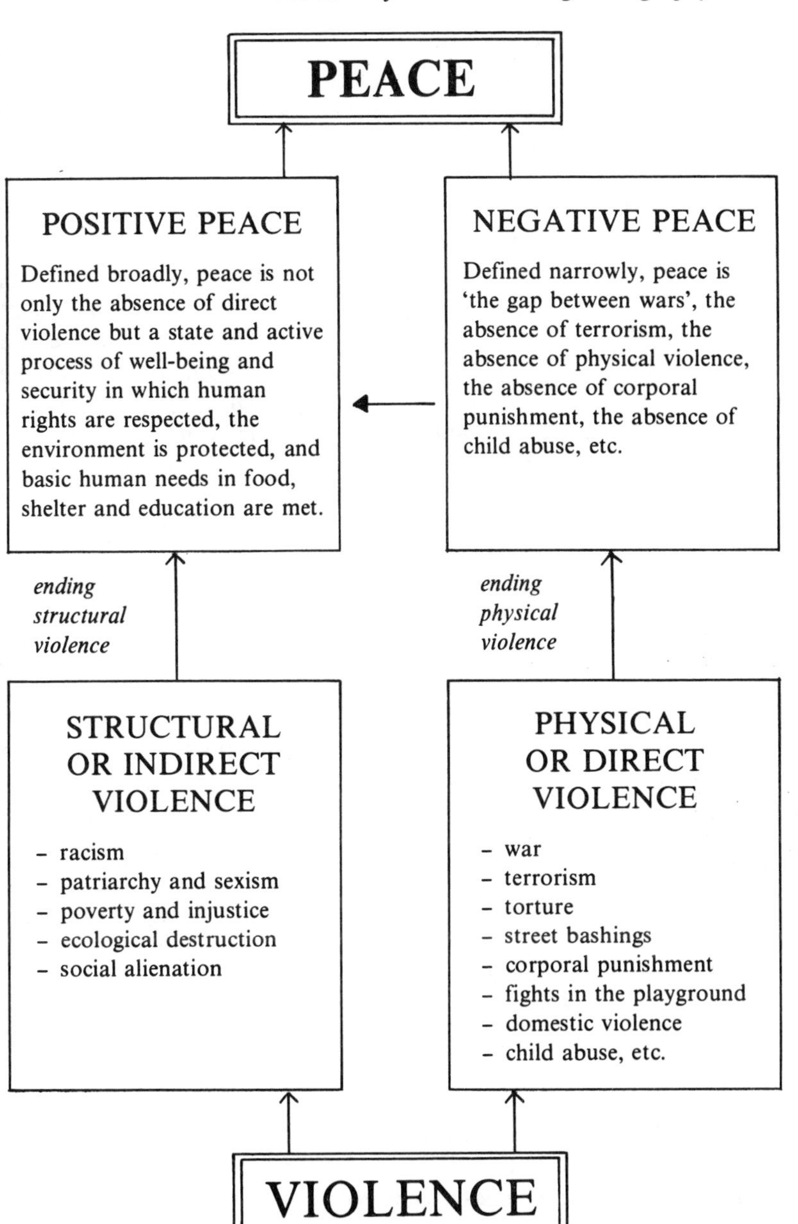

Figure 8.2: The concepts of positive and negative peace
(source: J. Fien and F. Hutchinson)

just economic and social order by seeking to uncover the root causes of inequality. Consequently, many radical geographers criticize welfare geography for offering only ameliorative solutions to personal and global problems through its failure to address these root causes. Johnson and Taylor (1986, 1987) argue that a view of the world as a single economic system that operates within and between two power blocks is necessary in order to understand the root causes of inequality. Basing their arguments on the world systems theory of Wallerstein, (1974, 1980, 1984), they show how the accelerating destruction of cultures and environments from both direct and structural violence is a result of the working of a capitalistic world economy (including state captialism). They claim that the entrepreneurial, corporate and state pursuit of profit and advantage makes undue demands on natural environments while motivating and controlling political activities at national and global scales. The uncontrolled pursuit of profit and advantage also generates problems of food gluts and famine, constrains individual freedoms, and threatens local cultures, thus producing the geography of unequal life chances studied by welfare geographers. Viewed this way, world systems theory provides a link between studies of direct and structural violence in geography. The various chapters based upon world systems theory in *Teaching Geography for a Better World* (Fien and Gerber, 1988). *Education for Peace* (Hicks, 1988b) and *A World Studies Workbook* (Hicks and Steiner, 1989) on teaching for human rights, anti-racist and anti-sexist teaching, development studies and environmental politics provide over fifty examples of geography curriculum units and activities that promote the knowledge, attitudes and action skills necessary to work for a more peaceful and just world. They are a guide for those who wish to educate for peace through geography. Peace education is not just about studying the 'problems of peace', however. Peace education also seeks to empower the individual as an agent of positive peace and, thus, places much emphasis on sharing success stories with students in which the work of individuals and groups in overcoming adverse economic and political structures are highlighted. The work of Greenpeace and other environmental groups in successfully obtaining an embargo on most whaling activities, and tree saving and re-afforestation work of the Chipko women of Uttar Pradesh, and the campaigns of The Wilderness Society and Australian Conservation Foundation in saving the beautiful Franklin River and the remaining rainforests of north-east Queensland are examples of success stories in the environmental area that may be used by geography teachers to good effect in this regard. The World Wildlife Fund (1988) teaching pack based upon the BBC television series, *Only One Earth*, and Timberlake's (1987) book from the series provide a number of other successful examples of positive peace-working from many different parts of the world. To complement this global emphasis, peace education seeks to empower students to be active agents for the betterment of their local communities, as well. This includes studies to improve communication and interpersonal skills, to promote the non-violent resolution of conflict, and to identify opportunities for individuals and groups to work for change. This is what is meant by the term 'thinking globally and acting locally', in peace education. Positive peace is built by people with the willingness and the skills to challenge the local, national and global structures with which the world economic system seeks to bind them. These structures include poverty, patriarchy, racism and militarism. Being aware of these structures is a powerful avenue for understanding one's own or one's group's position in the world and the things that must be taken into account in bringing about change. Burns (1986) writes that just as it is hard to resolve a conflict if it is not clearly articulated, it is difficult to do more than ameliorate problems if the underlying structures that cause and perpetuate them are not challenged.

Yet, while structures can (and do) bind and disempower the uncritical, it is important to realize (and to teach) that these structures are not immutable. Within these structures there is a role for human choice between alternatives and some encouragement to individuals and groups to challenge the structures and work to change them (Fien, 1988). This is the dialectic between social structure and human agency which Lee (1985) has described as 'the most fundamental idea to impart through education' because of its 'central importance to the future of human survival'. Thus, teaching the concepts, skills and values of political literacy which can empower and motivate individuals and groups to work for change has a major role to play in promoting positive peace. Practical examples of how this may be achieved through geography are provided in recent publications such as Huckle (1983c, 1988, 1989), McElroy (1988) and various chapters in Hicks (1988b), especially by Williamson-Fien on teaching about power and Huckle on environmental politics and political literacy. Among the examples used in these publications are ways of encouraging geography students to reflect and act upon their perspectives on environmental issues, nuclear energy and minority rights.

The importance of teaching approaches

Whilst the terms 'peace studies', 'peace education' and 'education for peace' are sometimes used interchangeably, there is an increasing tendency to draw distinctions. This is because peace *studies* has a dominant *content* focus, very much as was described in the previous section. However, peace *education* is interested in the hidden curriculum as much as it is in the formal curriculum. Burnley (1983) notes that:

> Peace education is not only *what* is taught – it cannot be equated with content. Its foundations lie in respect for children as people, the acceptance of their ideas and sensitivity to their feelings. The atmosphere of the classroom should be one in which co-operation and trust flourish.

Increasing numbers of peace educators prefer the term 'education for peace' because it highlights the need for compatibility between content and teaching processes. As Hutchinson (1985) says, there is

> ... little point in teaching about peace if we ignore how we teach. For a teacher to take a class in peace studies whilst brandishing a cane would be a contradictory process indeed. If the classroom context or the school as a whole is an unhappy, alienating and violent one for children, then by definition this cannot be education for peace. Peace educators stress how learning situations are inherently unpeaceful if they involve aggressive competition, little or no participation on the part of the learner, lack of dialogue between the learner and the teacher, and other forms of direct and structural violence. The term 'education for peace' is viewed, therefore, as making explicit a concern for a reappraisal of teaching methods as well as content to help ensure that the values of co-operation, participation, dialogue and positive peace are reflected in classroom activity and the relationships between teachers and children.

The geography teacher has at least two tasks in creating such an approach to learning. The first is in the selection and development of experiential learning experiences for students and it is here that *Earthrights* (Greig, Pike and Selby, 1987) and *Global Teacher, Global Learner* (Selby and Pike, 1988) with their 150 plus exemplar activities ranging from 'Globingo' to 'Woolly Thinking' are invaluable resources for student-centred co-operative learning strategies. The second task complements the first as it involves 'carefully limiting' one's own role from dominating the substance and direction of learning. Jenkins (1985, 205) recommends that while teachers might see themselves as authorities on certain matters, they should never act *in* authority because 'one has got a to create a classroom which is in some way a microcosm of the society one is trying to create'.

This is an important issue when considering some of the more controversial topics encountered in studying the causes of direct and structural violence and alternative solutions to the problems they cause. Topics such as racism, immigration policy, foreign aid, military spending, international relations and disarmament are only a few of the many over which the community is divided and, while it is vital that they be addressed where appropriate in the geography curriculum, by being careful not to act *in* authority teachers will be able to avoid the trap of consciously or unconsciously enlisting students in their own causes. By carefully evaluating their role in the classroom, teachers can ensure that students are free to explore many points of view, to formulate enquiry questions co-operatively, and to develop appropriate methods of investigation and tests for truth.

This does not mean that teachers should always be neutral. There is a well-tested difference between teacher neutrality and classroom objectivity (Burnley, 1988). In peace education, as in all teaching, teachers need to be free to choose the approach to analysing value-laden issues best suited to individual classes, situations and topics. Sometimes the 'neutral chair' will be the right approach; on other occasions, a 'balanced', a 'devil's advocate' or a 'committed' approach will be in order (Stradling, Baines and Proctor, 1984). By being active co-learners with students, teachers can abandon the 'banking' model of education and subject their views to the same critical analysis given to students' views, to those of visiting speakers, and to the text and other resources being investigated. By being prepared to make their views known to a class, and have them analysed, teachers can show students that peace is an issue over which it is important for citizens to form carefully considered views. Indeed, in relation to citizenship development, such teachers are modelling the democratic value that it is normal to take a stand on all issues without being dogmatic, and that one should expect one's views to be analysed and criticized by others.

However, parental and community support is vital for any change or innovation in education, especially when controversial issues are involved. To allay concerns that parents and school administrators may have about education for peace, geography teachers should seek to enlist their encouragement and support. The support and assistance of local politicians, scientists, doctors and parents in selecting and preparing lesson content, resources and learning experiences should be sought also. Peace education is an area where geography teaching can be seen to be public. However, more important than seeking support for what they teach, geography teachers, as educators, should seek endorsement for how they teach. Explaining to parents how a controversial issue such as the geography of nuclear conflict might be handled in the classroom – and even inviting them as helpers and observers – directly counters any charges of bias or indoctrination that may arise. Three areas that might be elucidated in this endeavour are the goals of any teaching unit, the process approach to teaching and learning to be employed, and the classroom climate that is created. For example, the goals of a possible unit on the geography of nuclear conflict might include:

1. To constructively air and deal with some student fears, thoughts and questions about a possible nuclear war.
2. To understand why the superpowers are in conflict and how this affects other countries.
3. To explore the variety of alternative viewpoints on a controversial issue.
4. To encourage students to make informed and reasoned decisions on issues, and evaluate alternative ways to act on them as responsible citizens in a democracy.
5. To value non-violent solutions to conflict and seek to maintain peace and co-operation in their personal relationships and in national and global affairs.

Secondly, in relation to the process approach to teaching and learning employed in education for peace, it should be explained to parents that on nuclear issues, as on any others, the teacher's role is not to teach students what to think, but how to think, and that this is done through a variety of ways, including:

1. Providing students with the background information in a variety of forms and giving students training and opportunities to find more information.
2. Ensuring that a wide range of perspectives is represented so that students see the value systems operating in the issues being explored and, thus, understand why society displays divergent views on the issues.
3. Training and encouraging students to assess the information they use by requiring them to differentiate fact from opinion, investigate and

verify sources and recognize claims that are difficult to prove or disprove.

4. Ensuring that students analyse the pros, cons and implications of each argument.

5. Encouraging students to evaluate the arguments presented by comparing, contrasting and clarifying them.

6. Using probing questions to help students identify the deep fundamental values that underlie the various arguments.

7. Encouraging students to clarify and take their own values into account when evaluating different viewpoints.

8. Providing opportunities for students to freely choose their position on the issue.

9. Insisting that students be able to give convincing reasons for their decisions and show evidence that they have considered the consequences and implications of their decisions.

10. Providing information and opportunities for students to explore various ways in which to act on their decisions and evaluate the wisdom and implications of that action.

Thirdly, there is a need to assure parents that when a class embarks on a programme over which there may be controversy, sensitive teachers are aware that they are dealing with issues over which the community is divided and many young people sometimes have grave concerns. It can be explained how teachers appreciate and empathize with these concerns and how they respond to them through building a warm and supportive classroom climate by:

1. Encouraging students to listen to what others say, whether they agree with their statements or not.

2. Not forcing their own views and opinions on students, but responding openly and honestly when asked.

3. Asking questions that help students to clarify their own thoughts and feelings.

4. Urging students to share their feelings and concerns to see that they are not the only ones who have those concerns.

5. Affirming life-valuing, social justice and democratic principles as the criteria for evaluating alternatives and making decisions on all issues.

6. Reassuring students that they are not alone in any fears they may have about the future and that many people, organizations and world bodies are working to create a safe and peaceful future.

Communicating with parents and school administrators about such procedures for selecting unit objectives, using enquiry-based teaching methods and creating an appropriate classroom climate can go a long way to overcome any concerns about teacher bias that may arise when the more controversial aspects of education for peace are being studied.

A whole-school approach

Thus far, the emphasis in this chapter has been upon the opportunities of an education for peace perspective in geography. Suggestions on the geographical themes that arise from the broad definition of education for peace and for the selection of appropriate teaching approaches have been explored. However, just as education for peace is not a specific subject to be included in the curriculum, it is not something that can be infused into one or two subjects. By itself, a peace-orientated geography curriculum is not enough if effective education for peace and justice is desired. Instead, whatever the geography teacher or department does should be integrated into an across-the-curriculum policy shared by the whole school. Such a policy ought to include amongst its aims those set out in Figure 8.3.

These seven aims give rise to a number of leading curriculum and school policy issues and to a range of curriculum ideas many of which are quite geographical. Geography teachers interested in developing a whole-school policy on education for peace might find it useful to engage colleagues in a systemic consideration of the policy issues and curriculum ideas which follow from these aims.

Conclusion

The scope, justification and curriculum possibilities of education for peace through geography have been described in this chapter. Attention has also been directed towards providing ideas and sources for developing content themes and learning experiences which can empower students with insights and skills to participate in working with others to create a more just and peaceful world. However, while there are many opportunities to educate for such a world through geography, whether or not individual teachers, geography departments and schools focus their teaching towards this end is problematic. It is a question of the choices *we* make between short-term self interest and long-term professional responsibilities. The pressures to avoid controversy through self-censorship (Maher, 1986) and the uncritical adoption of

AIM 1. A review of the nature of classroom and school structures and relationships to promote mutual respect and dignity for all involved in the educational process – students, teachers, parents and administrators. This includes a consideration of teaching styles, varieties of learning experiences, student involvement in school decision-making and discipline procedures.

AIM 2. The development of creative and peaceful approaches to conflict resolution, especially at the interpersonal level, but also at the intercultural and international levels.

AIM 3. The overcoming of prejudice based on racial, religious, gender or cultural grounds.

AIM 4. The promotion of a sense of justice and a commitment to work to help overcome the social and economic causes of poverty and oppression – locally, nationally and globally.

AIM 5. The development of respect and concern for planet Earth which provides the resources upon which all human life is nurtured.

AIM 6. The development of skills for problem identification, social enquiry, critical thinking and problem-solving and the skills of political literacy for democratic participation in society.

AIM 7. The development of a sense of self and history so that past, present and future can be interrelated, thus enhancing the visioning of alternative futures and ways of bringing them about.

Figure 8.3: The aims of an across-the-curriculum approach to education for peace. (source: Fien. Contact the author for further details of the curriculum questions and teaching ideas.)

biased conservative syllabuses and texts (Gilbert, 1984, 1986) are great. So too are the pressures of curriculum orthodoxy, government priorities in education, examination rules and the inertia of our own experiences, education and training (Naish, 1988). However, the demand for the socially relevant curricula of education for peace is great also. This demand comes from the fears and concerns our students have about the condition of their world, their needs and hopes for the future, and the aspirations of concerned and responsible parents and teachers. To teach geography for a bettter world, the tension between these conflicting demands must be resolved. Tipping the scales towards education for a just and peaceful world are the bleakness of not trying and the promise of the opportunities before us. As Bunge (1986, 291) urged:

> The geography of the heavenly planet *is* within reach ... We can have heaven; or we may have hell. In geographical terms, this planet is not too small for peace but it is too small for war. (my italic)

Chapter Nine
National Identification and International Understanding

Hartwig Haubrich

The chapter contains a quantitative and qualitative text analysis of essays entitled 'How I see my country', written by 15 year old students from 28 countries from all over the world. The author selected 51 content categories which he defined inductively and then used, together with intensity levels, connectivity factors and values to describe the different profiles of the cognitive and affective structures of the students' perceptions of their countries. The main result is that the students show very good psychological preconditions to combine national identification and international understanding through peace education for a better future.

In recent years I have travelled in many countries and met many geographic educators. These colleagues enabled me to ask 15 year olds to write an essay with the title 'How I see my country'. I have received reports from 28 countries and published them as reading materials (Haubrich, 1988a). The main function of this publication was to give the youth of the world an opportunity to become informed about different countries not only by adult textbook authors but also by youngsters who live in these countries. Students should write for students in the world in order to develop better understanding between the different nations in our world.

The second function of this project was to analyse how these young students perceive their countries, i.e.:

- which subject areas they select and write about;
- which ideas, feelings, fears and hopes they express;
- which values they prefer and stress;
- what kind of identification they show with their own country;
- what biases and stereotypes they have or try to avoid.

Because of the small number of students involved, the outcomes cannot be representative. But this pilot study can provide some ideas to stimulate more research in the field of international understanding.

Methodology

Content Analysis: The first step in analysing the cognitive structure which the students used to describe their countries was to find out the main subject areas or content categories they adopted. The author read the essays, selected topics and subtopics and coded them according to the following inductively worked out categories:

List of content categories and code number:

10 nature
11 situation
12 size
13 vegetation
14 animals
15 climate
16 soil
17 raw material
18 landforms

19 water resources

20 economy
21 foreign trade
22 industry
23 agriculture
24 mining
25 services
26 developing
27 technology
28 transport

30 culture
31 language
32 architecture
33 tourism
34 attractions

40 population
41 society
42 clothes
43 food
44 leisure
45 living standard
46 education
47 capital
48 home community
49 home country

50 social environment
51 settlement
52 mobility
53 history
54 inventions
55 religion
56 urbanisation

60 politics
61 military
62 war
63 international understanding

70 values/attitudes
71 identification
72 international co-operation
73 peace
74 image
75 human rights
76 future

Intensity Analysis: The second step was to grade the different subject areas according to the 'intensity' with which they were described. Dependent on the quantity and quality of reference the different categories received marks from 1 (lowest) to 5 (highest).

Value Analysis: The third step was to look for the values, i.e. whether the young students saw their topics positively (1), in a neutral way (2) or negatively (3).

Connectivity Analysis: Very often one paragraph was dominated by one category but this category was also connected with other categories – for example vegetation as a main category might be related to climate, landform, soil and situation. These connections were analysed and recorded.

Data Processing: Having finished the analysis according to the above methods the codes were typed into a computer with the program DATA-Entry and then processed by the SPSS-X package. The outcomes were two diagrams for each essay and an overview diagram of the cognitive and affective structure of all students' perceptions. These diagrams provided the basis for the interpretation of the results.

The cognitive and affective structure of the students' perceptions

Because of limitation of space, it is possible to show only a selection of categories and how they have been encoded.

10 nature:

> The high level of industrialization and the high living standard have their price. Our forests which are so characteristic of our country are becoming more and more ill. We speak about our dying forests. In most rivers we cannot swim because of their pollution. In some industrial areas the air is poisoned during bad weather conditions. And there are other problems against which we have to fight and are fighting. (Bastian Hilger/FR Germany p.41)

This quotation is an example for the category 'nature', an intensity level of 4, a negative valuation and connectivity with 'living standard', 'industry' and 'climate'.

13 vegetation

> In the far south, along the coastal belt, the mangrove or salt water vegetation is found while in the north-eastern region the vegetation thins out into the Sahel-Savanna. In the south, the agricultural products like coconut, swamp rice, cocoa, palm oil, cassava, maize and yams are grown, while in the north

groundnuts, beniseed, unpland rice and cotton are grown. (Nnaemeka Okpala/Nigeria p.113)

This example is encoded with the category 'vegetation', with the intensity level 5, valuation 'neutral' and connectivity with 'climate', 'agriculture', 'situation' and 'landforms'.

14 animals

Australia's animals and birds are fairly well known around the world. The best known ones include the koala and the kangaroo. Other Australian wildlife includes the brown snake, lizards like the frilled lizard and the gecko. Kookaburras, cockatoos, parrots, peacocks and galahs are common in this country. Some Australian animals are in danger of becoming extinct. These include the Tasmanian tiger, the bilby and the hairy-nosed wombat. As well, animals such as the koala are being given to overseas zoos. (Andrew Gerber/Australia p.9)

This paragraph has been encoded under 'animals'. It scored an intensity level 5, a negative valuation and connectivity with 'international co-operation'.

20 economy

Korea today is ranked as a newly industrializing country with a potential to join the ranks of the developed economies in the not so distant future. Korea has accomplished a successful economic development through series of Five-Year Economic Development Plans first implemented in 1962. The annual rate of economic growth during the period from 1962 to 1981 was 8.41 per cent. Korea's Gross National Product (GNP) per head increased from 87 US dollars in 1962 to 1.998 US dollars in 1984. (Kim, Sang-Hyun/Korea p.95)

This quotation was encoded with the category 'economy', an intensity level of 4, a positive valuation and connectivity with 'industry', 'living standard' and 'international co-operation'.

21 foreign trade:

Among the well-developed industries are garments, electronics, toys, clocks and watches. The exports of these industries are ranked very highly in the world. Hong Kong even produces electronic parts for the space shuttle. (Kwan Yu Bun/Hong Kong p.53)

The codes for this description are for content 'foreign trade', for intensity 5, for positive valuation and for connectivity 'industry'.

23 agriculture:

Even today, facing natural hazards, the farmers in Bangladesh manage to grow nearly two million tonnes of food every year, in an area measuring only

54 thousand square miles. The country receives a lot of aid from outside. Many factories producing jute, of which Bangladesh is the world's largest producer, have been established. The production of tobacco, another one of the cash crops of Bangladesh has been advanced. A large quantity of pulses, sugarcane, various seasonal fruits and vegetables is also grown in the country. The economy of Bangladesh mostly depends on agriculture. Despite of all the agricultural developments Bangladesh remains a land of green, struggling for survival. (Sabina Islam/Bangladesh p.12)

This is an example for the content category 'agriculture', with an intensity level 4, a positive valuation and connectivity with 'nature', 'food', 'vegetation', 'economy' and 'living standard'.

26 development

The economic development during the forty years after the war was not equal in the whole country. In spite of brotherly help, some territories have still developed slowly. Reasons can be found in different levels of economic development through history as well as in the unequal occurence of natural resources. (B. Pregelj and P. Campa/Yugoslavia p.153)

This quotation is encoded as 'developing' with an intensity level of 3 and a neutral valuation. There is connectivity with 'economy', 'history' and 'raw material'.

32 architecture

From these mountains, Jabal Amman, is the white stone of which all the houses and villas are built. They have a beautiful and nice architecture. In my opinion these are the nicest houses I've ever seen, considering that I travel a lot with my parents. (Rana Samawi/Jordan p.90)

This example illustrates the category 'architecture' with an intensity level of 3, a positive valuation and connectivity with 'mobility'.

41 society

In England, as in all countries, there is a social hierarchy. This is not as definitely defined as it was in the nineteenth and very early twentieth century, today the upper class and upper middle class merge together, the lower middle class and the working class merge together also.

The upper class consists of the royal family, titled aristocrats and important members of Parliament. The middle class is much more difficult to define. This is made up of Members of Parliament, business owners and important people in industry. The working class consists of 'ordinary' people, workers, tradesmen, shopkeepers, the unemployed – making up the majority of the population. There have always been more working class people than middle or upper class and with the help of unemployment in England, this is still true today. (Andrea Lyons/England p.28)

The category 'society' is combined with an intensity level of 5, a neutral valuation and connectivity with 'history', 'population' and 'living standard'.

43 food

Rice, either plain or cooked with other grains, is the main dish at all Korean meals. Rice is accompanied by a variety of side-dishes. Favourite side-dishes include bean-paste soup, pickled cabbage called 'kimchi', roasted beef and fish and steamed and seasoned vegetables. Soy sauce, soybean paste, red pepper paste, ginger root, sesame oil and sesame seeds are other seasonings, which are essential to Korean food. (Kim, Sang-Hyun/Korea p.97)

This quotation illustrates the category 'food' with an intensity level 4, a neutral valuation and connectivity with 'vegetation'.

45 living standard:

It is true Switzerland is a rich country. But even here the heavens do not rain money. Nobody suffers for hunger and everybody has his roof over his head. Nowhere can you find actually poor and criminal people in the streets.

But you have to know: Not every Swiss is rich. There are Swiss families who have to work very hard to earn their living. And those who are rich aren't so without reason. The richness has to be earned through much work. (Rahel Stauber/Switzerland p.134)

This paragraph was encoded as 'living standard' with an intensity level of 5, a positive valuation and connectivity with 'population', 'society' and 'economy'.

53 history:

I would like you to know the importance of the state of Israel to the Jews, that we are driven out of the country and were separated among the nations all over the world. No matter where we were, we were persecuted because of our different religion. Then the Nazis came and almost succeeded in exterminating us. Only then did we undersand that we cannot go on living without a country of our own and we returned to our old country of which we had diaspora. (Moshe Shaham/Israel p.68)

This category 'history' is described by an intensity of 4, with a negative valuation and connectivity with 'population', 'religion' and 'home country'.

60 politics

Denmark has nearly always been a kingdom and it is the oldest kingdom in the world. Our first king was 'Gorm den Gamle'. We don't know when he started ruling the country but he stopped about 950 years ago.

Right now we have a Queen called Margarethe the Second. She is the second Queen in Denmark's history and she is a descendant of the old king Gorm. She has not got much power and she doesn't exactly rule the country but leaves that to the Danish Parliament.

The Danish Parliament is elected by the Danish people who have the right of voting. To have the right to vote, you must be over 18 years. In Denmark both men and women vote. (Mette Humle Jorgensen/Denmark p.25)

This quotation received the category 'politics', the intensity level 5, a neutral valuation and connectivity with 'history' and 'population'.

61 military

We have many military aeroplanes, nuclear submarines and nuclear weapons and therefore we belong to the strongest states of the world. Indeed France's place is between the USA and the USSR, because it is not a member of the Nato. One isn't quite sure whether France acts with the USA or alone for itself. Thus France is able to play an important role to hold the military balance between the world powers. Besides that France is staying all over the world: in Africa, America, Polynesia and the Middle East. (Farouk Soufi/France p.46)

The codes for this paragraph are 'military', intensity 5, positive valuation and connectivity with 'identification', 'technology', 'international co-operation' and 'politics'.

62 war

My hometown Hikari, which has 50 thousand people, had a base of the Japan navy during the war. Many students, who had to work for the war, were killed by bombs. They are all my seniors and they were in junior high school then, forty years ago. (Koichiro Venatsu/Japan p.82)

Here we have the category 'war', the intensity level of 3, a negative valuation and no connectivity.

63 international understanding:

My country wants just warmth and peace with all the Arabic countries. (Ani Azriel/Israel p.65)

The category 'international understanding' is connected with 'peace', a positive valuation with an intensity level of 2.

70 identification

I will show what the main features are and what France means to myself. In a first part, I will describe France as a country of traditions, tourism and

> different landscapes. In a second part, I will show that France is an economically and strategically very important state and that it was also important in its history. In a last part, I will demonstrate that France is a country of liberty and human rights. This all means France for myself ...! (Farouk Soufi/France p.44)

This example is encoded as 'identification' with an intensity level of 5, a positive valuation and connectivity with 'culture', 'tourism', 'landforms', 'economy' and 'human rights'.

72 peace

> I want you to know that Israel wants peace with the Arab countries, but they want Israel to themselves, and if we give them Israel we won't have any other place to go to. The Arabs have many countries while we have only one and they want it to be theirs too. (Moshe Shaham/Israel p.68)

This quotation is encoded as 'peace' with an intensity of 4, a positive valuation and connectivity with 'international understanding', 'identification' and 'homecountry'.

73 image

> Most English people have a set picture in their minds of how they imagine foreigners to be. They have a different image for each country and this picture rarely changes even after visiting this country and meeting its inhabitants; the English are stubborn and do not change their minds so easily. So, probably, do all foreigners have their own set image of the English in their minds. At the turn of the century this image would have been one of upper class men dressed in tweed jackets and Hannet trousers [plus-fours], speaking with Oxford accents and playing bridge and watching cricket in their spare time. This image no longer exists. Unfortunately, for England, all the past couple of years an image of England as a nation of football hooligans has developed overseas. Both of these images of the English people are wrong but I cannot give an image of the average English person because within the country the people vary enormously. What I can say is that the typical English person is neither upper class nor a football hooligan, the majority of the population is working class and also law abiding.
>
> Most foreigners see the English as cool, unemotional and stand-offish. This is often referred to as the 'English reserve' and admittedly it does exist. (Andrea Lyons/England p.30)

This description is encoded by the category 'image' an intensity level of 5, a negative valuation and connectivity with 'population'.

74 human rights

> And now for the last symbol of France – to liberty! Indeed France is the first

> country which obtained, by fighting, the human rights during its revolution in 1789. This French declaration became the basis of the declaration of the human rights in 1948. Therefore we can characterize France as the country of human rights. France also belongs to the countries which signed the bill of children's rights on 20 November 1959. France protects and practices the right of sanctuary and the free movement of the unions. France together with five other states – possesses the veto right in the United Nations. The idea of liberty is – I believe – the idea of France. (Farouk Soufi/France p.48)

Farouk's description is encoded by the category 'human rights' with an intensity level of 5, a positive valuation and connectivity with 'history' and 'international co-operation'.

The above quotations illustrate the topics and interests of the young authors. Their perceptions are very complx and full of life compared with the abstractly encoded categories, levels of intensity, valuations and connectivities. But this reduction is necessary in order to be able to characterize the cognitive and affective structure of the single national perception and to compare the perceptions of the different young authors.

Comparison of the identifications of some authors

Because of limited space only two essays will be compared in the section which follows. Andrea Lyons, the English author, reports on many different topics and most of them, including population, society, living standard, image, culture, landform, industry and agriculture are described on the highest intensity level of 5. She is very strongly interested in the image English people have in the world. She mentions positive and negative sides of the English and summarizes her very differentiated image as follows: 'The English people have their bad points, but you will find that the majority of us are just like you, good people at heart, but we all have our faults.' The main areas of her essay are related to fields such as historical background, societal status, clothes, language, leisure, social environment, living standard, education and population structure. Politics do not belong to her main interests, which include the historical, social and religious basis of her society. She values the economic situation quite negatively, especially unemployment and relates her description of the economy to categories such as population, technology, services and international co-operation.

The identification with her country is the most critical of all the authors. She writes: 'I feel no strong patriotism to England or its rulers probably because of the terrible state that the country is in'. But she then moderates this valuation: 'After saying this I must admit that I could not live permanently abroad, because I view England as my home and have a sense of affection for the country.'

These few points are sufficient to show how different are the English author's perceptions of her country from those of the French author.

Farouk Soufi, the French contributor, sees his country only positively. There are no neutral or negative valuations. Farouk is especially interested in 10 main categories (Andrea in 19). These are image, international co-operation, human rights, economy, vegetation, landforms, culture, tourism, politics and military. Quotations for the categories 'military' and 'human rights' have already been given. Farouk shows the strongest identification with his home country compared with the other authors. He summarizes his essay as follows: 'Now I have shown you my France: landscapes, traditions, tourism, political strategy, economy, history with liberty and human rights. I think the best way to summarize all that I told you is to quote Charles de Gaulle (1890-1970): 'France cannot be France without grandeur!'

Farouk also describes French culture and tradition and relates them to the categories population, situation, social environment, history and international co-operation. Although Farouk describes less categories than the English author he describes them on the highest intensity level of 5.

Farouk and Andrea are only individual people and this pilot study does not provide a representative sample. On the other hand there are of course differences between nations and cultures. The world would be boring if people did not show such a variety of values, attitudes and behaviour. Should we not teach and accept that as Andrea writes:

> When visiting France last year I realized my own 'English reserve' on meeting the family with whom I was to stay. I had expected a friendly *Bonjour* and a handshake from the parents. But to my surprise and, I must admit, considerable discomfort, I was hugged and then kissed several times on each cheek by every member of the family. I got used to this ritual each morning before breakfast, and each evening before retiring, though never did I learn to enjoy this affection.

It is not possible to describe every national essay but, like Andrea, nearly every author is conscious of the difficulty of characterizing people because it very often means stereotyping. Therefore nearly everyone stresses that he or she is giving only his or her personal view about his or her country.

The main structures of the essays

It is possible here to select only those categories or topics which are educationally important or are described by the students on the intensity levels 4 and 5. These are 11 categories out of a total of 51.

A culture-orientation is typical for 14 of 28 countries. It has the highest priority. Within this context the students write also about language, clothes, food, education, architecture and attractions in their countries.

Eleven essays show a strong political orientation. Categories such as war, military and international understanding are important in this context and can be found under the connectivity ideas. Ten of 28 authors stress the category 'nature' and describe also many natural factors as situation, size, vegetation, animals, climate, soil, raw material, landforms and water resources. Some essays contain two or three sections about nature.

A social orientation can be found in eight reports. Population, living standards, home community, home country, capital and social environment are typical subtopics within this social context. The USA report contains five different small paragraphs about social issues.

Seven students stress the image their country has in the world. The English author is very much involved in treating this issue. Four different paragraphs contain the topics auto- and/or heterostereotypes. The Swiss author tries to correct the image Switzerland has in the world in three sections.

A very strong national identification is shown by six authors. These are Bangladesh, France, Jamaica, the Netherlands, Poland and Yugoslavia. But also the other authors show a kind of positive affection for their countries. An economy-orientation can be found in six of the essays. In this context the students write about foreign trade, industry, agriculture, mining, services, stage of development, technology and transport. The economy is of special interest and therefore very broadly described.

Human rights are important for France, the Netherlands and the USA. The other authors do not mention this topic.

The category 'future' is only stressed by three countries. These are Japan, Switzerland and the USSR. The category 'peace' is important in only two reports. The writers from Israel and China are the only ones who treat it very intensively. Within the other essays the issue of peace is not treated under the main categories but can be found amongst the connectivity factors.

Geography textbooks were analysed in the same way as the students' essays. The textbook chapters contained less categories than the students' reports. But the textbook paragraphs were more differentiated and contained more information. This difference shows that the students are more interested in a very broad approach and description of a country, i.e. they are not only motivated by classical geographic topics but also, and especially, by cultural, political and social features or by human issues.

Conclusion

The national perceptions of the 15 year old students from 28 countries from all continents contained 51 different main subject areas called content categories. But these categories were selected and treated quite differently. The sample of this pilot study is not big enough to build clusters of author types, but basically it can be said that the students are more interested in a broader approach to information about countries than textbooks normally offer. The cultural, political, social and human issues are of special interest as well as classical geographic topics such as nature and economy. The students do not hesitate to write about their values. Their identification with their own country is basically positive. A few writers, those from Denmark, England and Switzerland treat their national identification critically but not without a positive affection. The national identifications of the authors from France, USA and USSR are very strong and extremely positive. The Russian author summarizes his statement as follows: 'So in all spheres of our life, whether it is school education or work or leisure or medical treatment I permanently feel the care of my State about me'. A comparison with other countries can be found only in a few essays. The author from France writes for example: 'We belong to the strongest states in the world. Indeed France's place is between the USA and USSR'. The Japanese student admires Australia in such a way that his national identification seems not to be as strong as his love of Australia. In spite of some very strong national identifications there are no bad feelings expressed against other nations. Consciousness about the importance of peace and the future is quite weak but there is no chauvinism which could build a barrier against international co-operation. It seems on the basis of this pilot study that teachers have a very convenient basis on which to combine and balance national identification and international understanding through peace education for a better future.

Chapter Ten
Towards a Geography of Social Concern
David Lambert

This chapter presents a discussion on the value of radical geography both to the discipline as a whole and to geography in education. After a consideration of the rise of Marxist analysis in geography in the 1970s, and a brief examination of the problems associated with a full blown 'Marxist Geography', attention is focused upon more recent debate centred on structure and its relationship with agency and place. In this way, it is argued, a radical, Marxist perspective is brought into the realm of a real human geography. A radical stance also forces us to examine ideologies and this is an additional theme that runs through the chapter.

> It's a sociologist's paradise,
> Each day repeats,
> On easy, cheezy, greasy, queezy, beastly Beasley Street.
>
> John Cooper Clarke 'Beasley Street', 1981.

> There is no such thing as society. There are individual men and women and there are families.
>
> Mrs M Thatcher, reported in the *Guardian*, March 1988

It is hard to imagine a greater polarity of views as those contained within these statements. It is, of course, not surprising that the two individuals concerned should diverge so strikingly given their respective positions; one, the self-proclaimed 'punk poet' chanting about his home street in Salford, Greater Manchester, and the other the godmother of the strangely pragmatic amalgam of politics and economics which has become known as Thatcherism. Each, however, transmits a message to sociologists in particular – and perhaps social scientists in general – which it is important to consider; the assumption of powerful, deterministic economic, political and social *structures* which effectively shape and predict peoples' lives on the one hand, and the unswerving belief in the potential of the individual on the other.

If we can agree that geography in education has a role to play in examining issues of 'social concern' then the schism that these quotations illustrate needs exploration. One purpose of this chapter is to make such an exploration with a particular emphasis on radical geographies. Radical geography in the form that emerged in the 1970s through the writings of Harvey (1973), Peet (1977), Castells (1978), and others was a response to the search for 'relevance' to real-life issues that grew out of the perceived limitations of human geography. It will be argued that the Marxist critiques provided by radical geographers have been crucial in geography's development. It would not be possible to interpret our quotations above without the benefit of this critique and similarly, a geography without scrutiny from a radical perspective would be powerless and useless. However, a geography based solely upon orthodox Marxist dogma would be equally sterile. We go on, therefore, to evaluate some ways in which radical thought has developed in geography. Environmental education is briefly considered in this context.

There is, in this writer's mind, a considerable difference between discussing geography as an academic pursuit at the 'research frontier' and geography in school education. It would be untenable to deny any link at all between developments in geography in higher education and in schools, but it is also necessary to be cautious about the precise nature of these links. A school geography that centered upon the philosophical tensions in the discipline would be difficult to teach and, given the stage of intellectual development of the young people, difficult to learn. But this is not to say that the chasm separating the positions of the two individuals quoted above are to be ignored or glossed over. Quite the reverse, in fact, as the primary purpose of this chapter will be to explore how the insights and explanations of the radical critique can be applied in the secondary school setting.

A case for radical geography

There is a piece of graffito at the entrance to a railway tunnel in north London that simply reads 'Kropotkin lives', a reminder, perhaps, of the socialist-anarchist basis and long pedigree of radical and progressive thought in environmental and geographical fields of investigation (Kropotkin, 1902). The dominant influence on geography in the twentieth century has been something quite different, however. The search for academic 'respectability' required the adoption of 'scientific' methodologies and epistemology; this would enable geography to break out of the 'academic backwater, blissfully ignorant of the methodological and philosophical issues which enlivened other disciplines' (Sayer, 1985b, 159). The quantitative revolution, together with the narrow view of 'science' which it propagated, sealed the fate of geography for quite some time. The shortcomings of this era are numerous and are well documented (e.g. Harvey, 1973; Huckle, 1983a).

For the purposes of the present discussion it is probably sufficient to record just two of these, namely the ideological role that geography was fulfilling in terms of supporting the needs of advanced capitalism and the limitations of the intellectual heritage that geography laboured under, in the form of environmental and social determinism.

These points can be taken together 'the quantitative revolution was a social product', (Lee, 1985, 204); in other words it was a response to society's needs at that time. The belief in technological progress and the solubility of problems by the application of appropriate techniques (which were simply awaiting discovery or invention) was the context, and the product was only the very muted questioning of a system in which material inequalities amongst people persisted and even increased.

Writing on the 'quantitative revolution', Harvey admits to having been swept along, indulging in various technological wizardry, but finding 'to my consternation that I only managed to accumulate a drawer full of unpublished and unpublishable papers' (Harvey, 1969), which is a nice way to draw attention to the theoretical weakness of much of the academic output. Models were used, and taught, which bore little resemblance to actuality and it seemed at the time that this was the fault of actuality, not the models! Just think also of classical locational analysis which is quite openly a tool to measure profitability and makes assumptions concerning the economic structure (competition, 'economic man') which serve a clear ideological role. In a similar manner, the information field in geography at this time was seen as unproblematic; you simply collected it. As Sayer writes, 'this "scientific" geography rested upon the unacknowledged and unexamined concepts of common sense' (Sayer, 1985a, 165). This is an illustration, if it is not stretching the point too far, of how the power of a prevailing ideology produces, via an unhindered and value-free science, false consciousness. Researchers and teachers of geography did not purposely set out to mislead or obfuscate, but assumptions went unchallenged and alternatives went unexplored.

The power of this model-based geography to mislead is a serious concern, and results partly from theories whose origins lie in interpretations of Darwin. The Darwinian heritage in its various mutations is the most pervasive legacy of nineteenth-century thinking, and geography has not been immune from its contribution to influencing the way the world is interpreted. It has given us a framework in which we can organize the 'natural order' of things in both the natural and social worlds. Pepper recounts an interesting twist in the Darwin story and in particular the *social* Darwinist arguments which are deployed to legimate the status quo:

> To challenge the credibility of such fatalistic, do-nothing doctrines, it is worth studying their history. A remarkable fact comes to light, which is that the so-called 'natural order' discerned by biologists like Darwin, Huxley, Tansley and Clements, was in reality quite clearly and explicity *first* transferred by and *from* society *to* nature, before being transferred *back* from nature to society in social Darwinism or social ecology. Thus, as Engels noted, the principles of competition, struggle for existence and survival of the fittest were taken from ... observations of capitalist society and imposed, in Darwinian evolution, on to plant and animal behaviour patterns ... Then this supposed 'natural' order of plant succession, from simple to complex, was used in subsequent political legimitation of particular land uses. (Pepper, 1987, 73)

Further illustration of this point is contained in Figure 10.1 What clearer evidence do we need of 'pure ideology posing as science', an accusation often levelled, of course, at the radical perspective rather than the liberal science ethic?

A geography of social concern needs first to be aware of this deficiency and then needs to do something about it; it is not good enough to give the impression, by default maybe, that poverty in the inner cities is simply a 'natural' outcome of social processes. It is, though, in the interests of the continued development of capitalism to have the dark clouds of possible homelessness, unemployment and poverty to play 'stick' to the 'carrot' of material well being that rewards success – and compliance to the political and economic system. A geography of social concern, therefore, needs to ask questions not merely about spatial patterns and assumed 'spatial processes' but of the system itself. It can be noted, in passing, that welfare geography, though it arose from a 'general feeling that the discipline was failing to respond

Ecological Concept	*Animal/plant ecology example*	*Human ecology example*	*Political implications*
An 'environment' as an ecological unit	e.g. salt marsh	e.g. city	Analysis is restricted to locality
Natural processes	Biological competition for scarce resources	Economic competition for scarce resources	Market processes are universal and inevitable
Adaptation and specialization	Different species in different ecological niches	Occupation groups/land use classes in 'natural areas'	Class system is merely specialization which benefits all
Dominance and control of community	e.g. trees in a woodland community	e.g. Commerce and industry in the city	Dominant classes are as benign as trees

Figure 10.1: The 'nature' and politics of human ecology.
(source: P. J. Taylor, 1985 187.)

The reader should relate the summary provided in this table to, say, the best-known product of the Chicago school of 'urban ecology', the hugely influential zonal model of E. W. Burgess. The ideological position of this work is clear; as Taylor writes, 'the proposition that some human behaviour is "natural" is usually a justification for a particular status quo. Quite simply, dominant classes are not like trees, and the processes of their control are anything but natural and "purposeless"'. (Taylor, 1985, 188)

---

to contemporary social issues' (Smith, 1977, 4), runs aground in this respect. It is primarily concerned with redistribution and relies on the altruism of governments or societies. Questions concerning power, the ownership and control of wealth and in whose interest the political and economic system works, are muted.

The framework which facilitates the penetrating questioning which in turn supports radical enquiry, and which began to emerge in the geographical literature in the 1970s, is Marxism. Essentially what radical geographers have set out to do is to redress the balance by introducing political economy into the realm of human geography. Thus human geography adopts a critical view toward the concept of 'work', for example. It establishes through Marxist analysis (historical materialism) that it is productive activity and the way in which this is organized, which shapes society. The main productive force is labour and people have to enter into certain relations with each other in order to set production in motion. It is in this way that history is made.

As Peet explains:

> For Marxists, the crucial social relation of production is between the owners of the means of production and the workers employed to operate the means. Under capitalism, the socially produced means of production are privately owned. The private owners of the means of production control the conditions of the labour process and its products, including the surplus product that is the source of investment capital (Figure 10.2). Accordingly, they control the future course of economic and social development. (Peet, 1985, 6)

These social relations represent the economic structure of society and this structure in turn shapes appropriate social, cultural and political structures (what Marx termed the 'superstructure'). The political structure, for example, is both determined by and helps support the economic conditions.

The economic imperative under capitalism is the maximizing of surplus value (of private profit) and, by this analysis, it is not surprising that weak controls on toxic waste disposal into the North Sea, poor conditions of health and safety on oil rigs or the appalling indebtedness afflicting many of the poorer nations on earth are all features of advanced capitalism. These are examples of the symptoms of a complex of environmental crises and readers will be able to add many more to this list. For Marxists these crises are the expected outcome of capitalism. They are generated by the fundamental contradictions in capitalism that Marxist analysis shows up: the insoluble tension between production for need and production for profit, for example; or the equally intractable problem of reconciling the absolute necessity for capital accumulation (private profit) and a care for the natural environment (i.e. 'exploitation' versus 'conservation').

Figure 10.2: 'The exploitation of labour through the extraction of surplus value.'
Originally reprinted by permission of Fred Wright, United Electrical, Radio and Machine Water of America
(source: *Journal of Geography*, *84*(1), January 1985)

A case against Marxist Geography

In the briefest space, I have tried to make a case for radical – Marxist – geography and to describe, albeit in sketch-form, its position.

Fundamentally, its analysis shows that to understand geographical relations, we must first understand the social structure which itself is predicated upon the economic relations that exist.

But is there not more to it than this? Well, in a sense yes there is, for radicals talk of a *breakthrough* to Marxism which is both difficult and of fundamental importance:

> In the breakthrough from liberal to Marxist geography a leading role was played by Harvey ... who moved very quickly through the stage of liberal theory, to arrive at Marxism by the early 1970s. (Peet, 1977, 16)

It is difficult because of the need for 'all academics ... to "untrain" themselves' (Harvey, 1973, 149); that is to say, for people to cleanse themselves of their assumptions and to raise awareness of the purpose of 'normal science'. It is important because without Marxism our endeavours become counter-revolutionary 'in the sense that it allows the bleeding-heart liberal in us to pretend we are contributing to a solution when in fact we are not' (Harvey, 1973, 144). In other words, radical geography has as its objective not merely to *understand* society, but to *change* its basic character.

It is for this reason that radical geography is often equated with a full-blooded attack on Western societies and their replacement by some kind of state socialism. The latter part of this equation may be unfair, however, as Marxists are quick to point out that their analysis is appropriate to all societies. Indeed, they argue further that it is not their business to draw 'blueprints for the future shape of society' (Peet, 1985, 10). But, what we are left with then is a somewhat unsatisfactory confusion: a form of analysis which is committed to change but unwilling or unable to say with any clarity what form that change may take. It argues that peoples' consciousness arises out of their economic circumstances; the implication is that to replace the prevailing economic structure with something better, will produce better people – people who are not driven by egotism, competition and selfishness which are rational human characteristics under capitalism. In the absence of empirical verification for this a conundrum arises which remains insoluble: is capitalism a product of human nature or is human nature a product of capitalist relations?

Is this a fatal flaw of the Marxist critique? Some readers will be no doubt thinking that the flaw is with the writer, as introducing human nature and demanding empirical verification is certainly not within the realm of orthodox Marxist procedure. But, these are in fact not the only items I would wish to bring into the discussion. Marxist analysis runs a great risk of occupying a form of barren intellectual world consisting of general propositions which are place-less or at least are not place-specific. This is profoundly non-geographical. It reduces real places to points and reduces the people who live in them to pawns within a system of economic relationships. To put it another way, Beasley Street may not have been a very nice place in which to live and the inhabitants were disadvantaged, but it was different from streets, say, in the Fitzgerald District of Detroit and, although we know what Clarke means when he writes 'Each day repeats', to overemphasize the structures within which people live tends towards absolving men and women of any responsibility. In this way, the radical analysis seems deeply pessimistic as well.

The purpose of this chapter is not to conduct a philosophical assessment of Marxism and its value to geographical discourse. To delve too deeply into the complexity of argument and counter-argument would, I contend, deflect us from our real purpose. Even so, it is important to record that Marxist theorists would object to what they might regard as a caricature in the comments I have provided above. For example, it is false to accuse Marx of having suggested that history constantly repeats itself in the sense that human beings are quite impotent, alienated from nature and committed to a life of subservience and oppression. Points such as this are made freely in publications such as the Communist Party publication *Introducing Marxism*. For instance:

> It is important to recognize that such distortion and alienation in economic life are never absolute and all-pervading. Capitalist production could not survive for a day unless it did actually succeed in meeting genuine needs – in providing consumer goods and raising living standards. Similarly working life under capitalism is not completely devoid of genuine satisfactions, in spite of exploitation ... Marxist economic theory does not deny these real advances nor does it call for a return to less developed systems of production. (Simon, 1986, 25-26)

But in turning to a publication such as this we have perhaps complicated the situation even more, for political party publications do not necessarily provide pure or accurate interpretations of a particular philosophy, operating as they do in the arena of political expediency.

In many ways, and so long as we are content not to be hidebound by the 'scriptures' of 'what Marx said', we could most usefully sidestep the issue of whether there is a case for or against a Marxist geography. Far more useful might be to accept the existence of the Marxist critique, in the sense that it has informed our understanding of the economic processes that help shape societies, as a component of our investigatory kitbag. In other words, it would be difficult to defend or propagate a 'Marxist Geography' and in the end this would in any case be a distracting and not very interesting occupation. It is *not* difficult, however, to embrace a geography which is informed by ideas and perspectives which ultimately have their origin in Marx. Such a geography (crucially) would be open to ideas from other sources as well; and there are urgent concerns which geography must face – not least the various 'Green' problems on a variety scales – to which the narrow and, perhaps, rigid Marxist analysis cannot alone bring resolution. It is perhaps in this spirit that the political columnist in the *New Statesman and Society* has written that 'as a political party the CPGB [Communist Party of Great Britain] has absolutely no further reason to exist', whilst welcoming its attempts through recent publications to create a 'new, creative marxist theory' and introducing a 'better marxism' into political debate. (*New Statesman and Society*, 2 September, 1989, 21)

Structure and agency

Marxism presents us, in its orthodox form, with a narrow variety of structuralism. In doing so it reduces to a constant the real experience of real people. In its most extreme form individual roles are ignored completely and this is, ironically, a reactionary stance as its fails to recognize individual or collective actions of people in their various roles: as women, as blacks, as physically disabled and so on. Society is viewed as monolithic rather than diverse, simple rather than complex and, as we have seen above, usually without spatial context.

In reality, and without denying the existence of structures – especially the structures of everyday life such as finding shelter and food – we need to recognize the impact of human agency. As Lee writes of societies:

> They are made in conscious and less than conscious fashion by 'real people in a real context'. As a result, each society is in a perpetual state of becoming. Societies are always being made and remade. The underlying motor of this creative process of social construction and reconstruction is the dialectical relationships between 'real people' (or agents) and the 'real context' (or structure) which is made by people to provide their own conditions of existence. (Lee, 1985, 201)

The process described here is commonly referred to as structuration. It denies any purchase to the idea that societies are determined and are subject to a mechanistic and impersonal historical development, whilst at the same time it encourages us to expect creative human action which offers hope and optimism. Writings that have appeared in geography in recent years incorporating these perspectives are numerous (e.g., Gregory, 1985; Massey, 1984; Sayer, 1984). They urge upon us a form of radical human geography which takes on a *realist* theoretical stance, rejecting a simple, unproblematic empiricism and at the same time compelling us to discover and examine the relevant structural features of society which are not necessarily open to 'common sense' and straightforward to identify (Gregory, 1985, 71). Andrew Sayer emphasized this in relation to school geography. On the 16-19 Project 'A'-level syllabus he wrote of the inadequate treatment of *social* relationships and power, and the 'managerial' approach adopted in the syllabus to people-environment issues. He explains thus:

> The use of words like 'we', 'society' and 'mankind' may engender a certain identification with others and while that is no bad thing in itself it is pure mystification if it is based on the outrageous assumptions that 'we' all participate equally in making such decisions, that we all have the same interests and that, in a capitalist society, production is apparently simply for fulfilling human needs rather than for profit. (Sayer, 1985a, 91-92)

The argument is that class differences and the power relationships that arise are obscured in the overall tone of the syllabus; but perhaps Sayer fails to acknowledge fully the scope that exists in the syllabus to introduce the kind of analysis he suggests. The power in this respect lies in the hands of the teachers; it is not likely that a syllabus *per se* can itself be a radical document but many syllabus frameworks, 16-19 included, do not preclude teachers encouraging students to a critical attitude to knowledge and designing teaching and learning activities that challenge conventional wisdoms. (See, for example, 'An evening in the Capital Theatre', Palfrey, 1986.)

Of course, to be able to do this we need a framework in which to think, plan and organize. Realism enables us to do this; 'we will come to see', as Gregory notes, 'that *people make a difference and places make a difference*' (Gregory, 1985, 74; author's italic). Kirby puts it differently, emphasizing the role of structure:

> it is now seen to be not possible to break apart the 'big picture' and the small details; human agents recreate capitalism in specific ways, and in so doing they create tensions which have impacts upon the systems as a whole. Specific localities inherit the blueprints of a structure like industrialism in

different ways; agents impose upon it particular cultural meanings, particular priorities, with the result that there emerge different types of labour relations, different forms of legal practice and different social relations. Nor do these exist in isolation, for all parts of a complex economic system have then in turn some impact upon the whole; capital and labour are both mobile, and may move to take advantage of such variations. One more, the whole is continually reinterpreted and changed by individual, and in consequence, local action. (Kirby, 1987)

These comments are illustrative of the work going on which explicitly sets out to examine the role of space in the functioning of the capitalist economy. It might be helpful to set alongside this some further ideas which possibly will flesh out even further a framework which geography teachers may find supportive. Figure 10.3 presents a simple diagram which shows a rationale for the use of different spatial scales. It is derived from Taylor's work on developing Wallerstein's political-economic ideas and basically informs us that, although the economic

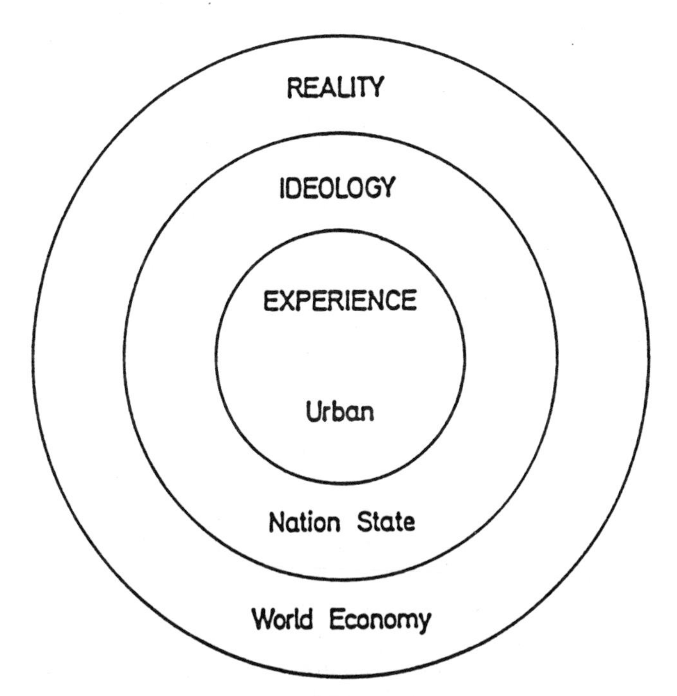

Figure 10.3: A rationale for the use of different spatial scales.
(source: Taylor 1985; Kirby, 1982)

system in which we all live is global in character, we must at various times change the spatial scale of analysis in order to understand the actual operation and outcome of the world economic system (Taylor, 1985, 30; also reproduced in Kirby, 1982, 7).

So, we are all caught within the global economic system (the 'reality'). But there are two further layers of understanding. Crucial to Taylor is the nation-state which functions as an ideological entity in a similar way to that which Marx defined, ensuring national loyalties and even nationalism for reasons of economic self interest. Beneath this, and quite distinct, is the urban scale which is the scale of everyday experience – of finding shelter, work and the other day-to-day needs. Taylor illustrated how these interact (albeit in a somewhat dated example):

> In a political discussion in the Wallsend Constituency in North East England I have observed that a major topic of concern has been the health of shipbuilding. This is only natural since the Swan Hunter yards are the major employer in the area. If the yards close, the resulting unemployment will affect the whole town, making Wallsend the 'Jarrow of the Eighties'. This is the scale of experience. It is at the scale of ideology that policy emerges however. The response to local pressures was for the Labour Government to nationalize British shipbuilding including Swan Hunter. This is ideological since it reflects only a partial view of the situation. It may protect jobs and ease the flow of state subsidies into the area, but it does not tackle the basic problem affecting shipbuilding. Both demand and supply in the industry are global. The current problems in the industry can be directly traced to the fall in demand following the 1973-74 oil price and the emergence of competitive suppliers from such countries as South Korea. Clearly a policy of nationalization is a long way away from solving the problems of Wallsend's shipyards. (reproduced in Kirby, 1982, 6)

This provides us with a rationale for examining issues at three spatial scales. It is proposed *not* merely as a convenient way of dividing up the syllabus content, but a framework to facilitate the introduction of a more critical (radical) school geography. It does this because different things happen at these different scales. For example, it is difficult to examine ideology at either the local or the global scale; similarly, it would be more meaningful to examine, say, unemployment at the local scale – investigating real cases or communities – than to aggregate up to the national or even global scale. And some issues such as acid rain or the pollution of the North Sea can be very usefully examined at each scale in turn; the *Daily Mirror* cartoon might provide a useful starting point for the latter (Figure 10.4).

Figure 10.4: 'Go on ... please. One more won't make any difference.'
(source: *Daily Mirror*, 31 August 1988, Reproduced by permission of C. Griffin, Mirror Group Newspapers.)

An imaginative reading of the cartoon may give us a way into investigating the local experience of living near to the threat of inadequately treated waste of a life-threatening industrial plant. The national context, in which such occurrences are allowed to persist, can then be examined. This may require looking at legal frameworks and also less tangible elements of an ideology, such as the 'not in my backyard' rationale, which has resulted in nations 'exporting' pollution via pipelines and tall chimneys. Finally, the cartoon features the Karin B desperate for a berth to unload its highly toxic chemical waste, which had been originally dumped in Nigeria. This is the reality of the global economic system in which firms are able to shift their products, their capital and their waste across national frontiers with the minimum of hindrance. We have an approach here which has the potential to focus students' enquiry on to the real issues of power and towards a critical position with regard to ideologies. The effect on real people in real places is also pursued.

And the Greens?

There is space here only to acknowledge 'Green politics' which is sometimes described as a new radical movement and which probably has had a significant impact on geography teaching and learning. Phrases such as 'encouraging positive attitudes to the environment' are common in syllabus documents at all levels in secondary schools.

However, it is important in the context of this chapter, to also make note of the searching debate going on both in and outside the various parts of the Green movement. Greens are critical about individual and collective human behaviours which reduce the quality of life and in some cases the very existence of life. They also put up imaginative alternative futures and, of course, encourage children to do the same. But, it is compellingly argued by the likes of Pepper (1984) and Weston (1986) that this approach often falls into the 'trap' of liberalism and pluralism – that is to say, ignoring the reality of power, and the power of capitalist ideologies – and also has a limited, even romantic, interpretation of 'environment'.

Huckle has argued that:

> Perhaps for too many green teachers the environment is equated with the earth's ecology and nature. Lessons stress the survival needs of rare species and habitats, ecological processes, and wilderness areas. There is a reluctance to recognize that most environments are socially constructed and that the environmental problems facing the majority of the world's people are problems of hunger, clean water, safe and satisfying work, housing and alienation. (Huckle, 1986, 11)

He is right, of course. These are the problems faced by people on a day-to-day basis and, to return again to Figure 10.2, should be studied on the scale of 'experience'. The additional understandings that Huckle urges us towards are attainable, I would argue, by analysis through the overlaying scales – of 'ideology' and 'reality'.

Conclusion

I have tried to show that radical geography has had and continues to have a vital role in the development of the discipline. In a sense it was a response to the sterility of the isolated state and the isotropic plain; but it also has been crucial in showing the way forward. We can reject a 'Marxist Geography' (the label is at the very least unhelpful) but we cannot ignore the critique that the Marxist perspective has provided, nor the related theoretical developments that have since taken place within geography.

Furthermore, I have tried to indicate that the introduction of radical geography to school is possible. It does not require syllabus changes, as most syllabuses do not exclude approaches and frameworks which would allow students to investigate issues critically. It is up to teachers to make certain conventional wisdoms problematic and to organize activities that give students access to real power relations and an understanding of who are the real decision makers.

These are relatively modest, yet still radical aims. Marx himself gave a specific meaning to 'ideology', as the *unaware* expression of a belief system within a society. 'False consciousness' is the result. Mrs Thatcher's quotation at the beginning of this chapter is clearly an attempt to bolster the ideology of individualism which is so powerful in Western societies. Through studying space and society, geography can encourage students to be critical, not only of John Cooper Clarke's doom and gloom, but of the ideology that guarantees the persistence of inequalities in material and social wellbeing.

Part Three
Resources and Learning

Chapter Eleven
The New Technology and Geographical Education
W. Ashley Kent

This chapter offers a critical portrayal of the context and realities of the use of information technology (IT) and in particular, computers in geography at school level in Britain. It focuses on the use made of computers in classrooms; the role of outside agencies; a newly published inservice pack and Project HIT. It outlines the research progress and needs in this field and shares some critical perspectives on such developments. Finally, it looks to the likely future of geography and IT by the year 2000.

Anna, our ten year old, came in from school and immediately sat down at the micro – a rather elderly BBC B and very much part of the furniture in our 'family' room. She proceeded to write and word process a play with parts for herself and her school friends. She then set up the equally ancient and rather primitive printer and printed off six copies. Then it was time for tea ...

To Anna and many of her generation, computers have very little novelty value. They are treated critically and used whenever needed – in our case, for instance, the SMILE maths programs and English programs such as WORDS, WORDS, WORDS. Mastery of such technology often puts technophobic adults to shame and extends to other technological elements of a modern Western house. Why *are* the children so much more adept than I at manipulating video players, digital watches and telephone answering machines? Schools (and not just middle-class parents!) have played an important part in fostering technological awareness in children.

Information technology (IT) developments have been particularly noteworthy and dynamic in schools in the 1980s. IT is an umbrella term which covers video, satellite imagery, televisions, computers, interactive video and compact disc players. For convenience and brevity, this chapter focuses on computers.

The changes in the use of computers in geography teaching over the decade have been well documented in a variety of publications (Shepherd et al., 1980; Walker, 1981; Watson, 1984; Hall et al, 1985; Kent, 1985; Kent, 1986a; Watson, 1987; Freeman, 1988) and it is not the intention of this chapter to cover the same ground. The 1970s could be described as the paleotechnic era (Hall's term, first used in Hall et al, 1982) since only a tiny minority of geography teachers were touched by computing. It took the arrival of the microcomputer via a government subsidy scheme and the establishment of the MEP (Microelectronics Education Programme) to herald the Neotechnic era for computers in schools. Great excitement was generated by the arrival of first the 380Z, then BBC micros in schools, to be shortly followed by MEP subsidised subject specific software. Arguably, the Aeotechnic era arrived in 1986 with the creation of the MESU (Microelectronics Education Support Unit) in the UK to enable teacher training at all levels to implement the now fashionable computers across the curriculum policy. Throughout these eras, geography has been a front runner in grasping the pedagogic potential of the new technology. A clear indication of this was the establishment as early as 1983 of a Computer Page (always an inaccurate estimate of its length) in *Teaching Geography* with articles and reviews of software. A further indication has been a steady flow of books aimed at supporting and encouraging the use of computers in geography, for example, Watson, 1984; Midgley and Walker, 1985; Kent, 1986b; Fox and Tapsfield, 1986; Kent and Riley, 1988. The three 'eras' roughly equate with the development of my own feelings towards computers in geography. In the Paleotechnic era, I was highly sceptical of the likely wide ranging impacts of the technology. However, in the Neotechnic era, I was enthused and converted to the cause of encouraging the use of the 'mighty micro'. Now, however, in the Aeotechnic era, my hopes are more realistic yet still tinged with an excitement and dynamism that make developments in educational technology so (dangerously?) seductive.

The purpose of this chapter is to portray the current situation with regard to computers in geography and to look forward to likely developments by the turn of the century.

The situation now

Throughout the 1980s there have been studies to determine grass roots level activity. One of the seminal pieces of research was that of Freeman

(1981), who studied Hertfordshire. More recent work, such as that of Rogers (1987) for Essex and Dove (1987) for Victoria, Australia, took a similar approach through questionnaires and interviews with teachers. More recently there has been the work of Baker (1988), through the Fawcett Fellowship at University College, London, and probably the most recent and comprehensive has been the work of Allen (1988a), at Cambridge in which he surveyed 100 geography teachers from East Anglia and the South East.

Use by geography teachers

There are many ways of categorizing the software and related learning used in geography education. Figure 11.1 shows one example, but the critical distinction which has emerged in the last few years has been that between general purpose (non-subject specific, content free, horizontal and generic) software and subject specific software. So far the majority of software produced and used is of the latter type but subject use of general purpose software is growing. For instance, a recent example has been the use of a spreadsheet to complement the Granada TV's programme on 'Trucking', part of an Information Technology series for schools. The spreadsheet is used to recalculate travel distances and costs of journeys the lorry driver makes between England and continental Europe.

It is uncertain exactly how much geography software is published and available but Foskett's list of geography software being compiled for the National Educational Resource Information Service (NERIS) on behalf of the Geographical Association had reached 165 programs by January 1989 and was not thought to be comprehensive. Sadly, there is no one library in the UK where all educational software is housed – in spite of the efforts of this author![1]

Allen's survey (1988a) suggests that popular uses of the microcomputer include: the micro as electronic blackboard in geomorphology, weather and climate; drill and practice in mapwork, and statistical/quantitative work for fieldwork, not least geomorphology. He also discovered that word processing was being increasingly used by pupils for projects and reports as well as by teachers who used them a great deal for administration and teaching materials production and thereby as a 'way in' to the use of computers.

The situation with regard to hardware is even less clear. By 1985, the average number of microcomputers in schools was 10, but by 1989 it was probably nearer to 20, with some schools having several networks

Software is often categorized by its style; thus we have general purpose and subject specific software. General purpose programs are those in which the actual material is entered by the user – the software simply 'handles' the material. This material can be on any subject matter, so that programs can be of interest to physicians, linguists and historians, for instance, as well as geographers. Into this category we put:

- word processing
- data handling and interrogation
- spreadsheets
- desk top publishing
- viewdata
- modelling

Subject specific programs are ones in which specific content – in this case geographical content – has been incorporated. This type can include an enormous range of styles, using 'style' here to refer to the design of the software itself. Thus there are:

- quizzes
- tutorial programs
- simulations
- educational games
- role plays
- problem solving
- graphics
- statistics

Figure 11.1: Classifying software
(source: *Learning Geography with Computers*, NCET, 1989)

and laboratories adding up to 70/80 or more microcomputers. Most schools have at least one computer laboratory which may be networked, in addition to other micros scattered around the school. The numerically dominant micros are still BBC Bs and Masters but clearly the Nimbus has been bought in very great quantities recently across the country so the picture is patchy. Increasingly, geography departments have their own micros, usually a BBC but now the occasional Nimbus.

Geography teachers have remained positively inclined towards the use of computers throughout the decade and according to Allen's recent survey (ibid.), identify the following advantages in the use of computers, and in this order of importance:

- interest and motivation engendered in the children;
- development of problem solving and decision making skills;
- development of IT literacy and mapwork skills.

The limiting factors are considered to be:

- access to the hardware
- time needed to gain expertise in this area

- lack of expertise and confidence
- suitability of software
- the limited potential of much software in values education

These latter perceptions are a direct result of a lack of recent, relevant inservice training of geography teachers who clearly need help in addressing the most commonly asked questions (Figure 11.2).

HOW DO I INTRODUCE THE MICRO INTO MY GEOGRAPHY CURRICULUM?
(or what I've always wanted to ask but never dared)

Is this all as difficult as it appears?

Computers frighten me, how do I overcome this fear?

Whom do I ask for advice?

What group of children should I start with?

What program should I use first?

How do I find out about software?

What teaching strategy should I use first?

What preparation is required?

What programs can I move to?

Should the school and department have a policy about computers?

Where else do I go for information about computing?

How do I cope with only one micro and a class of 30?

How do I use the computer laboratory since it is the only way I can get access to micros?

Figure 11.2: How do I introduce the micro? (source: Kent, for *Learning Geography with Computers*, NCET, 1989).

Role of outside agencies

The Geographical Association (GA) as an 'insider' agency for geography teachers, has been an active force for change in this area. Particularly helpful has been the role of the educational computing working group of the GA which has published a good deal through its members (e.g. Fox, 1984; Fox and Tapsfield, 1986; Kent and Riley, 1988), and has contributed to most GA annual conferences throughout the decade. Also, it has overseen the Computer Page in *Teaching Geography* which includes software reviews.

However, the major influence on change has been the Government's drive towards technological awareness in schools. As early as 1982, there was a 'Year of Information Technology' and as the decade has passed the IT across the curriculum movement has gained in momentum, helped by government backing. Hardware subsidy schemes were influential in the early 1980s in getting greater numbers of micros into schools. However, it was the MEP followed in 1986 by the MESU (now an arm of the National Council for Educational Technology) which more directly affected geography teachers. MESU, through the humanities team leadership of Andrea Tapsfield, has been an important mechanism for 'training the trainers'. It has also produced some helpful publications on weather satellites, Domesday and fieldwork.[2] However probably its major influence will be seen to have been the *Learning Geography with Computers Pack*, about which more in a moment.

Another encouragement and support for geography teachers to incorporate new technology in their work has been the appointment of education support grant (ESG) teachers, some of whom have geography expertise. These are paid for by the 1988 £10 million Technology for Better Schools scheme and alongside geography/humanities advisers with a commitment in this area, have brought about considerable changes. Also, TVEI funding for some schools has meant a considerable boost in hardware availability and some geography teachers have taken advantage of this. Finally, GRIST (Grant Related Inservice Training) money now available has allowed locally-based courses on IT and geography to be run, since technology is a priority area in the new GRIST structure.

The learning geography with computers pack

Potentially, however, the biggest single encouragement for geography teachers to incorporate IT in their curricula is the recent publication by MESU of the *Learning Geography with Computers* INSET pack (NCET, 1989). Its outline (Figure 11.3) illustrates its richness as an inservice and initial training resource for geography. It was compiled by Michael Milton at the Institute of Education in 1986-87 and was edited by Deryn Watson. A network of university department of education tutors has been set up by MESU as regional co-ordinators for subsequent inservice work based on the pack. As an innovative distance learning package for geography teachers it is unparalleled, yet there are still fears that without imaginative local facilitators it could be under used or badly used. Alongside the pack MESU have produced a video of classroom case studies (Learning Geography with Computers, Short Video Case Studies, MESU, 1988) which together with a video produced by this author[3] support the inservice potential of the pack.

Project HIT

Another innovation supported by MESU has been the establishment of Project HIT (Humanities and Information Technology) for a two-year period from September 1988. The centre for the project is the Institute of Education, University of London, where Alaric Dickinson (History) and this author (Geography) are its directors and the original National Co-ordinator, Andy Phillips. The project aims to support teachers' groups in history, humanities and geography who wish to explore ways in which IT can be effectively used. These groups (11 for 1988-89) produce materials in the form of modules or units illustrating particular ways of integrating IT into the geography curriculum. One group of teachers, for instance, is based in Cumbria and is supporting and extending the GCSE geography resource materials already produced by the Lake District National Park.

Evaluation and critiques

The near indecent pace of the developments in IT during the 1980s has not been matched by a similar emphasis on evaluation. Funders are more interested in development and product and consequently the reflective questions are not sufficiently posed, yet alone answered. Some research has been undertaken (see Kent, 1984), but it tends to be small scale and piecemeal. Probably the largest element of research completed has been at MA/MEd level by geography teachers as researchers. In particular, the London Institute of Education has generated 12 MA

LEARNING GEOGRAPHY WITH COMPUTERS

What is included?

The eight modules contain:

- a guide to using the pack
- case studies illustrating the use of software in classrooms
- examples of classrooms and INSET activities
- advice on using computers in the geography curriculum
- articles on the role of information technology
- checklists to help you organise and evaluate the use of computers
- classroom materials, including commercial software

What are the modules?

- Starting Out ... Learning Geography with Computers
- Using ... Learning Geography with Computers
- Development Studies
- Economic Understanding
- Physical Processes
- Population and Settlement
- Reading About ... Learning Geography with Computers
- Materials For ... Learning Geography with Computers

Data handling, oracy, fieldwork and other cross curricular themes are covered across the modules.

What software?

• CHOOSING SITES	Longman
• CLIMATE GRAPH	Andrea Tapsfield
• FRONT PAGE EXTRA	Micros & Primary Education
• GRASS	Newman Software
• HUMAN POPULATION GROWTH	Longman
• SAND HARVEST (BBC only)	CWDE (Longman)
• SLOPES (BBC only)	Granada
• DRAINAGE BASIN SIMULATION (RML only)	ILEEC
• STARS	Advisory Unit, Hatfield

Also data files on weather, population, development, occupations, census.

What computers will be needed?

Learning Geography with Computers will be available in two versions:

BBC for BBC B and Master computers

Research Machines for 480Z and Nimbus computers
(NB some software may not be available for all machines)

Who has the pack been written for?

- teachers
- teacher educators
- INSET providers
- advisers and advisory teachers

For use with school based GRIST, 'Baker' days, PGCE courses, INSET courses, curriculum diplomas and certificates or as a self-study pack.

Figure 11.3: Pack description

(Source: *Learning Geography with Computers*, NCET, 1989)

dissertations on computers and geography since 1978. A summary of their findings can be found on pages 89-96 in Graves et al, (1989). Grumitt (1978) and Hassell (1982) analysed alternative teaching strategies; Robinson (1982) attitudes; Lawler (1986) fieldwork; Leonard (1984), Cummings (1984) and Jefferys (1987) focused on classroom case studies; Freeman (1981), Dove (1987) and Rogers (1987) analysed the extent of adoption; Cracknell (1985) analysed teacher training strategies; and Thomas (1985) carried out an evalution of software. Few opportunities are available for researchers to share experience, though twice-yearly research seminars have been held at the London Institute of Education for five years. Occasionally a more international group of research workers are brought together, as in 1986 when an ESRC funded international research seminar entitled 'The Use of Computers in the Humanities and Social Sciences' was hosted by the Institute of Education in London (Kent and Lewis, 1987). Two major research exercises have just been set up which could provide helpful insights for geography education.[4]

Additional to specific research conducted into IT and geography, have been various critical perspectives aired over the last ten years or so (e.g., Lyon, 1988). In the face of overpowering, persuasive and well funded developments these must not be lost. They include:-

- a concern that children will interact more with machines than with people;
- a concern that IT (the tail) may too readily wag the geography curriculum 'dog';
- a concern for the opportunity costs of these IT developments;
- a concern that the vocational relevance of IT programmes below graduate level is often overplayed;
- a concern that educators and their educational objectives are powerless in the face of a powerful computer/industrial lobby;
- a concern that an extension of IT can reinforce power, extending exploitation and control;
- a concern that there seems to be increasing polarization between children in certain schools with a richness of IT experience (e.g., City Technology Colleges or TVEI schools) and those in less favourable circumstances. Is the logical extension of this a majority of IT illiterate and deskilled pupils and a minority of powerful IT literate?
- a concern for gender imbalance in the ways IT across the curriculum is delivered in schools (see Hoyles, 1988).

A particularly helpful contribution to this critical perspective is the chapter on 'Social and Political Literacy', written by John Huckle in the 'Reading Around' module of the *Learning Geography with Computers* Pack (NCET, 1989). Huckle points to the danger of the apparent greater legitimacy of computers in the eyes of children and the need for IT to be a vehicle for social literacy, not control. In particular he outlines a six-fold model of criteria to use against software (see Figure 11.4).

Geography 2000

By the turn of the century the national curriculum will be well established. Each of the core and foundation subjects will have to deliver an element of information technology given its own context. Indeed, each subject working group set up by the Secretary of State for Education during 1988-89 was asked to consider the scope for using computer and information technology in its subject and to frame appropriate attainment targets. As the Design and Technology working group put it: 'All areas of the curriculum provide contexts in which the use of IT is appropriate and through which pupils will develop general IT capability'. To respond to that challenge should not be too difficult for geography since there is a recent history of ten years or so in which the potential of IT in geography has been explored. In other words there is a foundation of experience on which to build.

Even so, looking ten years ahead is fraught with difficulties, particularly in a field as unpredictable and rapidly changing as IT. The most comprehensive effort to foresee the future of new technology in the teaching of secondary school geography by the year 2000 was undertaken by Roderick Allen in 1988 (Allen, 1988b). As a part of his PhD research at Cambridge he employed a panel of 24 experts with national reputations and credentials in computer-assisted learning in geography. Using a Delphi Study he was able to describe a consensus view on expected change. The following is a brief synopsis of that consensus:

> The experts felt that computers will be regarded as a routine resource similar to paper, pencil or book and used in all areas of the curriculum. Teachers will be keen to use the new technology, will be adequately trained and will play a more facilitating role in classrooms where more pupil-centred and enquiry learning will be used. The technology will play an emancipatory role, removing boring mechanical tasks and encouraging sophisticated graphicacy skills via the use of graphics packages, plotters, three dimensional projections, digital mapping and the like. Computers will play a

1 Relevance

Does the package deal with a significant social situation or issue which affects pupils' present or future lives?

2 *Knowledge*

Is the situation packaged in such a way as to ensure that teachers and pupils gain a critical theoretical grasp of what is going on?
Does the package explain or merely describe the social world?
Does it develop appropriate concepts and theories?
Does it allow teachers and pupils to consider alternatives to the social arrangements presented?
Does it allow teachers and pupils to construct and refine their own knowledge?

3 *Social Change*

Does the package offer explanations of how the situation arose and how it is likely to change?
Does it acknowledge conflict over the present and future nature of society and allow pupils to recognize their own role as potential agents of change?

4 *Skills*

Does the package develop intellectual, communication and social skills?
Are these merely coping skills or do they allow social criticism and effective participation in society?

5 *Values and Politics*

Does the package contribute to values and political education?
Does it promote values awareness, clarification and analysis?
Does it develop the knowledge, skills and attitudes which contribute to political literacy?

6 *Action*

Does the package facilitate both reflection *and* action on society?
Does it give pupils increased control over their learning, their lives and the decisions which affect them?

Figure 11.4: Criteria for evaluating software (source: Huckle, *Learning Geography with Computers*, NCET, 1989).

greater part in the testing aspects of the national curriculum, though this was not generally welcomed.

Databases and datafiles will increase in importance with enhanced skills of data handling and analysis required by teachers and pupils. A much wider range of datafiles will be commercially available not least on CD-ROMS, allowing vast amounts of storage. A geographical information system (GIS) will be in operation and teachers will make fairly routine use of huge on-line data banks and picture banks like NERIS and Campus 2000 (the result of the merge in TTNS and PRESTEL). Computer simulations will be more accurate and realistic and will be able to handle more qualitative and values-orientated situations. Content free problem solving programs such as RESOLVE, FORUM and PROBLEM SOLVER will be used with specific geographical subject matter. Interactive video (IV) will be much cheaper and easier to use and OS maps and atlases on IV will be in fairly general use as will detailed discs on many countries. Hard copy of IV images will be easier to obtain and generally IV will be much more used, particularly for data retrieval and imaginative simulations. Also both 'live' and 'non-live' remotely sensed images will be in greater use and the skills to interpret them will be a part of the geography curriculum.

The most significant change predicted by the experts is the greatly increased use of word processors by pupils. Course-work of a variety of types will be word processed, enhancing the presentation of pupils' work and desk top publishing will be often used. On the other hand, electronic mailing either for teachers to share ideas and teaching resources or by pupils to communicate with other children, is unlikely to be used much more than at present. Developments of generic software and a closer affinity between educational and industrial software will emerge. It was felt that WIMP environments (Windows, Icons, Mice and Pull Down Menus) would be user-friendly and pervasive. Finally, the group felt that greater use will be made of software produced by commercial organizations which it was felt had its dangers.

Discussion and conclusions

In many ways these predicted changes concerning IT and geography in 2000 AD are likely to be inevitable. Inevitable because of the national curriculum and its insistence on IT across the curriculum and inevitable because of the inexorable tide of new technology in society. This poses a vital challenge to educators to see that their priorities are at the forefront of IT developments in education and not the priorities of the computer business. Furthermore, the bandwagon effect of all this needs tempering with critical perspectives as illustrated earlier in the chapter. The challenge for in-service training of teachers is massive (see Figure

11.5). MESU has made a start and the *Learning Computers with Geography* pack (NCET, 1989) is a rich support, but the scale of the inservice need is huge. Will it be met adequately alongside the other inservice needs of teachers in these momentous times of a changing curriculum?

Figure 11.5: The challenge of the micro (source: *Learning Geography with Computers*, NCET, 1989. Reproduced with the kind permission of the National Council for Educational Technology.)

The future of subject specific software development is uncertain and not entirely rosy. Similarly, the hardware battle between UNIX and OS2 will no doubt continue and the outcome is equally uncertain. What is certain is the need for greater technical support for teachers and a need for administrators to build in the costs of obsolescence of the hardware. Neither is at all adequate at present.

Finally, two major opportunities lie in the path of geographers in the next ten years. On the one hand IT provides a convenient focus for greater collaboration between higher education and secondary school geographers. School teachers have led the way with exciting enquiry based CAL geography lessons. On the other hand, higher education geographers are doing highly exciting things with geographical information systems (GIS) (Economical Social Research Council, 1988) and satellite imagery. There is a real opportunity here for constructive, mutually beneficial dialogue. The other major opportunity is the possibility of realizing Papert's dream in 1980 of the computer being the 'carrier of powerful ideas' and the 'sower of the seed of cultural change' as well as the developer of 'new relationships with knowledge'. He, envisaged the computer playing an exciting and innovatory role in children's learning. The pedagogic opportunity is undoubtedly there. Shall we grasp it?

Notes

1. Efforts to achieve funding for a National Software Library at the University of London Institute of Education have as yet proved fruitless in spite of considerable support for the idea and an obvious need. It would be based on the existing National Reference Library for Schoolbooks and Classroom Materials at the Institute.
2. These include: Reynolds, R. (ed.), 1988, *Using Weather Satellites in Schools*, NCET; Bilham-Boult, A. (ed.), 1988, *Using Computers in Fieldwork*, NCET: NCET, 1988, *Domesay Ideas*.
3. *The New Technology in Action in Geography Classrooms. A Video Project.* This was co-ordinated by W. A. Kent and was launched at the 1988 IGU Geography Education Commission meeting in Brisbane. It is a video of eight classroom case studies where new technology is being used in geography classes. It is supported by a set of teachers' notes and is intended as an inservice resource.
4. Kings College, London, is engaged in a large-scale research exercise evaluating computers across the curriculum. It is entitled 'IMPACT: An Evaluation of the Impact of Information Technology on Children's Achievement'. The Institute of Education and the Advisory Unit for Computer-Based Education, Hatfield, are co-ordinating a Modelling Research Project, started in 1989 and funded by the Training Agency.

Chapter Twelve
In Defence of Textbooks
John Lidstone

While textbooks in geography are frequently criticized, their predominance in many geography classrooms continues unabated. This chapter reconsiders five of the criticisms that are frequently levelled at textbooks; suggests that textbooks serve us well in the areas of the substantive subject of geography, new ideas on pedagogy and in contributing to students' understandings of matters of social and environmental concern; and comments on various ways in which teachers could use their textbooks to greater effect. The writer concludes that textbooks, like any tool, can only be as effective as the skill of their users, whether these be teachers or pupils.

In 1948, Bartlett commented that:

> The textbook as used in geography teaching has not been the subject of much research, yet as one of the most common aids to teaching geography, it should possibly have done so.

Twenty years later, in 1968, when undergoing initial training as a teacher, I was disconcerted to find that, not only was no mention made of textbooks and their use during the entire three years of my course, but that their use during periods of teaching practice was positively discouraged. And this, despite the fact that my observation of experienced classroom teachers suggested that textbooks played a major part in their work.

In preparing this chapter (in 1989) I am still surprised that textbooks get such a bad press. The terms 'textbook knowledge', 'a textbook teacher' and 'textbookish' are used derogatively, and one wit has even defined a textbook as 'a book no-one would read unless they had to'. Despite this view, both the relatively healthy market for them and the comments of practising teachers point to the continued importance of textbooks in schools, although the amount of space in professional journals and books on geography teaching which are devoted to the use of this most common of teaching aids remains dramatically less than that devoted to other teaching and learning resources, such as computers. Furthermore, the relatively little attention which is paid to textbooks frequently appears to focus on criticisms of the books themselves rather than on their effective use in classrooms.

While textbooks in general have been the focus of criticism for almost as long as geography has been taught in schools, it may be argued that effective development and progress in the subject may be measured through the publication of new and innovative textbooks. Only when new approaches to the subject have become enshrined in the textbooks may they be said to have been truly adopted by the majority of practitioners and therefore of real significance in the education of young people. This implies no disrespect for the philosophical contributions of those in the vanguard of curriculum development, but is based on the power of numbers. I would contend that a small change in the education of a larger proportion of school pupils is of greater long-term significance to geographical education than a large change in the education of a minority.

Why are textbooks criticized?

Textbooks have been criticized for a number of real and perceived failings. These include allegations such as:

1. textbooks are composed of expository text which must be 'learned' by students. In this context, textbooks have been equated with the worst aspects of a 'reception' model of learning;

2. textbooks consist solely of the *results* of geographical enquiry – either factual or interpretative – presented as findings to be learned by students. Thus, textbook authors are seen as presenting the student with *their* interpretations of evidence rather than presenting evidence and encouraging students to undertake their own interpretation;

3. textbook knowledge is out of date and irrelevant to the lives of today's students;

4. textbooks are biased and give inaccurate or only partially accurate accounts of the world;

5. textbooks are too difficult to be read by the students for whom they are intended.

In this chapter, I should like to suggest that much, though of course not all, of the criticism of textbooks is ill-founded and that the problems to which the criticisms allude stem more often from a failure by the critics to consider textbooks in their proper classroom context than from faults inherent in the books themselves.

Whilst acknowledging that textbooks of widely varying quality are currently in print and that examples of books which exhibit all the faults implied by the criticisms listed above may be found in our schools. I suspect that criticisms are often a matter of the worker criticisizing the tools rather than acknowledging that there may be some failing in the way in which they are being used.

The five criticisms which have been levelled at text books will now be considered in more detail.

Criticism 1. Textbooks are composed of expository text which must be 'learned' by students.

The materials presented in the textbooks of today are not intended by most authors to be compendia of facts to be committed to memory. While this may have been the intention in the past, when there were advantages in the clerks of a trading nation having a functional knowledge of the world map, such an approach is less relevant to a generation which has grown up with nightly television news bulletins and documentary programmes from around the world, many of which include excellent maps to help the viewer to locate the places mentioned. Recent concerns in the United States that the television generation is still quite unaware of the location of many of that country's fields of battle are, I suspect, unlikely to be alleviated by a return to a geography dominated by rote learning. Many writers on the history of geographical education have leaped with glee at the introduction of the Rev. J. Goldsmith's *A Grammar of General Geography* (1823) in which the author stated:

> The proper mode of using this little book to advantage, will, it is apprehended, be to direct the pupils to commit the whole of the facts to memory, at the rate of one, two, or three per day, according to his age and capacity.

However, even at the height of this period in the development of geographical education when rote learning was highly valued, not all books for young people were compendia of facts. Vaughan (1972) has described a number of books in which, then current Quaker philanthropic concerns such as slavery and prison reform were presented to the readers as part of real or imaginary travellers tales. One such book by Mrs Priscilla Wakefield (1751-1832) described 'A family tour through the British Empire' taken by a group of children who, on a visit to Liverpool, 'warmly declared their abhorrence of buying and selling their fellow creatures' although during their visit to a cotton mill 'our travellers had the satisfaction of seeing here a thousand children employed usefully, and learning an early habit of industry'. In such cases, the message went far beyond the specific incidents described.

Even if we accept that the majority of textbooks in those early years were mere compendia of facts, it is perhaps unfair to lay the whole blame for the inadequacies of the geography teaching of the time at the door of textbooks and their writers. Keltie, in 1886, emphasized that until teachers with a specialism in geography were trained, there could be little progress. The summer schools for geography teachers organized by A. J. Herbertson at Oxford University (Jay, 1965) were amongst the first attempts to rectify the situation and would today be described as 'in-service training activities'.

In the absence of adequate in-service training, it may be appropriate to regard textbooks as playing an important role in introducing alternative approaches both to geography and to teaching.

Such guidance may be discerned in the approaches adopted by many writers of geography textbooks published in the last decade or so. A review of the Prefaces and Introductions to the current generation of textbooks reveals such statements as:

- 'Many problems are designed to be open-ended in the hope that their solution will involve reasoned discussion either among pupils or between pupil and teacher' (Rice, W. F., 1983),
- 'to help pupils develop skills of observation, mapwork and recording and depicting data' (Grenyer, 1979),
- 'Maps, plans, charts and graphs are an integral part of the series: pupils draw maps and use them as sources of information' (Slater and Weller, 1982),
- 'Data is provided to be thought about and analysed and worked on' (Beddis, 1982),
- 'to confront pupils with real world issues and to encourage them to present their own knowledge as well as received knowledge' (Ghaye and Ghaye, 1983)
- 'The *Living in Our World* series is focused on things that people need: home, jobs, food, recreation, the environment and social organization. Activities encourage students to evaluate new situations using the geographical skills and concepts they have acquired ... Each unit uses an

inquiry as the vehicle for students to learn about geography and to develop geographical skills' (Gerber, Lidstone and Mead, 1989)

In Queensland, as elsewhere, many teachers are still ill at ease with the idea of enquiry-based learning. Figure 12.1 shows how one textbook explains the approach to enquiry encouraged in the Queensland junior high school geography syllabus for the benefit of teachers and pupils alike, in graphic form.

Even in books written in a more expository style, statements of aims are couched more widely than mere acquisition of facts. The Marsdens (1983) introduce their *World in Change* with the statement that:

> the introductory chapters provide a physical and cultural framework ... Each section is accompanied by sets of exercises, varied in style and designed to test graphicacy, application and problem-solving skills, as well as recall, recognition and comprehension.

Criticism 2: Textbooks consist solely of the *results* of geographical enquiry.

Few textbook writers today would, I suspect, claim to present a definitive interpretation of the features, issues or phenomena which they describe. A publisher's statement on the back cover of *The Fabric of Geography* (Rice, W. F., 1983) states that 'Each study requires students to assess the value of geographical ideas and to practice their use'.

Most textbooks published during the 1980s contain a wide range of data sources in the form of text, maps, diagrams, tables, graphs, and photographs, either created by the authors themselves or taken from newspapers, government reports, journal articles and the publications of special interest groups. Many textbooks also include activities which are designed to encourage students to create their own interpretations based on the source materials provided.

The criticism that textbooks admit of only a single interpretation was perhaps most justly levelled at books based on the division of the world into natural regions as proposed by Herbertson in the early years of the twentieth century and in common use in schools at least into the 1970s. However, even with books such as these, to level such criticism at the textbooks rather than at those who presented them to pupils, is to ignore the interrelationships which should take place between teacher, pupil and book. That the fault does not lie mainly with the textbook, but elsewhere, is suggested by Jay (1965) who wrote that:

> In his concern to reduce the great mass of geographical facts about the

Figure 12.1: What do geographers do?
(source: Gerber, Lidstone and Mead, 1989)

> numerous countries of the world into a simplified scheme of about fourteen regional types, Herbertson unwittingly may have tempted some teachers to place undue reliance upon learning by rote as the mode of assimilation by pupils, and to stress the short sentence or phrase which summarizes the climatic conditions over a wide area of the earth's surface at the expense of the more detailed description which gives a region its character.

Similarly, Hall (1976) commented on the difficulty experienced by students in understanding the major climatic regions of the world. He pointed out that

> one reason for difficulty in learning is that *world climates are never taught as distributions derived from a model.* The movement step by step from a simple Greek division to something that would satisfy Herbertson, checking the argument and testing its approximation to an atlas, and then relaxing more assumptions, is rarely undertaken, not just because of the time involved, but because climatic regions have become absorbed into the dogma of real geography of which they are an essential part, not the behavioural result of a simulated model.

It is perhaps not surprising that so many people have fallen into the temptation of criticizing those books which include regional descriptions for not pointing out the origins of the models on which such descriptions are based. It is, however, salutary to ask why we, as teachers, have been so in awe of the textbook that we have failed to criticize, and furthermore, failed to encourage our students to interact with, and perhaps even challenge, the materials presented to them.

Criticism 3. Textbook knowledge is out of date and irrelevant to the lives of today's students.

Marsden (1988) has illustrated how, in the early years of this century, some textbooks went through tens of editions, selling hundreds of thousands of copies, and remained in schools for many years. More recently, the life of textbooks has been much shorter, and publishers have become much more aware of the need for books to be up to date. However, care must be taken not to confuse being up to date with the inclusion of the very latest factual detail. One textbook published in 1987 includes consideration of such issues as growing populations, soil erosion, the effects of natural hazards, world food supplies and atmospheric and oceanic pollution. While the reader of the present chapter will probably be able to suggest case studies pertaining to each of these issues which have emerged since 1987, the general principles to be considered in examining such issues as presented in the textbook are still valid.

Ward (1988) writes of an Australian student who, preparing a piece of work on native fauna, used the modem on the family computer to access an American database. He found information on echidnas so recent that it had only been entered by the Smithsonian Institute three days before, and he may well have been the first person in the world to have accessed that information. However, exciting as finding such recent data may be, there is no guarantee that the student's capacity for researching, analysing, interpreting and suggesting solutions to current issues is enhanced by working only with the most recent information.

Criticism 4: Textbooks are biased and give inaccurate or only partially accurate accounts of the world.

A frequent concern, initially in the United States but more recently elsewhere, has been that textbooks include inaccurate or only partially accurate accounts of the world. The results of this concern have been seen in the large number of content analyses which have been published. Such content analyses have concentrated on the treatment of specific areas of the world, specific groups within populations, specific political viewpoints and specific ideas and skills which can be discerned in various textbooks. One such study, undertaken by Boden (1977) investigated the images of other countries presented in textbooks from France, West Germany, India, Japan, Kenya, Venezuela and the United Kingdom. Boden found that many textbooks from all these countries suffered from:

(i) inaccurate statements in the form of text, photographs and maps;
(ii) omission of basic and essential historical and geographical information on a country (as seen by an evaluator from that country); and
(iii) misleading interpretations and opinions.

Hicks (1980, a and b) investigated ethnocentric bias in textbooks and discerned attitudes to racism ranging from 'radical' through 'liberal' to 'status quo'. Similarly, Wright (1981, 1983, 1985 a and b) and Wright and Pardey (1982) have discerned textbook biases emanating from the range of photographs, maps and statistics presented in a number of books, and have suggested that such books may leave students with very misleading impressions of the countries covered.

With very few exceptions (Wright and Pardey, 1982), these content analyses have been descriptive rather than prescriptive although perhaps their authors are implying that the books in which various biases are identified are unsuitable for use in schools. Furthermore, while sincerity, honesty, integrity and truthfulness are obviously qualities essential in all textbook authors, and teachers, there seems to be little suggestion that the biases discerned in the books represent any evil intent. Amongst the few writers to imply such motivation is Donaldson (1971) who investigated the ways in which negro children in the United States could relate to their social studies textbooks and defined the approach taken by geography texts to black Americans at that time as the '4-D approach: distortion, deletion, denial, dehumanization'. Even here, however, it is unclear whether his allegations are directed at textbook authors as individuals or at the society which they represent.

Marsden (1988) draws our attention to the imperialistic attitudes and overt racism present in many of the textbooks written by well respected textbook authors between 1930 and 1960. He points out that even at the time of their publication, there were a number of people who were critical of the stance to race implicit in many syllabuses, and presumably, by extension, in many textbooks.

With the benefits of hindsight, we may regard many of the great authors of the past as misguided, but does the evidence suggest that they were any less caring than we are today? Why other than from a sincere concern for the state of the human condition would Fairgrieve (1926) have penned:

> The function of geography is to train future citizens to imagine accurately the conditions of the great world stage and so help them to think sanely about political and social problems in the world around?

Why else would Howarth (1954) have made his plea for imperial geography as the foundation stone for imperial citizenship on the grounds that 'the more truly these stones are laid, the less occasion, in the long run, for racial misunderstanding and segregation'?

It may be argued that the attitudes implicit in textbooks should be viewed in the context of the times in which they were written. The work of the well-respected geographers who wrote the books of the past may be regarded as reflecting the dominant ideology of their times. David Wright has pointed out that what we see depends very much on the spectacles we are wearing. Perhaps the worst that can be alleged of textbook writers of the past is that they tried to encourage students to see things through their own spectacles, rather than through the multifocal lenses so fashionable today. Whilst it will be suggested below that it is an important duty of teachers to encourage their students both to analyse and to challenge the ideology implicit in any teaching resources, it is sobering to ponder on which aspects of the work of today's writers and teachers will be found to be biased and deeply offensive by geographers and geography teachers of the future.

Criticism 5. Students cannot read their textbooks.

This observation has been made by teachers for many years and the blame has been levelled at either the textbooks or the students. Presumably because it was perceived easier to change the textbook than the students, a demand was created for books with large amounts of graphic material and a minimum amount of simple text. When techniques such as readability formulae, cloze tests and maze tests, for assessing the readability of text and the abilities of students to handle specific pieces of text came into common use in the 1970s, there was an increased demand for such textbooks. The process of writing in simpler language, as defined by the readability formulae, became known in the United States as 'dumbing down the textbook'. Educators hoped that by lowering reading levels, lower-ability students would be enabled to gain mastery of the important subject matter, concepts, and skills of a course without being stymied by too demanding or frustratingly difficult reading passages. Smith (1988) comments that the results have not been good, and reports on the new trend in the United States to 'smarten up' textbooks.

The rationale behind this trend is that by being presented with more demanding materials, students will be challenged to greater intellectual efforts and brought to expect more of themselves. In the United Kingdom, Harrison (1979) and Graham (1981) investigated the readability of textbooks in social studies and science and found that in almost all cases the books studied had higher readability levels than the ages of the students by whom they were being used. Lidstone (1985) investigated the use of textbooks in a number of geography classrooms and found that while the readability of the textbooks was frequently above the mean age of the students, cloze tests revealed that most students were able to use the book productively with the instructional help of the teacher, despite the fact that only a minority could apparently have used the books independently. This finding is significant in view of the findings elsewhere in Lidstone (1985) and those of Lunzer and Gardner (1979) that the geography teachers who were studied very rarely required their students to study their textbooks independently, but rather worked with their pupils on the text, ensuring that they identified the main ideas and concepts being presented. Once again we must ask whether the criticism that students cannot read their textbooks should be made of the books or of those responsible for their use.

What functions do textbooks serve well?

The defence of textbooks requires more than the refutation of generalized criticisms. The positive contributions of textbooks to the development of geographical education must be considered in more detail. In examining the contributions of textbooks, consideration must be given to their role in terms of *1.* the subject of geography; *2.* new ideas on pedagogy; and *3.* the contribution of geography to students' understandings of matters of social and environmental concern.

The role of the textbook for new geography graduates entering the teaching profession is different from that for geography teachers in mid-career or for those who are faced with geography teaching but who lack academic training in the area. It may be expected that new geography graduates are comfortable with recent thinking in at least some aspects of the subject at the academic level, although they may be uncertain as to how best to introduce these ideas at school level. On the other hand, more experienced teachers may find difficulty in adapting to new ideas in academic geography, while having developed high levels of skill in classroom management.

1. Textbooks and the subject of geography

Geography at university level is an area of academic research. As such, the nature of the subject at the academic frontier is constantly changing. Naish et al. (1987) comment that:

> In the sense that geography is to be used as a medium for education, there is no requirement that all new academic developments should necessarily be translated into the school context.

On the other hand, a refusal to consider the applicability of new developments to school level geography could lead to a fossilized school subject lacking all academic rigour and based on tenets which have been rejected by the community of academic geographers.

For many teachers, keeping up to date with the latest approaches to the subject becomes an almost impossible job. For such teachers, textbooks, ostensibly written for their students, may become invaluable sources of updating. It may be argued that this is an inappropriate way for teachers to update their subject knowledge, and that content-focused in-service education would be preferable, but the fact remains that opportunities for any type of in-service education remain rare. Williams (1988) has described the problems inherent in the continuing education of geography teachers and, in support of the increased need for greater opportunities for teachers to update their knowledge and understanding, quotes Preston James' statement on the pace of change in geographical education of two decades ago that:

> The pendulum used to swing back and forth with intervals of many decades. Now the pendulum is producing a new geography almost every year with thoroughly confusing results.

It was in such a context that the present writer surreptitiously discovered the relevance to school geography of the skills associated with the 'quantitative revolution' of the 1970s from such series as *The Oxford Geography Project, Harrap's Course in Reformed Geography* and Cole and Beynon's *New Ways in Geography* (1968-72). Some readers will remember that the latter series was originally written for pupils of primary age. A few years later, when the initial euphoria with quantification was fading a little, Beddis (1982) introduced the *Teachers' Guide* to the *A Sense of Place* series by suggesting that:

> this series of three books attempts to bring together those elements of the more traditional descriptive geography, the theoretical geography of the 1960s and 1970s, and the more recently advocated 'humanistic' geography, that would seem appropriate for young people in the first three years of secondary school.

A further example of textbooks serving an informative role for teachers may be seen in the case of studies of the so-called Third World. While most geography syllabuses specify study of developing countries, many teachers in mid career, if they received any training in development studies at all, would have been introduced to the topic through the application of a deficit model. The publication of such textbooks as *Patterns in Underdevelopment* (Bale, 1982) and more recently the Teaching Development Issues series of books published by the Development Education Project team (Cooke et al., 1985), may mark the introduction of many teachers to an alternative model of development, as well as to that branch of academic geography which was described by Peet as 'radical geography' as long ago as 1977.

2. Textbooks and teaching methodology

While textbooks may be used to introduce teachers to new areas of geography with potential for classroom adoption as 'a medium for education', they may, at the same time, serve to introduce teachers to new approaches to the management of learning. Classroom applications of various quantitative techniques, the use of simulations, techniques for exploring individual perceptions of different environments and ways to assist students to interpret written text have all been presented in textbooks published in recent years. Beddis (1982) writing in the Introduction to *A Sense of Place* informed teachers that:

> each double page spread contains a number of ideas and these are identified [in the Guide] ... It is hoped that this will help teachers in preparing lessons, especially if they are non-geographers ... The methodology is firmly based on the principles of enquiry-based learning. Data is provided to be thought about and analysed and worked on.

Slater and Weller, in their series *Skills in Geography* (1982) claim that

> Maps, plans, charts and graphs are an integral part of the series: pupils draw maps and use them as sources of information; graphs are used to record and provide data; and other graphical devices are introduced such as food webs and flow charts

and go on to state that

> Pupils are encouraged to look at geographical problems from the standpoint of other people so that they can appreciate the complexity of many geographical problems ... Problems without clear cut solutions are outlined using games and dramatization to show the interplay of different groups of people and pupils have to explore the attitudes and needs of the people concerned to make their own judgements of what ought to be done.

3. Textbooks and matters of social and environmental concern.

Peet (1977) advocated a radical approach to geography in which

> We should reconsider the traditional ways in which we have looked at person-to-person relationships, social system-to-social system relationships, and social system-to-environmental system relationships. By reformulating those relationships, radical geography aspires to the evolution of a non-destructive society.

Robinson (1985) describes such radical geography as a close relative to humanistic geography but wedded to action rather than to contemplation. While Robinson suggests that an explicitly radical geography would be impossible within the confines of a controlled estblishment system such as public education at secondary level, there has been a considerable move towards the consideration of matters of social concern in geography lessons, and this trend has been enshrined in government publications. In 1985, the DES document *Better Schools* (DES, 1985b, 14) set out six broad aims for learning in secondary schools. Of these six, two in particular referred quite explicitly to affective matters:

> ... to help pupils to develop personal moral values, respect for religious values, and tolerance of other races, religions, and ways of life;
> ... to help pupils to understand the world in which they live, and the interdependence of individuals, groups and nations.

The implications of these two aims have been summarized by Rawling (1987) as follows:

> Whereas traditional approaches to geography were concerned predominantly with description and explanation, newer approaches give greater consideration to evaluation, prediction and to moral and ethical questions arising from people-environment situations.

While initially matters of social concern were introduced into geography curricula by a committed few, such innovative areas of study have become institutionalized through textbooks. While some books such as John Bale's *Patterns of Underdevelopment* (1982) and the two volumes of the *New Wave Geography* series written for schools in Victoria, Autralia (Stowell and Bentley, 1988) have taken an openly radical stance, there has been a 'knock-on' effect on other textbooks, so that few textbooks of recent date fail to include some discussion of, or even passing reference to, matters of social and environmental concern.

Such 'passing reference' may be considered by many to be too little to be useful for achieving the kind of world advocated by Peet, or even to meet the requirements of the DES aims of learning. However, they may serve as a reminder to teachers and pupils alike to look at the matters raised through a variety of spectacles and through a range of textbooks. Thus, the most traditional description of plantation agriculture in one book may be read critically and compared with a more radical account in another, and in the hands of an aware teacher, may even serve to emphasize the imperialistic philosophy underlying the plantation system more effectively than overtly radical descriptions in a more 'committed' book.

'Traditional' textbooks also have a major contribution to make to the study of current environmental concerns. The greenhouse effect, possible climatic effects of nuclear war and industrial pollution of the atmosphere are three areas which are often raised in geography classrooms. Unfortunately, such matters are often taught using newspaper reports and forecasts which may be treated by students as if they are the last word on the subject. However, if such issues, raised in newspapers or the electronic media, were to be considered in school in the context of a textbook in which global circulation patterns and the structure of the atmosphere are explained, pupils would be able to consider the validity of the various forecasts for themselves in the light of a theoretical background. They will then be better able to suggest possible courses of future action. Of course, some textbooks may consider such issues in their full geographical context, but the absence of a consideration of the latest environmental issue need not be taken of itself as indicating a weakness in the textbook.

How can teachers use textbooks better?

Textbooks may be used effectively in schools in three main ways. They may be used by pupils 'as is', they may be analysed critically by students and teachers and they may be used by teachers as aids to the teaching-learning process. In order that these three types of use may be accomplished effectively, it is necessary that: *1.* pupils are helped to interpret the textbooks with which they are expected to work; *2.* pupils and teachers work together to analyze textbooks critically in order to seek out the truth inherent in the situations described; and *3.* teachers themselves are confident in their own abilities as geographers as well as teachers.

Of the three conditions listed above, only the last will be addressed here in detail. Regarding the first two, a number of techniques for helping pupils to become precise readers of expository text are described in Lidstone (1989). Wright (1985 a and b, 1988) has addressed the issue of detecting bias in textbooks and describes a number of techniques which, although designed for use with teachers and student-teachers, can be adapted easily for use with students of secondary age. Berry (1985) has described how one of his classes put geography textbooks 'on trial' on a charge of failing to demonstrate adequately the effects of apartheid on the peoples of South Africa.

It is the third condition which will receive attention here, since it is the basic tenet of this chapter that teachers must bear the main responsibility for the use of textbooks in their classrooms.

Preparing teachers to use textbooks effectively

A study undertaken into the use of textbooks by teachers in a number of geography classrooms (Lidstone, 1985) showed that the interrelationship between teacher, textbook and pupils is far from simple and that, frequently, the classroom interactions are designed to overcome many of the weaknesses for which textbooks themselves are criticized.

The teachers in that study invariably used the textbooks to support their own interpretations of the subject regardless of the specific structure of geography or teaching style suggested by the author of the books. Those teachers who were less confident in their interpretation of the topic under discussion made greater use of the structure offered by the textbook author, but all were agreed that close teacher-pupil interaction was of the greatest value in the teaching-learning endeavour.

Furthermore, when the classroom interactions between teacher, textbook and pupils were examined in the light of basic research on learning from printed materials, it appeared that strategies which may be expected to increase the capacity of pupils to learn were already being adopted. The problems which would be identified by analysis of the textbook alone were, it seemed, being circumvented within the total classroom context.

This is not to suggest that all was well in the classrooms that were investigated. The study suggested that the most important influences in these classrooms were the teachers' existing ideas on the nature and scope of geography teaching and the constraints under which they perceived themselves to work. The central issue for these teachers was not the provision of appropriate teaching materials in the form of textbooks, but their personal decisions on the fundamental aims of geographical education. While teachers were prepared to learn new techniques of teaching and adopt new information from a good textbook, neither their fundamental aims nor their conceptualizations of the nature of geography appeared to be strongly influenced.

The implications of this for the present examination of the role of textbooks would seem to be that teachers should be encouraged to undertake continuing education in their specialist areas. Appropriate in-service education may be expected to help teachers both to be suitably critical of textbooks and to be willing to learn from the innovative approaches to both the subject and teaching which they may include. The problem of geography textbooks is really the problem of how they are used in geography classrooms.

Conclusion

Since those far-off days of initial training and the guilt feelings engendered by using textbooks, I have overcome such feelings and begun a search for the perfect textbook. I have never succeeded in this quest, but in the process, have come across many techniques to reduce any adverse effects of textbook teaching. Perhaps the textbooks even prevented my pupils from suffering my own biases. No textbook can be, or should attempt to be, teacher proof. It is salutary to note the comments on the use of textbooks made by the writers of the book published by the Incorporated Association of Assistant Masters in Secondary Schools on *The Teaching of Geography* (1954);

> Class teaching and textbook supplement and reinforce each other. But the textbook must always be subservient to the teacher ... an aid to teaching and not a substitute for it. ... The satisfactory relation of the textbook to his [sic] class lessons forms one of the teacher's most difficult problems. He has to steer between the Scylla of too slavish adherence to the book and the Charybdis of such complete disregard of it that it becomes practically valueless.

Chapter Thirteen
Is Mapping in Schools Reflecting Development in Cartography and Geographical Information?
Rod Gerber

Maps are distinctive graphics and the development of competence in their use is a complicated process involving the development of understanding and competence in their elements, skill in designing them and abilities to interpret the geographical information that they contain. Current practices in teaching mapping skills in schools have not kept pace with recent developments in cartography and geography. The challenge for geography teachers, textbook authors and commercial publishers is to understand what these changes are in order to accommodate them in their mapping resources. Ways to meet these challenges are suggested. These include focusing on: the linkage of mapping more closely to learning; the selection of appropriate maps for different groups of students; the use of an effective sequence of mapping education; the education of textbook authors and map publishers in cartographic communication and the development of in-service teacher education programmes.

The singer-songwriter Neil Diamond (1976), although not writing directly about maps, encapsulated many of the challenges associated with them in the following lyrics:

> Signs that burn like shooting stars,
> That pass across the night-time skies.
> They reach out in their mystic language
> For us to read between the lines.

Signs like moments hung suspended
Echo just beneath the heart;
Speak in voices half remembered,
And half-remembered play their part.

Whether these graphic representations that we call 'maps' are generated manually or by a computer is immaterial. What is important is to realize that maps are complex graphic representations whose meanings are established by the people who read them. Their complexity occurs because of the following unique attributes:

1. Maps consist of a range of signs that do not carry fixed meanings, e.g. a green triangle may represent a nuclear reactor, a forest or a playground.

2. Map signs have location, i.e. each sign on a map is placed carefully on an area to indicate its location relative to other signs.

3. Consequently, maps are not the territory that they represent, but they have similar structures to those of the territory represented. These structures are maintained by the use of proportional areas, retained shapes, proportional distances and topological properties so that, for example, the spatial relationship between New Delhi, Beijing and Singapore will be evident on an accurate map of East Asia.

4. Maps are a presentational form of communication in that they are simply a set of encoded signs made on a plane surface. The signs and the concepts that they encode, unlike spoken or written language, are displayed all at once and in no particular sequence.

5. They possess a quality of image in that maps are space representing space. This quality is necessary for spatial cognition since people who design and use maps must be able to imagine what features look like from a plan view before they can encode or decode the relevant signs.

The current situation

The current situation of mapping in schools occurs because most geography teachers do not realize the above-mentioned complexities about maps used in classes and neither do many authors of geography textbooks and school atlases. Therefore, it is still possible to find geography curricula for young adolescents in many countries which place an emphasis on reading and interpreting topographical maps. Similarly, the emphasis on small-scale mapping using maps of continents and the world instead of large-scale mapping using maps of the school ground or the local street is a prevalent practice.

The examination systems in many countries have been a major influence on the type of mapping undertaken in geography lessons. This is typified by the analytical investigations conducted in several countries. For example, Okpala (1988b, 31-39) has demonstrated how the West African Examinations Council through its insistence on the reading and interpretation of topographic maps has increased the difficulty of map work in Nigerian schools. Cooper (1988, 609-613) in analysing the mapping skills required by geography students taking the General Certificate of Education at Advanced level in the United Kingdom notes the variable ways by which the different examination boards focus on map interpretation. He makes a plea for a greater use of thematic maps, other than topographic maps, and for map drawing. Stimpson and Yeung Pui Ming (1987, 137-152), in their analysis of variations in the map drawing ability of secondary students in Hong Kong, concluded that one reason for variations in this ability is the lack of opportunity and need in examination classes to draw maps.

A more positive observation can be made concerning the influence of textbooks and atlases on the current mapping skills development. Geography textbooks are playing important roles in the development of map interpretation skills. Books such as *People and Environment: A World Perspective* by Graves, Lidstone and Naish (1987); *Worldwide Issues in Geography* by Hart (1985); *Understanding Landforms* by Hilton (1984); *World in Change* by the Marsdens (1983); *People on Earth* by Robinson and Jackson (1984); *New Wave Geography* by Stowell and Bentley (1988) and *Living Geography* by Van Noorden (1985) all contain a range of exercises that emphasize the interpretation of thematic and topographic maps. They do not focus directly on the development of specific mapping skills. Rather, their focus is on the use of mapping skills that have been developed elsewhere.

School atlases and atlas programmes on the other hand have moved very deliberately into the development of mapping skills. Analyses by Sandford (1987) and Gerber (1984b) indicate the extent to which this is so for a wide range of school atlases that are used in many countries. The most thorough sources of print resources for developing mapping skills are to be found in the range of skills books that have been published, some in isolation and some as a part of an atlas programme. The most comprehensive sets of these books include the *Mapstart* series by Catling (1985) and the *Jacaranda Atlas Programme* (Butler et al., 1983-5). Here, the specific skills associated with the design, use and interpretation of maps are developed based on sound research and implemented via realistic learning experiences.

Mapping has always been seen as an integral component of geography. Whenever skills in school curricula are discussed, it is common practice to emphasize the central role of mapping skills as the basis of the graphic element of geography. Generally, there is an emphasis on making maps to record data in an organized graphic form and on the use of maps in the analysis and interpretation of geographical data. Implied in this statement is the expectation that, in so doing, the students will develop an understanding of the elements of maps and a competence in their use. There is some concern as to the extent to which all of the above aspects of mapping that are included in these curricula are actually put into practice in the geography classrooms around the world.

One further indicator of the current situation is the extent to which mapping skills education is part of teacher education courses in geography. In many institutions of higher education, there are courses in geographical techniques which cover the development of some mapping skills. These generally focus on map drawing, design and interpretation. Increasingly, computer-assisted applications are being added to these studies to keep abreast of the recent developments in technology. In actual teacher education courses, there are very limited inputs on how to teach selected skills. At best, students may expect a single session on teaching mapping skills. More likely, there will be a session on teaching skills in gegoraphy lessons and specific types of skills will be mentioned, but limited opportunities will be available to practise actual strategies for developing mapping skills. Maybe this is why there is such an emphasis on map interpretation skills in geography teaching.

In order to answer the question 'Is mapping in schools reflecting developments in cartography and geographical information?' it is essential to appreciate what recent developments have occurred in cartography and geographical information. Then, it should be possible to identify gaps in current school practices in geography teaching. Once these gaps have been pinpointed, a number of recommendations may be made on the actions needed to minimize any of the identified gaps.

Recent development in cartography

Cartography has undergone quite a change in the last decade. This change has been related to advances in technology, the use of different forms of data and the increasing concern for user-oriented cartographic products.

Computers have had a major impact on cartography to the extent that manually-generated products are becoming a thing of the past. The recognition by computer software companies of the potential of computer-assisted mapping and drafting applications has led to the proliferation of a host of packages to enable maps to be generated from geographical data stored on computer files. From the early days of *Symap* through to *Auto Cad*, *Arc Info* and *Map Info*, these software packages have become more sophisticated and can be used on personal computers rather than having to rely on larger mini or mainframe computing hardware. The main challenges that faced cartographers revolved around the digitizing of large amounts of data, the regular upgrading of this data and the palettes of symbols that have been included in the software packages. Not all of these palettes were designed by cartographers and so they were not all most appropriate for useful cartographic symbols. It was a case of computer programmers and not cartographers designing symbols for maps. Despite these challenges, cadastral, topographic and a host of thematic maps are generated on computers. Papers such as those by Baker and Drummond (1984) on digital cartographic data and Stefanovic and Vries-Baayens (1984) on computer-assisted relief representation typify the impact of computing on cartography.

The use of a broad range of data has evolved in cartography. Especially in the automated processes of map production, there have been a series of advances associated with the use of different data forms for cartographic representation. Aerial photography has been an important source of geographical information. Modern stereoplotters have refined the retrieval of geographical information from pairs of aerial photographs. Remotely-sensed images obtained from sensors aboard satellites revolving around the earth's surface provide essential digital information that may be used to map seasonal changes in land use, the extent of irrigation, damage in forest fires or urban expansion. Satellite imagery can also be used to a depth of 15 metres to provide economical data to map shallow water tropical environments. Statistical data, e.g. census data, is being maximized using CD-ROMs to generate a range of thematic maps on socio-economic themes. The increase in the range of thematic data being used for mapping purposes continues to expand as cartographers find uses for this data. Thematic data associated with social issues such as sport, recreation, politics, employment and tourism, typify those more recent cartographic studies.

The concern for user-driven cartography is as important in recent years as the focus on technology. The emphasis here is on the belief that maps will be most useful when they are designed to contain the geographical information that users want and they are presented in symbols that these users can understand. The Cartographic Communication Project (Gerber and Lyons, 1984a) encapsulated the basic requirements of user-oriented cartography. Further studies by Gerber (1984a) and Gerber and Lyons (1984b) have demonstrated how to design such user-driven cartographic products and the factors that influence their effective use. This focus on cartographic communication has led to the development of a distinctive sequence for designing such maps (Bos, 1984) and the increased emphasis on thematic and not topographic maps in the use of user-oriented cartographic products (see Figure 13.1).

These developments have lessened the emphasis on standard mapping for topographic and cadastral purposes and emphasized thematic mapping. They have taken the emphases from the cartographer and placed them squarely in the hands of the user. They have also decreased manual methods for map compilation and emphasized computer-assisted ones.

Recent developments in geography

The expansion of humanistic studies in geography has been notable in the last decade or so. These studies have heightened our awareness of the human conditions around the world and have offered more opportunities than previously for using one's values in making geographical studies. A direct consequence of these studies has been the increased demand for thematic maps on a host of socio-economic themes that geographers may use in their studies. This range of themes may be typified by those in *The State of the World Atlas* by Kidron and Segal (1981) and in *The Gaia Atlas of Planet Management* edited by Myers (1985).

A second development that has reshaped approaches to geography and handling data is the development and refinement of geographical information systems (GIS). These constructs have been developed largely to produce inventories and to anlayse resources in geographical environments. Authors such as Burrough (1986), Peuquet (1984) and

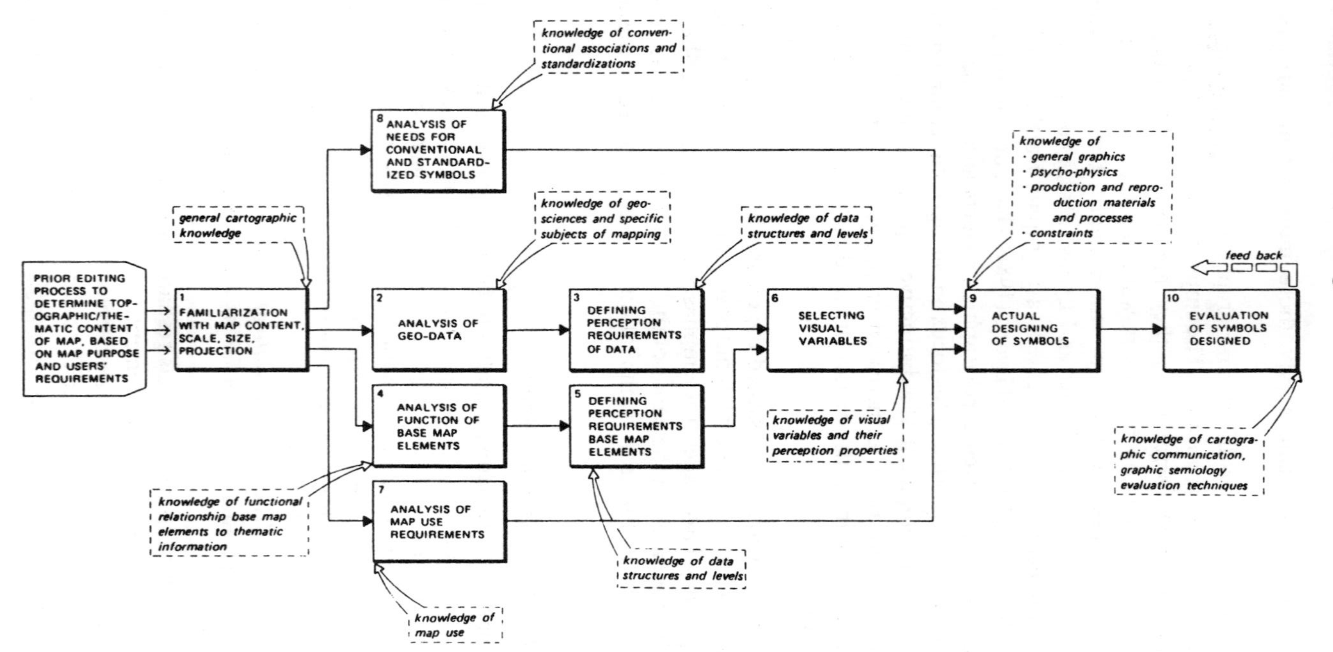

Figure 13.1: Scheme for designing cartographic symbols (source: Bos, 1984)

Tomlinson (1984) have explained the data structures that are necessary to design a GIS, the technology that is necessary to link together separate sets of spatial data and have demonstrated how they are different from computer graphics. Geographical data describe features in the world in terms of (a) their position as expressed as co-ordinates, (b) their attributes, e.g. density, size, breed, rank or age, and (c) their spatial interactions. Computer graphics focus on the display and manipulation of visible material only and pay little attention to the non-graphic attributes. Therefore, a geographical information system may be regarded as a model of the real world. In this model, the data may be accessed, transformed and manipulated interactively. Therefore, it can be used for investigating specific environmental processes, e.g. the impact of salinity, for analysing trends, e.g. the irrigation usage in a region, and for predicting the results of planning decisions, e.g. the impact of tourist development on a littoral zone.

The technological advances in cartography, especially those associated with computers, have made the rapid manipulation of data possible, facilitated the storage of large data files and enabled the production of a large range of cartographic, graphic and non-graphic products. As a result, geographical information systems are popular tools for studies in resource management.

Gaps between recent developments in cartography and geography and practice in mapping in schools

The above observations, when synthesized, indicate that practice in mapping in schools has not taken cognizance of all of the recent developments in cartography and geography. In fact, it could be argued that much of the mapping skills work in schools relies heavily on cartographic thinking that is at least twenty years old. This thinking was based on the clinical design of maps and focused mainly on the reading or interpretation of maps that were prepared by academics or publishers who were remote from the schools that used their products. In fact, many of the maps used in geography classes were not designed primarily for educational use. They were rather designed for use by military people or by other cartographers. School atlases were the main exception to this generalization, although many of these were designed by cartographers for general reference use.

The resulting gaps between current practice in schools and the recent advances in the disciplines of cartography and geography may be noted as:

1. The concept of user-driven cartography in which maps are designed for particular groups of users who give meaning to the encoded symbols on each map. This encapsulates the idea that maps are made for identifiable groups of people who have detectable abilities and experiences with maps. Here, the cartographers consult with these groups of users before they design maps for them rather than the too-common experience of designing maps in isolation from the users.

2. The use of geographical information systems as a means for structuring the geographical information needs users prefer on their maps. This is related to the above-mentioned user-driven aspect of cartography in that the user should identify the key geographical data that they want on a map so that the cartographer can design the symbols for it in such a way that the map highlights the key data and downgrades the peripheral background information.

3. The focus on cartographic communication to emphasize the relative linkage between the cartographer as the designer of maps, the user as the receptor of cartographic information who gives meaning to the encoded symbols and the map as the medium for communication. Although this concept is twenty years old, it has never been taken seriously by the bulk of the textbook and atlas publishers.

4. The concentration on making or designing maps rather than reading or interpreting them. As early as 1965, Bartz called for geography teachers to focus on map-making in their classes rather than making more use of map reading (Bartz, 1965). She believed that students would come to a better understanding of mapping skills and realize that maps should be clear, simple and useful. A prime reason for emphasizing making maps rather than reading maps is to allow students to demonstrate the degree of their understanding of the elements of maps and then to build on this situation is a constructive manner.

5. The use of computer-assistance in the design and production of thematic maps. When schools possessed microcomputers with limited memory the process of working with an amount of digitized data to construct simple thematic maps was not feasible. However, software packages such as ATLAS and MAPINFO are now available to be used on IBM-type computers to design these maps. The continued expansion of memory space on personal computers through the installation of hard disks at very economical prices means that thematic mapping packages can be used in schools.

What should be done to improve school mapping studies

Recognition of these gaps is one thing. Doing something about them is quite another. As in all aspects of living where changes occur, they will not be adopted widely unless there is a constructive, informed approach to promoting their effective use. This is, of course, based on the premise that the change proposed is both desirable and beneficial to living. The judgement made throughout this chapter is that such changes in mapping skills development are encouraging greater relevance and usefulness of mapping to the normal living of people in their society. What is needed, therefore, is a number of suggestions on what should be done to improve mapping studies in schools.

These suggestions may take the form of broad guidelines for action or they may consist of actual exemplars of actions already taken. They focus on the following aspects: *1.* linkage of mapping more closely to learning; *2.* selection of appropriate maps for different groups of students; *3.* use of an effective sequence of mapping education; *4.* education of textbook authors and map publishers in cartographic communication; *5.* in-service teacher education programmes.

1. Linkage of mapping more closely to learning

It is now almost a decade since the author demonstrated the linkage between competence and performance of adolescents in understanding and using maps (Gerber, 1980). This study showed that students do require an understanding of the elements of maps before they can either draw them or read them in an interpretative sense. Other studies have teased out the links between mapping development and: way finding (Scholnick et al., 1987; Ottosson, 1987), cognition (Winn, 1987; Sutherland and Winn, 1987), giftedness (Gerber, 1987) and perception (Gerber, 1982). On another track, cartographic researchers have demonstrated how learning about maps is a complex process involving a mixture of perception, understanding and visualization. The extensive research on graphic information processing by Bertin (1981, 1983) typifies such investigation. Still further, the investigations by developmental psychologists such as Piaget and Bruner that have been adapted by educational researchers such as Collis and Biggs (1979), Rhys (1972) and Stringer (1976) have indicated the important role of thinking in learning about graphics such as maps.

These collective theories and research findings are useful to geography teachers when they are translated into clear guides for

Figure 13.2: Sequential development of mapping elements
(source: Butler et al, 1984)

PLAN VIEW		ARRANGEMENT OF FEATURES		PROPORTION AND SCALE		DISTANCE		DIRECTION		REFERENCE SYSTEMS	
• Horizontal ↓ Oblique ↓ Vertical views of discrete objects ↓	M	• Reproduction of arrangement of small numbers of discrete objects in unlimited space ↓	M	• Relative sizes of large-scale objects ↓	M	• Estimating and measuring short distances ↓	M	• Random estimation ↓	M	• Verbal and written descriptions of objects in the immediate environment ↓	M
• Horizontal ↓ Oblique ↓ Vertical views of objects and areas at differing scales ↓	M + A1	• Reproduction of arrangement of clusters of objects in large-scale area of local environment — limited space ↓	M	• Relative sizes of groups of objects ↓	M	• Estimating and measuring medium distances (⟶30 m) ↓	M	• Random estimation of N, S, E, W ↓	M	• Reading and constructing concrete grids on two-dimensional surfaces ↓	M
• Maps drawn at differing scales	A1 + A2 + A3	• Reproduction of arrangement of classes of objects in areas of differing scales ↓	M + A1	• Relative sizes of groups of objects at a smaller scale ↓	M	• Measurement on large-scale maps (increasing accuracy) ↓	M + A1	• Perception and knowledge of the 4 cardinal points (4-point compass rose) ↓	M + A1	• Reading and constructing 'street directory'-type grids from large scale to small scale ↓	M
		• Description and analysis of large-scale area patterns ↓	M + A1 + A2	• Expression of simple ratios ↓	M	• Measuring on small-scale maps (with increasing accuracy)	A1 + A2 + A3	• Use of N, S, E, W on maps ↓	M + A1	• Reading and constructing area references on maps of varying scales ↓	M + A1 + A2
		• Description and analysis of small-scale area patterns ↓	A1 + A2	• Introduction to scale ↓	M			• Perception and knowledge of an 8-point compass rose ↓	M + A1	• Identifying main lines of latitude and longitude ↓	A1 + A2
		• Interpretation and application of arrangement at differing scales	A2 + A3	• Using a simple linear scale and statement of scale ↓	M + A1			• Use of a compass to calculate accurate angular measurements ↓	A2 + A3	• Reading and constructing 6-point grid references ↓	A2 + A3
				• Using abstract line scales ↓	A2			• Practice in the application of direction on a range of map forms and the globe	A2 + A3	• Use of latitude and longitude ↓	A2 + A3
				• Representative fraction	A3					• Map projections	A3

MAP LANGUAGE

Map signs		Colour		Size and shape		Base data		Representing relief		Lettering/numbers	
• Recognizing the relationship between type of sign and reality, e.g., line, point, area signs to represent line, point and area features ↓	M + A1	• Use of colour to arbitrarily discriminate between features on a map ↓	M + A1	• Size and shape of signs to discriminate between features on a map ↓	M + A1 + A2	• Thick coastline and rivers Few coastal features named Selection of main rivers Thick political boundaries ↓	A1	• Simple verbal description of local relief ↓	M	• Recognizing that different sizes and styles of type can be used to distinguish between classes of features ↓	M + A1
• Classifying and labelling the types of signs ↓	M + A1	• Use of conventional colours, e.g., blue for water ↓	M + A1 + A2	• Size and shape as discriminators between signs on thematic maps	A1 + A2 + A3	• Finer representation of coastline Variety of coastal features named General representation of river systems Finer representation of political boundaries ↓	A2	• Hill shading (large scale) ↓	M + A1	• Identifying different sizes and styles of type on a map ↓	A1 + A2
• Increasing sophistication of signs from real to abstract ↓	M + A1 + A2 + A3	• Use of colour to discriminate between signs on thematic maps, e.g., density of colour indicating density of distribution ↓	A1 + A2 + A3			• Finer representation of coastline Wide range of coastal features named River systems defined more accurately Finer representation of political boundaries	A3	• Hill shading (small scale) ↓	A1 + A2	• Classifying different sizes and styles of type in a key ↓	A1 + A2
• Developing hierarchies of signs within each class ↓	M + A1 + A2 + A3	• Use of colour on political maps ↓	A1 + A2 + A3					• Layer colouring ↓	A2 + A3	• Classifying different sizes and styles of type on a map	A1 + A2 + A3
• Use of signs that measure amounts	A1 + A2 + A3	• Layer colouring to show relief ↓	A2 + A3					• Contours	A3		
		• Conventional representation of colour on a topographic map	A3								

Key:
M *Moving Into Maps*
A1 *Atlas 1*
A2 *Atlas 2*
A3 *Atlas 3*

action. One such guide is that proposed in the *Jacaranda Atlas Programme* (see Figure 13.2). Here, the collective findings of research into students' learning about maps has been translated into a sequence of learning for each of the elements of a map. It demonstrates to teachers that there are identifiable steps in the development of competence in these elements that can be the bases of activities. Then, specific tasks are developed for each page or part of the programme to indicate what the authors' intentions were and how learning can be maximized using specific pages. Figure 13.3 shows this in practice for a page on introducing the concept of a key or legend to young, concrete-level thinkers.

2. Selection of appropriate maps for different groups of students

The question of 'Which maps should I use with my class?' should take on a new meaning for geography teachers. Previously, teachers were very pleased to use whatever maps they could obtain in their geography lessons. This led to the practice of using a range of maps that were based on very abstract symbols with students who could not decode the geographical information on maps with any degree of sophistication. As a result, the meaning on topographic or Ordnance Survey maps, complex planning maps and maps of ecosystems, was lost in the range of pretty colours on the map surface. While the age of people is not a good guide to their ability to understand maps, it can be used to consider their ability to think and to make environmental decisions.

What, then, can be done to select appropriate maps for students who possess differing levels of intellectual development? The following guidelines could be useful:

(a) Diagnose the students' understanding of the concept of a map by asking them to write their own definition of a map.
(b) Diagnose their competence with different levels of map symbols. This can be achieved by asking students to draw symbols for particular geographical features and to attach labels to symbols that have been prepared for their interpretation.
(c) Have students draw a cognitive map of an area that is well-known to them in order to determine what level of abstractness they will impose on their own symbols.
(d) Establish from students the extent of their previous experiences in using maps. This survey will expose students who have had an enriching experience with maps and those who have had an impoverished experience.

Let's go scuba diving!

You are scuba diving on a coral reef.

All the things in the picture of the reef can be divided into four groups: sharks, fish, shellfish, and other things.

Below the picture are four divers with labelled nets. List the things that would go in each diver's net. Then draw a sign for each thing next to its name. (Use different colours, shapes and sizes to make your signs very clear.)

You now have a **key** that you could use to make your own picture of the reef.

Figure 13.3: Developing the concept of a legend with younger learners
(source: Butler et al, 1983)

(e) Redraw maps so that they contain only sufficient information for the purpose of the geographical study and so that the abstractness of concreteness of the symbols match the mapping abilities of the students who will use the maps.

(f) Make as much use of thematic maps as possible in geographical studies. The thematic maps will contain differing numbers of layers of information, e.g. an economic map could contain information on manufacturing and mining activities, transportation networks, settlement patterns and administrative boundaries. Usually this amount of information is represented on maps in an abstract form as a mixture of coloured areal shadings, different coloured lines and dot forms. It could be more useful to extract the one or two themes that are relevant to the aims of the inquiry and to redraw them in as abstract a form as the students can understand. This could focus on pictorial symbols for younger adolescents and abstract geometric shapes for older adolescents.

3. Use an effective sequence of mapping education

The above research has confirmed that students will not have an effective mapping education if they spend most of their studies in geography in interpreting maps. It is possible to identify three distinct processes in mapping education: competence in the elements of maps, designing and making maps, and interpreting maps. Further research (Gerber, 1985) has confirmed the need for competence in cartographic language before effective performance can be demonstrated by students. These conclusions can be translated into effective action for educators if mapping skills are sequenced so that students, working at their own ability levels, can firstly develop competence in the elements of maps. Then, they should undertake a range of experiences involving the design and drawing of maps using symbols that can be understood by each student. Finally, once their competence in maps has been confirmed, the students should engage in deliberate interpretative activities. This sequence is not widely used in the design of mapping skills programmes or in geography textbooks. It is time that changes of this nature were implemented. One good example of such a sequence is to be found in the first three chapters of the *Skills Book for Secondary Schools* (Butler et al., 1985). The extract from the Table of contents in Figure 13.4 demonstrates how the proposed sequence can be developed into an educational sequence: Chapter 1 emphasizes the discrete elements that students need to focus on in their competence phase; Chapter 2 gives a range of map-making experiences; and Chapter 3 highlights different types of maps and associated interpretative tasks.

1. What's in a map?

2. How do you make a map?

3. How do you use a map?

Figure 13.4: Sequence for developing effective mapping skills
(source: Butler et al, 1984)

4. Education of textbook authors and map publishers in cartographic communication

One very effective action to improve the development of mapping skills would be to conduct a series of workshops with the authors and publishers of geography textbooks and school atlases. A prime focus of these workshops would be a number of activities designed to inform these influential people about the nature of cartographic communication; to structure a range of interactive experiences to clarify this concept and to give them opportunities to demonstrate that they can accommodate it in the student-based tasks that they incorporate in any future cartographic product. It is a reasonable assumption that these people are influential in geographical education because they are responsible for the development of many of the basic resources that geography teachers and students use in their teaching and learning. For example, all of these people should be competent to implement guidelines for effective map design such as:

(a) All maps should contain a precise statement of purpose in the form of an exact, comprehensive title.
(b) Labels on maps should be clear, unobtrusive and well-oriented.
(c) Each map should contain a clear figure-ground relationship.

(d) All maps should contain a complete legend, a scale, a direction indicator and a spatial reference system.
(e) All symbols should possess the qualities of good signs and be commensurate with the abilities of the users.

5. *In-service teacher education programmes*

While it may seem that the major preventative actions for textbook authors and publishers are to understand the cartographic communication process and to practise it in their products, it is equally important that the 'experts' who are to implement these activities – the teachers – come to understand the ways by which students learn mapping skills. Once such understanding is achieved, the teachers need to become competent at implementing strategies to enable students to learn mapping skills effectively and efficiently. This may be achieved through a range of in-service education experiences. Such experiences are not suggested in any sequential manner. Rather, they need to be organized to suit the local educational context in which groups of teachers arrange their in-service programmes.

The scope for such programmes will vary according to the professional needs of the geography teachers. However, important experiences that geography teachers should undertake in regard to mapping include:

(a) Workshops in computer-assisted mapping that will give them opportunities to digitize limited amounts of geographical data, to select from data files suitable information for thematic mapping purposes and to generate either on a screen and/or in hard-copy form a simple thematic map.
(b) Workshops on the concept of geographical information systems, the access of data to construct a GIS and the structuring of this geographical information in a GIS for selected users.
(c) Workshops on the use of the cartographic communication process in developing mapping skills with students at different levels of schooling. These workshops will demonstrate how meaning is derived from maps, highlight how cartographic language may be used as a graphic code and emphasize ways to maximize the design of maps.
(d) Practical sessions on developing mapping skills' programmes for students that build on the students' existing abilities and experiences. These sessions will aim to put into practice the proposed learning sequence of competence in the elements of maps followed by map-making and then map interpretation. There should also be some practice at selecting appropriate mapping resources for different groups and levels of students.

Conclusion

As Neil Diamond's lyrics remind us, signs 'reach out in their mystic language for us to read between the lines'. The extent of 'reading between the lines' which is achieved in regard to maps really depends on the competence that students as map users have developed in their mapping studies. How well they have developed competence in understanding, designing and interpreting maps will depend on the mapping skills they have learned, their knowledge of the learning that has occurred and their use of appropriate exemplars while developing the mapping skills. This chapter has attempted to show that the current practices in schools in regard to mapping have not kept up with the developments over the last decade or so concerning both cartography and geography. While it is quite easy to identify the gaps that exist between these recent developments in the disciplines and the current mapping practices in schools, it is more important to propose directions that geography teachers may follow in order to bring mapping skills in schools into the 1980s and 1990s. These glib comments do propose the desirable directions for mapping education. Space does not permit the inclusion of comprehensive in-service programmes or detailed learning activities. Access to some of the references that are highlighted will asist in this regard. In fact, the best response to the problem is to customize the suggestions in this chapter to the particular local or national context and to formalize the development of mapping skills. This formalization process is not aimed at developing mapping skills in isolation, but rather at developing them and using them in the context of a coherent geography programme. Then, mapping in schools will reflect recent developments in cartography and geography.

Chapter Fourteen
Remote Sensing
Keith Hilton

*The history of remote sensing in geographical education is outlined, from air photography to current satellite systems such as the Landsat series of earth observation satellites. The educational implications of the system's repetition, resolution and use of colour is described. Two products are reviewed (*Landsat Satellite Images in the Classroom *and* Spaceview UK*) and their educational context and background discussed to illustrate the range of learning implications. The quality and quantity of environmental data from satellite remote sensing will increase in the future and the section concludes with mention of four factors affecting its future – the technology of delivery, the organization of remote sensing, student reaction and the nature of the educational system.*

Windows are set high in the walls with only the sky visible – the design of many Victorian classrooms seemed to exclude the real environment. Room design may have changed but to many teachers its limits remain something to overcome. Incorporating the variety and splendour of the world beyond the local environment has long been part of the challenge of geographical education and its supporting technology. Magic lanterns have been replaced by videos and our textbooks and curriculum packages transformed by modern design criteria and printing techniques. A small part of this classroom 'escape process' has been the use of remote sensing.

Remote sensing is the collection of information about an object without being in physical contact with it, or more precisely 'the use of electromagnetic radiation sensors to record images of the environment which can be interpreted to yield useful information' (Curran, 1985). In terms of geography teaching this means the use of airphotos and satellite images.

This chapter outlines the history of remote sensing in geographical education. It then pays particular attention to two products which have been made available to teachers, the issues they raise and the practical and research experience on which they have been based. Finally, in the spirit of Norman Graves' work at the Institute of Education, the chapter looks at the prospects and problems of the next decade of educational remote sensing.

From air photography to satellite image

The educational use of remote sensing since its primitive beginnings in the early nineteenth century has been closely linked to its technical development. Remote sensing has been available as long as 'platforms' and 'sensors' have existed. The first platforms were balloons and the use of aircraft as platforms began in this century, receiving substantial impetus in both World Wars. For most of this time cameras were the sensors, with oblique, vertical and stereo pairs as their products. Developments in photography saw the appearance of films sensitive to infra-red radiation, the use of colour and finally the use of colour film sensitive to the infra-red.

The use of low level aerial oblique photos has become common in geography texts during the last half century as *illustration*, in a regional or systematic framework, and in association with the teaching of map *skills*. Vertical air photography on the other hand has had a more chequered place in geographical education. Air photo reconnaissance played a significant intelligence role in World War II and the arrival of peace saw the first discussion of its use to geography teachers. In 1946-7 the journal *Geography* carried no less than four articles on the topic (Kendall, 1946; Linton, 1946 a and b; Rawson and Beaver, 1947). Whilst the potential of aerial photography was being introduced it is interesting that comments on the problems that teachers would have in obtaining these new tools were also raised. This availability problem has persisted as a feature of the recent satellite remote sensing era. The two decades which followed the appearance of these four papers saw few major developments, although by 1965 the *Source Book for Geography Teachers* did give some addresses where teachers could obtain photos (Unesco, 1965).

Over the last two decades there has been evidence of general acceptance of air photographs as a tool for geography teaching reflected in their use by authors, publishers and examination boards. By the mid 1980s two GCE 'O' and five 'A' level syllabuses explicitly required the use of aerial photographs, and their use in many others was implied (Steele, 1986). Examination board guidelines also included mention, the London board for example stating that 'work should be undertaken with the help of relevant materials, such as photographs and remote sensing data'. These are indicators of the maturation of remote sensing in geographical education. This maturation is also reflected in texts and few well illustrated books published in the 1970s and 1980s contain no oblique or vertical air photos. Their use has varied from an 'illustration' inserted at a late stage in book production to situations where authors exploited their rich information potential. The *Oxford Geography Project* (Grenyer et al., 1979) provides examples of both illustration and data uses and in Book 3, 34 per cent of the 'non people' photos are remote sensing plates. Books like the *Global System* (Spicer, et al., 1977) and products such as the BBC filmstrips (e.g. *Europe from the Air)* were also part of this phase. A number of books were also published with a central focus on vertical air photos and their interpretation, Blair and Simpson (1984) and the *Atlas Of Landforms* (Scovill, 1966) being examples.

During this maturation phase air photography also began to occur more frequently in teachers' books. In *The Geography Teachers's Guide to the Classroom* (Fien et al., 1984) for example they were discussed in relation to concept acquisition and fieldwork. The 1986 edition of the Geographical Association's *Handbook* also contains mention (Boardman, 1986) and the 1982 Unesco handbook stated that remote sensing 'leads students to an understanding of concepts, to the describing and explaining of spatial patterns and the derivation of generalizations, models and even theories' (Slater and Spicer, 1982).

Whilst aerial photography had become by the 1980s a common illustrative resource and a useful but minor part of enquiry-based learning, the situation in satellite-based remote sensing is less clear cut. The term satellite remote sensing implies the use of satellites as platforms and non-photographic means of obtaining environmental information.

Satellites have a whole range of platform attributes which distinguish them from aircraft. They orbit higher and continuously, thus scale (the size of area depicted in their images) and repetition (the reviewing of an area as days pass, seasons change and years progress) enter our consideration. Satellites also use non-photographic means of recording information, they measure radiation in and beyond the visible spectrum as digital data which is computer processed. These three factors, *scale, repetition* and *spectrum* have given geography teachers a whole range of new teaching opportunities and problems.

Satellites can be divided into two types, weather and earth observation, but any classification also involves considering whether they are in high or low orbits. The first category, meteorological satellites, are the ones most familar to pupils as their images are interlaced with TV weather forecasts and their 'real time' reception is now possible in schools. Weather satellites in *geostationary* orbits 36 000 km above the equator give continuous hemispheric views. Meteosat, the one of this circumequatorial family familiar to Europeans, goes East and West to Americans. Their resolution is typically 2.5 km at the equator, directly below the satellite, but this deteriorates towards the edge of the global view. In contrast the lower *polar-orbiting* satellites, like the American NOAA series and Soviet Meteor, swing near pole to near pole, giving images of smaller areas in somewhat greater detail.

Earth observation satellites have been a later development, starting with the American Landsat 1 in 1972, continuing through to the current Landsat 5 launched 1984, and the French SPOT in 1986. These satellites are in lower orbit, 910 km for Landsat 1, 2 and 3, 705 km for Landsat 5 and 830 km for SPOT and revisit at intervals of 14 to 26 days. Earth observation satellites use line scanners that build images from picture elements or *pixels*. Landsat 1's pixels were 80m, SPOT's multispectral is 20m and its panchromatic 10m. Pixel size determines resolution or the size of the features which can be detected. Civilian earth observation satellite images, whilst having coarser resolution than air photos, cover substantially greater areas at lower cost and their coverage now extends globally over many years. (Figure 14.1 is an example of how aspects of repetition and scale have been introduced in a recent curriculum package).

The illustrative potential of satellite remote sensing in geographical education is thus immense, whether it is meander migration, the ITCZ or urban land use, satellite remote sensing can provide a 'real life' illustration. It is therefore not surprising to find in the 1980s that authors, textbook picture researchers and publishers began using satellite remote sensing to show phenomena that an earlier generation would have used artwork and text for.

Whilst the scale range of satellite remote sensing has been used in geographical illustration its repetition potential has been less well exploited. Weather system development has seen its most useful

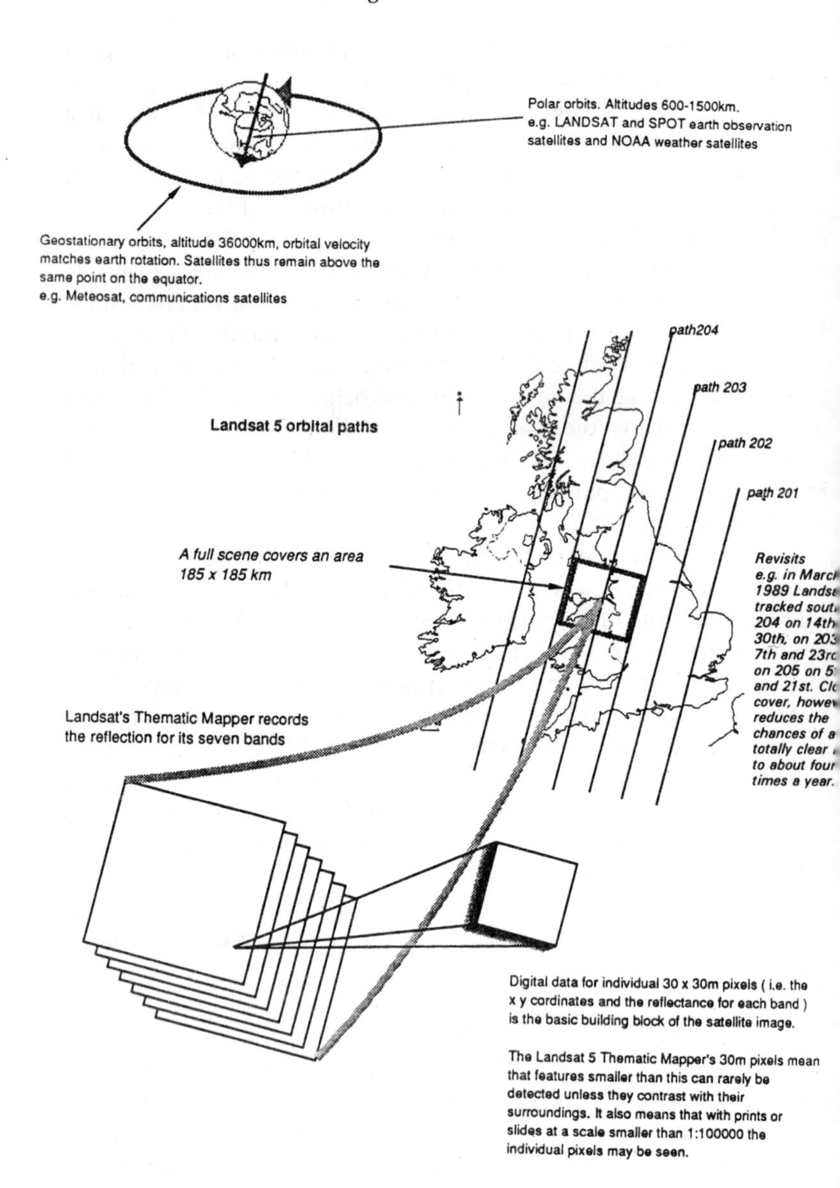

Polar orbits. Altitudes 600-1500km.
e.g. LANDSAT and SPOT earth observation satellites and NOAA weather satellites
Geostationary orbits, altitude 36000km, orbital velocity matches earth rotation. Satellites thus remain above the same point on the equator.
e.g. Meteosat, communications satellites
path204
path 203
path 202
path 201
Landsat 5 orbital paths
A full scene covers an area 185 x 185 km
Landsat's Thematic Mapper records the reflection for its seven bands
Digital data for individual 30 x 30m pixels (i.e. the x y cordinates and the reflectance for each band) is the basic building block of the satellite image.
The Landsat 5 Thematic Mapper's 30m pixels mean that features smaller than this can rarely be detected unless they contrast with their surroundings. It also means that with prints or slides at a scale smaller than 1:100000 the individual pixels may be seen.

Figure 14.1: Orbits, repetition and scale (source: Hilton, 1989)

deployment (Reynolds, 1982) but earth observation satellite images illustrating 'before and after' situations (hazards, urban growth, deforestation, etc.) sadly represent less than 1 per cent of its educational use.

The largest cluster of opportunities and problems arguably relate to the third factor – the spectrum. Most earth observation satellites passively record reflected radiation. The electromagnetic spectrum is divided into a series of bands, each satellite system having its own numbering arrangements for these. In simple terms the blue end of the visible spectrum is of little use in remote sensing because of atmospheric scattering. Shifting sensing into the infra-red gives substantially more environmental information about factors such as soils, soil moisture, ground cover, plant species, plant health, ground thermal characteristics and so on. Whilst this is good news for professional users of remote sensing it has posed a challenge to the educational user as this infra-red has to be 'invented' for us.

A single infra-red band can be processed by computers as a black and white image. This may look superficially like a black and white picture, but some care may be needed in interpreting the light and dark tones although shapes and associations of shapes may be more familiar guides.

When bands are combined as colour composites the situation becomes complex. Landsat's Thematic Mapper for example has seven bands, any three of these can be assigned to the red, blue or green colour guns in a VDU. Bands can be combined and ratioed so the possibilities are almost endless. (Figure 14.2 is an example of simplifying this complexity from the teachers' section of a recent curriculum package.) The area being imaged is itself also dynamic as reflectance varies when tides ebb and flow, crops grow, soil moisture changes and so on. Because of this complexity, coloured satellite images, unlike maps, can have no universal colour key. The meaning of colour can vary with the bands chosen, which colour is assigned to each band, the character of the area and the date.

The issue of colour is thus central to educational considerations. Its complexity raises the need for some degree of technical background before image interpretation can be used by a teacher. Colour also adds to the cost of the media, particularly in books and especially with those texts designed for the smaller markets such as GCE 'A' level. The positive dimension of colour in satellite images is, however, their visual excitement, their aesthetic appeal and the fact that the human eye can ultra violet visible infra red

The human eye only detects a part of the electromagnetic spectrum

i.e. radiation between 0.4 and 0.7 the former we perceive as violet , the latter as red and between them the various colours of the spectrum

Satellite sensors can detect radiation beyond these limits, into the infra red

The sensors are designed to be sensitive to particular wavelength divisions called BANDS

visible near infra red thermal infra red

Landsat 4 & 5's Thematic Mapper has seven bands, three in the visible and four in the infra red

1 2 3 4 5 7 6

Sensing in the infra red allows better discrimination of vegetation,soils,geology and thermal differences

Image analysis computers can take digital data for these bands and present them -
a) as single band scenes with 256 grey scale levels
b) as composites of 3 bands

Colour Composites

Natural colour composites involve assigning TM bands 1,2,3 to Blue,Green and Red colours

B G R

This gives a vegetation = green effect

False colour composites involve assigning any three bands to blue, green and red.

In 'Cheshire from Space' TM band 3 has been assigned blue, band 4 to green and band 5 to red

B G R

The meaning of the colours is described in the notes for each slide and a language of false colour for this band/colour arrangement is summarised in a figure.

Each satellite system has its own band limits. Landsat's Multispectral Scanner [MSS] for example has four bands.
In this case-
Natural colour composites uses B G R
A typical false colour uses B G R

Some of the slide library uses MSS data

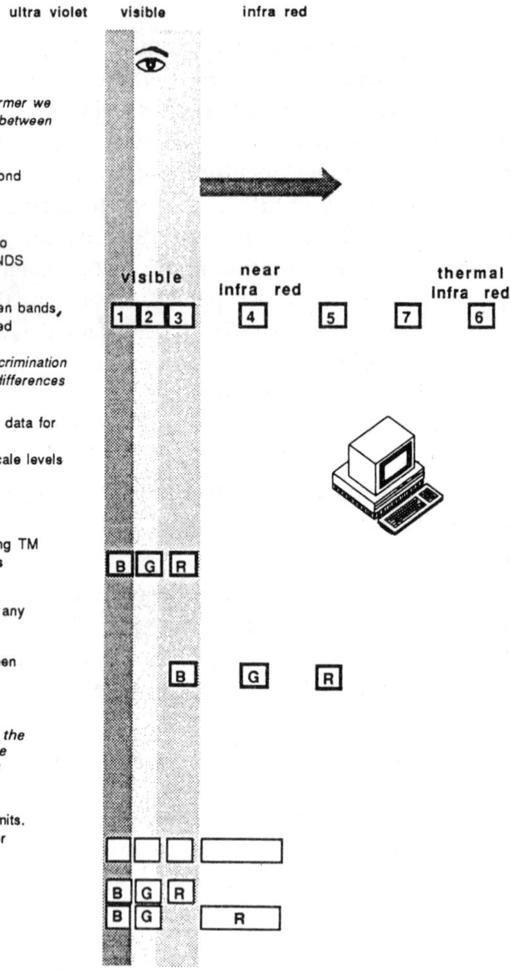

Figure 14.2: The electromagnetic spectrum, satellite sensor bands and colour composites (source: Hilton, 1989)

distinguish substantially more colour variations than those in a grey scale. Their information content and stimulus is therefore substantially greater.

Two products

The practical opportunities and problems of using satellite remote sensing in education can be illustrated by examining two products which have attempted to link this technology to established teaching situations.

The Australian *Landsat Satellite Images for the Classroom* was promoted as 'a series of kits bringing the latest advances in space technology into your classroom' (Falconer and Gerber, 1978). It contained Landsat multispectral scanner (MSS) OHPs and overlays, slide sets, coloured prints and maps based on city centre areas in Australia together with a teacher's handbook. The handbook claimed that Landsat MSS offered a 'new way of looking at regional geography'; it suggested treating the OHP as a map, adding successive overlays of place names, contours, water features and communications. Treating the satellite image as a map is a theme suggested by many (for example Hatt, T., 1987; Ritchie, 1987). An interesting part of this Australian project was the way in which the concepts from the Queensland Syllabus were used (Board of Secondary School Studies, 1977) which identified four basic spatial concepts – location, distribution, association and movement. Figure 14.3 outlines the approach of the kit (the example is from the Brisbane materials) and the way in which it linked syllabus-derived concepts to the classroom use of the kit's Landsat 1:1,000,000 MSS false colour composites, overlays and slides.

The kit's handbook commented on how Landsat MSS could contribute to the classification of single and multiple feature regions. Also included were points about hypothesizing with examples from physical and economic geography, Finally there was a short comment on Landsat images and the development of aesthetic appreciation. Each slide contained a paragraph on 'content' and a paragraph on 'suggested use'. For example one slide contained four bands of the Brisbane area. The 'content' section explained these and the 'teacher use' section suggested a class discussion of what is 'visible' leading to a clarification of the infra-red. Some slides were false colour composites, some had annotation and scale grids and there were a number of subscene enlargements.

Given the date of its production this series was an excellent product

Concept	Aspects	Examples of Pupil use of Landsat MSS
Location	**Distance**	*How far is it from Brisbane to Toowoomba?* *Why would it take longer to travel from Brisbane to Boonah than Brisbane to the Gold Coast, although the distances are similar?*
	Direction	*What is the direction of (list of Queensland towns) from Brisbane ?*
	Site	*What factors would have influenced the decision to found the earliest penal settlement at Radcliffe in 1824 rather than Brisbane ?* *Why is the Wivenhoe dam being constructed on the Brisbane River?*
	Situation (relative location)	*Where is Brisbane located with respect to (list towns)?* *Suggest why Brisbane is the major urban centre in the region ?* *Indicate some problems in building a main road west from Brisbane?*

The handbook also suggested the four aspects of location could be integrated -

Concept	Aspects	Examples of Pupil use of Landsat MSS
		by asking pupils to identify the water storage areas, identify the largest and comment on its site. *Methods suggested involved tracing overlays on the hardcopy, with work as individuals or groups.*
Distribution The arrangement of one phenomenon on the earth's surface. Distributions produce aerial association.	**Density**	*Using a grid calculate the density of land use.*
	Dispersion	*Activities involving measuring aerial extent*
	Centralization	*Trace and locate Brisbane and x other towns. Insert main roads, railways and describe the pattern and how it relates to physical features?*
	Patterns of Distribution	*Describe the facilities of the Port of Brisbane and suggest why new facilities are situated at the estuary mouth ?*
Association The degree to which one distribution is similar or different to another. Raises the question of causal relations		*Describe the distribution of irrigated farmland and explain why a dam is important to this pattern ?* *Trace upland areas,and dense vegetation.* *Suggest how upland distribution influences the distribution of dense vegetation ?*

Figure 14.3: Geographical concepts and the Jacaranda kits
(source: Board of Secondary School Studies, 1977)

exploiting the spatial coverage of Landsat's multi spectral scanner (185×185km) and working within the limits of its resolution (80m). The attempt to link the material to an existing geography curriculum was in retrospect its major contribution.

The second product selected for description here, *Spaceview UK* (Hilton, Stewart and McMorrow, 1988), is different for a number of reasons. Published a decade after the last exemplar an initial difference is in the basic satellite data, unlike the Jacaranda kit which used early Landsat MSS data, Spaceview UK used Landsat Thematic Mapper imagery, with its improved 30m resolution. Secondly it was a non-commercial effort to produce low cost hardcopy (i.e. sets of ten 30×30cms 1:100,000 scale colour prints). Collaboration between the National Remote Sensing Centre (NRSC), General Technology Systems Ltd., Serco Ltd., the Field Studies Council, the Remote Sensing Society and the Geographical Association's Satellite Remote Sensing Working Group saw the project to fruition. Thirdly *Spaceview UK* was produced in the context of a different educational system. Finally, and the reason for describing it here, it tried to incorporate the results of the intervening period's classroom experience and research.

The small amount of enquiry undertaken in the field of educational satellite remote sensing in the UK has been largely completed by practising teachers undertaking personal, unfunded, research for higher degrees. Their sample sizes and range of topic coverage has inevitably been small. Only one survey of use, teacher opinion and the policy of 'providers' (publishers and the remote sensing institutions) has been undertaken and this was restricted to south-eastern England (Steele, 1986). Experience, research and survey had, however, thrown up three interrelated issues in connection with satellite remote sensing use: problems of perceived cost, teacher knowledge and interpretation.

High cost had been a frequent criticism of educational satellite remote sensing. This hardly applies to some products; slide sets are a case in point. Those from Britain's National Remote Sensing Centre (*Introduction to Remote Sensing*, *Coastal Processes*, and *Applications in Geology*) and commercial sets have prices similar to those of other educational slide sets. Posters, with their large print runs, are a low cost 'hardcopy' provision and in 1989 the NRSC had a number available (e.g. *Britian and Ireland* a mosaic in simulated natural colour, *The Third Planet* a Meteosat view, *The Isle of Lewis* false colour, *Antarctica* and *Europe* a NOAA AVHRR simulated natural colour mosaic). Whilst suitable for wall decoration and general stimulus the temporal/seasonal span within mosaics can cause problems. However the cost of colour photographic prints, for example those ordered in single copies for local or field work areas, has been high and this has undoubtedly been perceived as a real barrier to geography teachers using satellite remote sensing.

There is some research evidence that sets of hardcopy generate more pupil talk, thinking and responses (Homewood, 1987; Ritchie, 1987). They are also more flexible in school use than slide sets or videos, which require the kind of viewing facilities still not present in the majority of rooms. Slides also tend to be used in the 'illustration mode' (Hilton, 1981) and are difficult for pupils to use in enquiry and group work. For such reasons it was decided to produce prints in the Spaceview package. By limiting the selection to ten areas, a viable print run could be achieved and the per print cost reduced (to less than 40p at 1988 prices).

Teacher knowledge (or rather the lack of it!) has been frequently mentioned as a limiting factor in the geography teachers' uptake of satellite remote sensing (Curran and Wardley, 1985). Most products reviewed in the *Remote Sensing Source book* (Carter, 1986) take this into account with technical briefings on satellite orbits, sensors, bands, image processing and interpretation. There are also now a number of texts specifically aimed at undergraduates and postgraduates which are accessible to teachers and for the United Kingdom situation the British National Space Centre has produced an introductory booklet *The Earth Below* (Hilton and Morgan, 1987) The NRSC has also responded to the problem with its series of free *Factsheets* and its series of videos (e.g. *Introduction to Remote Sensing*, *Towards a Greener Planet* and *Image Processing*.) The NRSC mobile exhibition unit *This Earth From Space* did an extensive national tour ending in the autumn of 1987. It typically spent a week in a town around which schools and colleges had been mailed so that school parties accounted for more than 70 per cent of its use. The Science Museum's 'Exploration of Space' gallery which opened in October 1986 had a section on remote sensing including the Globetrotter interactive audiovisual display.

The 'teacher knowledge' limiting factor has therefore improved through the kind of initiatives described above. There has, however, been little expansion in teacher education either at the initial level or through in-service training (INSET). The scale of INSET required may be quite modest. Kirman, in reviewing Canadian teacher training needs, suggested five workshop hours with time in between for reflection (Kirman, 1984) and the experience of the Geographical Association's

Working Group is similar.

The third limiting factor is the 'need to interpret' remote sensing imagery. Whilst scale and lack of annotation (feature names) have been issues, the central interpretation problem mentioned earlier has been colour. Learning the 'language of false colour' is a real perceptual problem facing teachers and their pupils. Dependent as it is on sensors, bands, image processing, ground area character and season, colour can easily bewilder the novice. Yet colour enhances environmental information, provokes thought and stimulates emotions, three educationally worthwhile outcomes. This has been a fundamental dilemma. A geography teacher is primarily interested in the information in a Landsat or SPOT scene. He/she feels unwilling to offer a course in remote sensing before commencing the geography. Such unwillingness reflects a lack of scientific confidence and an awareness of the demands of crowded syllabuses. The need for cross-subject co-operation is obvious, as indicated in the Centre National d'Etudes Spatiale (CNES) pack on Corsica (Gauthier and Vauzelle, 1986), achieving it is a recognized key task for the next decade (Stewart, 1987; INRP, 1987).

For the geography teacher the problem is reflected in the pupil's simple question 'What do the colours mean?' A number of solutions have been tried. Firstly the provision of colour keys. This is possible with a single image for a specific date, but is less easy with mosaics such as some posters of the NRSC and those North American scenes marketed by ASP in Vancouver. This approach was common in the early years of Landsat MSS false colour composities when tables of colours with typical interpretation points and comments on seasonal differences for a range of images were produced, for example those produced for *Mission to Earth*. This approach gives a feeling of false confidence and *Spaceview UK* did not provide such a universal table.

A second solution to the colour problem is the provision of text comments and explanations. Depending on the anticipated readership the detail has varied from simple 'colour x is item y', to more complex attempts at explaining the colours. *Spaceview UK*, because of the seasonal and environmental range of its nine images, adopted this approach. It attempted in its teacher's handbook to give concise colour keys for all images, but expanded on the reasons for the differences in a number of cases. A part of its strategy was, however, restricting the complexity. The pack uses only Landsat TM bands 3, 4 and 5 assigned to blue, red and green respectively. The thrust of the text explanation was thus on only *one* satellite system and *one* processing option, so that the environmental and seasonal effects could be explored without undue technical distraction.

A third solution is to use simulated natural colour. The initial Landsat MSS composites were most frequently represented as false colour composites. Various attempts, however, have been made to create a 'green mode' when vegetation is green rather than the reds of false colour. As Mueller-Wille wrote 'normal colour makes it easier to recognize familiar landscapes' which justified their use in atlas and map products like *Images of the World* (Mueller-Wille, 1984). The advantage of natural colour lies in its familiarity to the novice and in the fact that the human visual system is most sensitive to greens and yellows. The other side to the argument might mention that false colours usually have greater contrast and contrast is *vital* in differentiating features on an image. False colour, when data from the near infra-red is used also contains far more environmental information.

Experience with pupils using both natural and false colour conventions has been mixed. Whiteman (1982) had found that ability in using Landsat products increased with age of secondary school pupils. Homewood (1987) carried out some experiments comparing false colour and near natural colour for the same image/area/date. She found the same relationship between IQ and performance. Homewood's results showed overall no significant difference between the groups using false and those using natural colour images, but she did conclude that natural colour might be better for lower ability pupils when the children had limited experience of remote sensing. Her detailed results, however, led her to conclude that false colour produced higher scores for tasks related to urban, port, vegetation (except woodland) and physical features. She also found that false colour was better for tasks which involved detecting smaller items. As a result of considering these kinds of findings *Spaceview UK* was produced using false colours, but using only one combination. In this it contrasts with the earlier Jacaranda kit which had used a range of colour conventions.

A fourth strategy lies in starting pupils with images of their local areas or those with which they are familiar from their normal teaching and field work. Such a strategy of starting with an already known area, often with basic skills, had been shown to be productive (Kirman, 1977; Whiteford, 1985 and Ritchie, 1987). Not only can the issue of false colour be attacked directly by the pupils by their emulating the professional remote sensor's search for 'ground truth' but issues like image scale, resolution and so on can also be explored on familiar territory. Normally other forms of environmental information are at hand such as topographic and land use maps, planning department documentation and personal knowledge of local environmental issues.

Before leaving *Spaceview UK* one area needs to be mentioned for completeness – image scale. 1:100,000 images were produced. This scale was selected as a compromise. 1:50,000 would have enabled immediate comparison with British maps but the individual pixels would have been visible. For desk top use print size is also a consideration as anything much larger than A4 becomes unwieldy, easily worn and difficult to store. The selection of a 1:100,000 print scale thus allowed substantial detail to be detectable for a reasonably sized area and the addition of a margin grid eased pupil uses. The geographical areas selected were very much influenced by potential market. Strategy four (above) was a consideration and field work areas, particularly those studied by 14-16 year olds and well documented environmental issues (like the Broads and National Parks), were also relevant. The inclusion of urban areas, Merseyside and NE London, rounded out the aerial and topic coverage.

Many of the small scale studies have shown that pupils like remote sensing but once the novelty factor wears away the utility of it in the secondary school needs to be on a firmer base. Steele's survey (1986) had showed that 'A' level (16-19 years) was the largest group with which remote sensing was used. Evidence from Homewood, Ritchie, Whiteman in the UK and Kirman's work in Alberta (Kirman, 1984) had suggested that younger pupils could use Landsat. *Spaceview UK* therefore followed on from the suggestions made earlier by the Geographical Association's Satellite Remote Sensing Working Group in their January 1987 *Teaching Geography* article (Hilton, et al., 1987) and included exercises for the whole 11-19 age range.

Prospects

Assessing the prospects of remote sensing means considering the interplay of a number of factors, but as this is 'a technology-led innovation' (Hilton, 1981) a convenient starting point is with the platforms and sensors themselves. The scheduled launches of the satellite platforms (Figure 14.4) will ensure 'continuity and stability of data until the twenty first 'century' (Eosat, 1988). During this period resolution will improve (e.g. Landsat 6 will have 15m), new oceanographic applications will be developed (e.g. Landsat 6's sea wide

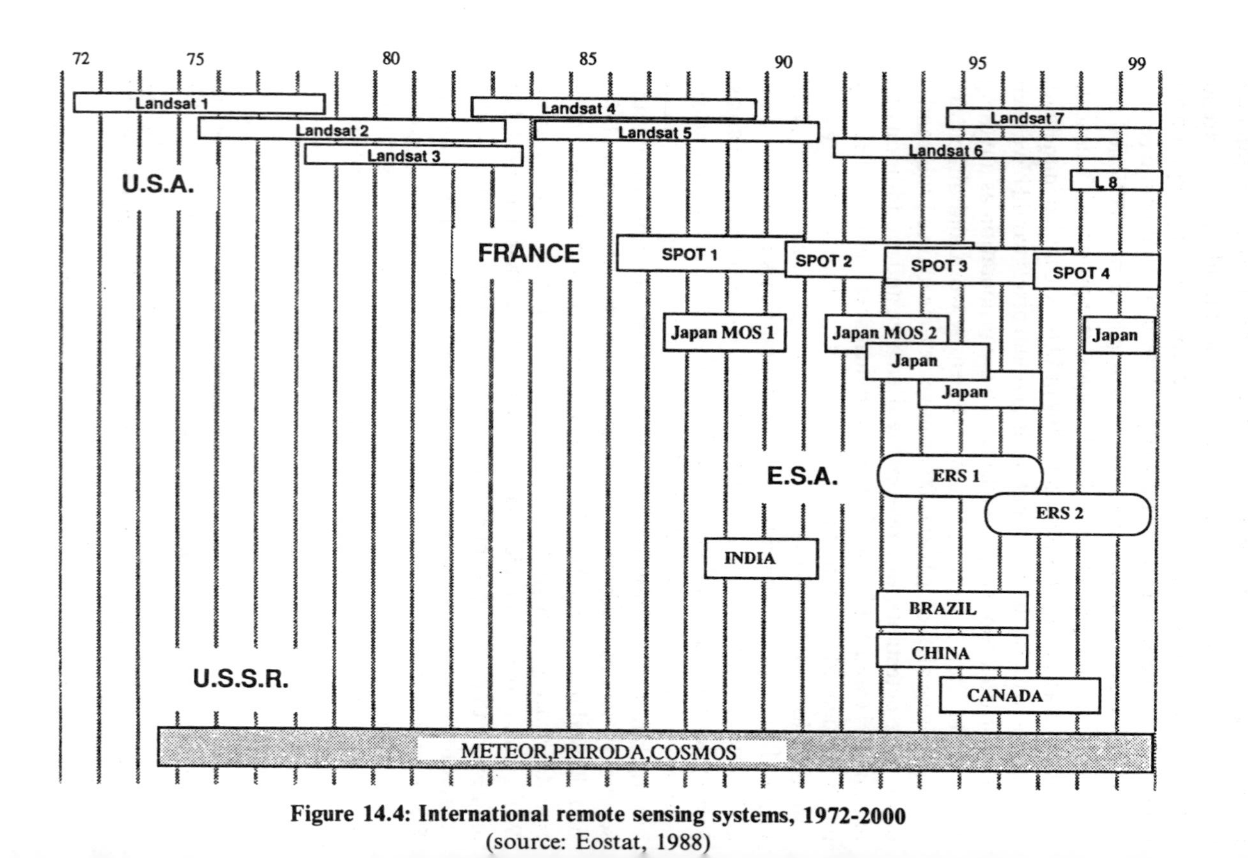

Figure 14.4: International remote sensing systems, 1972-2000
(source: Eostat, 1988)

field sensor), bands will multiply and all-weather capability will arrive (e.g. with ERS 1).

The technology for delivering this explosion of data to educational users is likely to contain elements of continuity, in the forms of books, curriculum packages, slides and posters. Anticipated products in the UK at the time of writing included, an environmental issue study pack supported by the World Wide Fund for Nature, to include satellite imagery in ten issue-based units such as rain forest destruction, desertification, mining, urban expansion and pollution (Hawkins, 1989). Slide sets for individual counties, for example the Derbyshire package (O'Hare, 1989), will continue to be produced. Individual colour prints will continue to be high cost but for small orders advances in colour copying will allow teachers to obtain local or field work area prints at less than £1 per copy.

Real-time analysis of satellite data can be expected to continue in terms of weather satellites, at costs of £1-2K for microcomputer based systems. The large steerable dishes required for earth observation satellite data reception means that their digital data will reach educational users as floppy discs (as they already have through the pioneer Dundee University BBC micro based packages), CCTs or CD ROM discs. To use this data microcomputer based (e.g. PC 286/386 or Archimedes based) image analysis systems will continue to develop. A number of these exist at present e.g. ERDAS from the USA. They are, however, likely to remain well beyond the financial reach of individual schools, perhaps Avon's purchase of an LS 10 system for use in an environmental studies centre and Somerset's project involving the installation of 40 Archimedes based image enhancement systems and local area Landsat data will be emulated elsewhere. Any development of reliance on microcomputer based systems to deliver remote sensing to geography pupils will inhibit universality, consigning access to the computer laboratory, and excluding remote sensing from the vast majority of geography lessons.

The second factor is 'industrial organization'. A feature of the 1980s has been the commercialization of satellite remote sensing and a search for returns on the huge investments in design, construction, launch and tracking. Landsat satellites were handed over to EOSAT in 1986 and SPOT has been commercial since its inception. The net effect of this is that data costs have risen. Whilst a multinational oil and mining company or a trader on the Chicago grain futures market may be able to pay for such environmental information, education rarely can. In addition the organization of the industry excludes educational users from its decision making, so that the products made available lack continuity of availability and linkage to teaching reality.The proposed establishment of an Earth Observation Centre to replace the NRSC (Large, 1988) seems likely to perpetuate the past pattern. Less than 1 per cent of the costs of such organizations would radically transform educational availability and use.

The third factor is the pupil. As has been mentioned earlier there is a lack of substantive research evidence on which to base future provision. Preliminary work in the UK, cited above in connection with the Spaceview product, and elsewhere (Tindal, 1978; Milne, 1979; Kisman, 1984) provides promising evidence for its educational potential. Questions of image scale, colours and the efficiency of different learning strategies, however, remain largely unknown.

The nature of the educational system is the fourth factor and its detail is beyond the scope of this chapter. The HMI report *Geography from 5-16* nonetheless stated:

> In recent years remote sensing from satellites has improved our knowledge of weather systems, contributed to resource exploration and to land use mapping, and aided systematic monitoring of natural disasters and the environmental impact of human activities. The study of geography should make use of the information which can be obtained from such sources. (HM Inspectorate, 1986)

In connection with the National Curriculum it is stimulating to note the range of possibilities for educational remote sensing embedded in the science 5-16 statement (DES, 1988c) and geography (DES, 1990).

The preceding paragraphs focus on satellite remote sensing. Conventional air photography will continue: it is familiar to pupils, teachers, authors, picture researchers and examination boards. The future of satellites in education is less clear. Data from space will increase substantially in amount, quality and coverage. Its penetration into school geography where it can stimulate and illustrate as a service to humanities is likely to continue. Its challenge comes in terms of its data-base potential (where low cost products will be required) and also in terms of its potential as a vehicle for cross curricular activities which link science, technology and the humanities. Before the twenty-first century remote sensing will be fully integrated into geographic information systems (GIS). The development of these is highly significant as the Chorley Committee outlined (House of Lords, 1984).

More recently the chairman of the ESRC stated 'Crucial questions about the functioning of society and the economy are amenable to investigation using GIS techniques. A basic familiarity with what GIS has to offer should be a part of the training of all social scientists' (Newby, 1988). Whilst only an academic minority of our geography pupils will need to be so trained, many of them may work in environments where GIS is a fundamental information handling tool and all of them will live in a society shaped by decisions made with its help.

The palaeolithic hunter who used a hilltop to look for game realized the equation 'elevation+intelligence = understanding'. Geography teachers using oblique air photos have long realized this. The challenge is adding the extra elevation and information that satellites can bring to environmental understanding.

Part Four
International Perspectives

Chapter Fifteen
International Geography: The IGU Commission on Education
M.J. Wise

In 1952 the International Geographical Union's Commision on The Teaching of Geography in Schools was established. The record of the Commission is traced. First established to provide a better case for the teaching of geography, especially as an aid to international understanding, changing objectives over time are indicated. The Commission's work, founded as a link between educational and geographical research, has yielded advisory and practically-oriented material for use in schools. The Commission's response to the problem of adapting general objectives to regional needs is discussed. Problems in organizing international co-operation are mentioned.

Norman Graves has been so active in developing international co-operation in research on geographical education and in improving the standards of teaching the subject that it seems appropriate to include in this volume some remarks on the work of the Commission on 'Geography in Education' of the International Geographical Union of which he was a member from 1968 to 1988 and Chairman from 1972 to 1980.

Balley (1972) has provided a review of discussions in the Congresses of the Union on the teaching of geography, especially in those Congresses in which a section of the agenda had been devoted to geographical education. Schneider (1972) also refers briefly to the Commissions on the Teaching of Geography, first created in 1904 only to disappear until 1952. From 1952, though the titles have varied and, of course, membership has changed, commissions in this field have been established at every four yearly Congress.

In the years after the Second World War, with the building of peace and the widening of international understanding much in mind, attention turned to the contribution that geographical teaching could make to these aims. Fairgrieve's observation of 1926 that

> the function of Geography in school is to train future citizens to imagine accurately the conditions of the great world stage and so help them to think sanely about political and social problems in the world around (Fairgrieve, 1926)

was much quoted. Geography was also seen as a relevant subject for encouragement in schools in developing countries where improved knowledge of the environment could assist in the tasks of raising living standards. Such considerations may have been among those which led to the holding of the Unesco Conference on the Teaching of Geography at MacDonald College Canada, in 1950. *The Unesco Handbook of Suggestions on the Teaching of Geography* first appeared in 1951. There was also concern amongst teachers of the subject that the aims and methods of geography in its modern form were not well understood by the public or by educational administrators. In some countries, as in the United States, geographical teaching was under threat from social studies: in others, old-fashioned concepts and methods were still employed. It was time for an international drive to present the value of the subject as an educational discipline, to illustrate the contribution that it could make to national educational aims and to urge again its potential value to international understanding.

Progress of the Commission 1952-68

One of the leaders in framing the proposal of 1952 to the International Geographical Union for a Commission on Educational Geography was undoubtedly Dean Neville Scarfe, then of the University of Manitoba, Winnipeg, earlier of the Institute of Education in the University of London. The proposal, brought forward during the 17th International Geographical Congress in Washington D.C., at which there was a substantial section on education, encountered little difficulty and a Commission was established under the title of 'Geography in Schools' (IGU *Newsletter* IV, April 1953). Scarfe was appointed Chairman. The members, it is worth recording, were Dr T.F. Barton (Secretary) (USA), Dr C.A. Alaqoz (Turkey), Dr I.R. Khan (Lebanon), Dr Gladys M. Hickman (UK), and Dr C.D. Carvallo (Brazil). Six consultants were also appointed, Dr Eric W.H. Briault (UK), M.R. Fichaux (France), Mr J. Reumert (Denmark), Dr A. Sømme (Norway), Dr Clyde Kohn (USA) and Dr B. Brouillette (Canada). News of the existence of the Commission was widely circulated. The initial aim was to produce a report setting out the case for geography in schools and suggesting improved methods of teaching. The time had arrived, it was felt, for an authoritatively agreed statement about geography: geographers should 'put their philosophy or point of view more clearly and forcibly before the ordinary public, and particularly educators' (Scarfe, 1953). As a first step, a statement which included a list of objectives was cirulated widely for comment. The Commission intended to investigate and evaluate the present status of, and recent trends in, the teaching of the subject at elementary and secondary levels. It hoped then to be able to recommend what the geography programme at these levels should be and how it might be implemented in the classroom. It also intended to press the case for geography as a major integrating science in the curriculum. Evidence is shown in the statement of the threat to the subject from advocates of social studies. School work in many countries separated people from nature, the humanities from the natural sciences. Geography could 'make good this neglect'. Geography, further, had suffered in the past from bad teaching or presentation in old fashioned forms. The study of 'man-land relationships in the wide sense in which modern geographers view them 'offered' a fine basis for integrating the whole school curriculum'.

Constructive replies were received to the statement and a questionnaire was formulated and sent out in December 1953 and January 1954 to every state in the United States, every province in Canada and to 28 other countries. By July 1954, Dean Scarfe reported that while every province of Canada had replied, as had 12 states in USA, only six other replies had been received, from Finland, Sweden, Netherlands, Germany, Italy and France. Nevertheless a start was being made on drafting a report for presentation to the 18th International Congress at Rio de Janeiro in 1956 (IGU *Newsletter* V, July 1954).

The Report was drafted by Scarfe (Scarfe, 1956). It met with some criticism in the discussion at the Commission meeting held in August 1956, though there was also much praise for Scarfe's initiative. The report, of 32 pages, was a substantial piece of work on his part: it included in addition to a general statement on the aims and methods of modern geography, a summary of the replies to the questionnaire and statements of the current position in USA, Canada, Turkey, France and India. A case was made for a 'correlative' role for geography among the subjects in the school curriculum, for its value, when well taught by vivid and practical methods, as 'excellent educational training', and for fuller realization of its socially valuable function. Much remained to be done to put the subject into a healthy position in schools. Every country should 'redouble its efforts to train teachers of geography more effectively and provide better facilities for geography teaching'. Geography 'had a most valuable part to play in total education by its unique contribution to the cause of international peace'.

The new Commission on the Teaching of Geography in schools established in 1956 had a different membership. Professor Benoît Brouillette of Montreal became Chairman and only Dean Scarfe remained from the preceding Commission. The new members were Professor Josef Barbag (Warsaw), Tom Brown (Headmaster of King's School, Gloucester, UK), René Clozier, who became Secretary (Paris), and Professor Juanita Gonzales (Uruguay). The Commission met in Paris, in January 1957, resolved to continue the work of its predecessor and to provide a programme for the teaching of geography in schools having regard to the age of the pupils and of the various possible methods. An enquiry was quickly put in hand among its members and correspondents on a number of questions concerning the teaching of the subject. This was preliminary to the devising of a major questionnaire based enquiry to be carried out in 1959-60 (IGU *Bulletin* VIII, 2, 1957, 40). By May 1958 replies from 20 countries had been received. In some countries, notably USA where Clyde Kohn was very active, special committees had been organized. Tom Brown and Gladys Hickman had gathered together a working group in the United Kingdom. Fruitful work was also in progress in West Germany, France, Canada, Switzerland, Japan, Iraq, India, Poland and other countries. Co-operation with Unesco had been well established and a report to Unesco on 'The teaching of geography and adaptation of syllabi to the mental level of pupils' was prepared for the Commission by M. René Clozier. Also in train were discussions on the possibility of undertaking for Unesco a study on the role of geography in facilitating reciprocal understanding between East and West as part of a wider Unesco project (IGU *Bulletin* XI, 1960, 46-49).

A mandate to undertake this and other tasks was duly obtained at the 19th Congress in Stockholm, 1960. Brouillette continued as Chairman, Neville Scarfe and Juanita Gonzales dropped out of membership and Hisao Aono (Tokyo) and S.P. Chatterjee (Calcutta) came in. Among the new corresponding members who now began to be active in the Commission's work may be discerned the name of N.J. Graves. The main objective of the re-established Commission was to produce for Unesco what was at first described as a manual for the teaching of geography in primary and secondary schools. The text was to be submitted for comments before publication to teachers in countries in Asia, Africa and Latin America with a view to completion in 1962. The first task, as Benoît Brouillette wrote in his Foreword to the publication of 1965, was to decide on the function of what came to be called a 'source book'.

> Should the book try directly to show how geography helps to improve relations between peoples or, alternatively, to give teachers practical advice on how to improve their teaching methods?

The second option was chosen in the belief that geography could not possibly achieve the first objective unless it were well taught.

Among other discussions which took place on the text of the source book was one in Bangkok in March 1962 held in co-ordination with the IGU Regional Conference in Kuala Lumpur and Singapore. The need for an essentially practical, rather than a theoretical, book was urged. Perhaps of even more long reaching effect was the suggestion that what was needed was 'a regional textbook produced by geographers well acquainted with local problems'.

Looking again at the *Unesco Source Book for Geography Teaching* which was eventually published in French, English and Spanish in 1965 (Unesco, 1965), one is struck particularly by the practical recommendations, notably in the two substantial chapters by Norman Graves on 'Teaching techniques: observation and indirect observation'. Clearly his influence in the Commission was already strong. However, according to Graves (1976b), it was Brouillette who was primarily responsible for the production of the Source Book.

One other development of the period 1960-64 should be mentioned. The Chairman of the Commission, Benoît Brouillette, had contributed in 1961 a paper on 'La place de la géographie dans un enseignement adapté à l'époque moderne' (Brouillette, 1961). Unesco was interested in a programme of studies, comparable to what became the Source Book but adapted to the special needs of certain major regions. The Commission was, especially with the experience of its Bangkok meeting in 1962, to become heavily involved in this project.

This became a major aim of the Commission established again at the 20th Congress in London, 1964. The Commission's meeting in London was especially notable for its practical emphasis on teaching problems and resources and on field studies (Brown , 1967). New members were Nafis Ahmad (Dacca), Shokei Birukawa (Tokyo), S.V. Kalesnik

(Leningrad) and H.J. Warman (Clark University). Tom Brown continued as the British member though he was shortly to move to a post in Kenya. Once again, the new Commission was swiftly at work, planning in Paris, in December 1964, a colloquium on the place of geography in the economic development of African countries with, as a subsequent activity, discussions with geographers in North Africa, Tropical Africa and, possibly, other parts of the continent. Looking ahead to the planned Regional Conference in Mexico City, 1966, the Commission saw this as an opportunity to carry its 'regional' work into Latin America. Meanwhile in order to facilitate reciprocal studies, three sub-committees of the Commission were authorized to work in and from Great Britain, USA and Canada, and Panama (IGU *Bulletin* XVI, 2, 1965, 96-97). Norman Graves, it must be mentioned, was, together with Gladys Hickman, directly involved in these discussions.

Plans for the African colloquium matured in December 1965 with a meeting in Addis Ababa where the organization owed much to the work of G.C. Last who had had wide experience of teacher training in Ethiopia. A plan for a manual suitable for teaching objectives and conditions in Africa was devised. A practical outcome was the creation of a Centre for Geographical Documentation in Addis Ababa.

Less than two years later, in 1967, a colloquium of Latin American geographers, held in Santiago, discussed the possible preparation of a manual adapted to conditions in that continent. Meanwhile, progress had been made in collating material for the African volume though, as a review of the situation at Montpellier in July 1967 showed, much remained to be done. A further colloquium was held at Accra in September 1967. A proposal for an initiative in southern and south-east Asia was also under consideration (IGU *Bulletin XIX* (2), 1968, 37-41).

So, by 1968, the Source Book had been produced and widely discussed and the plans for adapting its ideas and approaches to conditions in Africa, Latin America and Asia were making progress. The problems of teaching geography in schools in the developing world had been widely explored and a report issued.

Progress of the Commission, 1968-1972

A vigorous review of all IGU Commissions took place at the 21st Congress in New Delhi 1968. The Commission on the Teaching of Geography in Schools was replaced by a Commission on Geography in Education with wider terms of reference. The Commission was asked

> to study and improve the world-wide status of geography at all levels, not only in schools and universities, but also in adult education, mass media, newspapers, radio, television and cinema. (IGU *Bulletin* XX, 2, 1969, 18-19)

Ferdinando (Dino) Gribaudi (Turin) became Chairman, with Benoît Brouillette as Secretary. New members were appointed including Norman Graves (London), Professor A.R. Irawathy (Madras), Professor K. Ivanicka (Bratislava) and Professor J. Vilà Valentí (Barcelona). Gribaudi, a much loved figure in international geography, died, alas, in January 1971 and Brouillette resumed the Chairmanship.

To undertake its widened terms of reference the Commission established three sub-commissions, one of which, on the teaching of geography in schools, carried on actively the plans of the previous commission. An important review of the objectives of the Commission was initiated by Gribaudi and discussed at the Rome meeting in June 1970. Gribaudi outlined a number of important developments in society and education, including the advent of more general access to education, technical change and new methods of communication, the emphasis on economic development and education as an investment, the increasing awareness of ethical and moral issues and the transference of the focus of instruction from the community to the individual. Geography teaching, he argued, must adapt, especially at the secondary level. He also attempted to indicate how, as an educational discipline, geography contributed to desirable skills and abilities, e.g. study of the true meaning of space, skill in locating phenomena with precision, the search for relationships, stimulus towards mental adventure and research, humility in the face of nature's grandeur and strength (IGU *Bulletin XXIII* (1), 1972, 23).

Another important discussion on aims took place in Budapest in August 1971 when Clyde Kohn and others successfully proposed a resolution calling for progress in developing common learning materials on

> environment-man relationships, including resource management, air and water pollution and other issues arising from the interrelations of the human natural environment and from activity components of the world ecosystem.

Changes in the Commission's thinking about the aims and objectives of geography teaching may thus be discerned; among them a more sophisticated approach to 'environment' relationships embracing systems concepts and the investigation of 'spatial' questions.

Meanwhile, the previously planned meeting of geographers from

Arab countries was held in Cairo in December/January 1968-69. A further meeting of African geographers took place in Yaoundé in July 1970. Work on the Unesco Source Book on Africa was by now almost completed. A third regional meeting for the Latin American project in Mexico, November 1970, made progress in critical study of draft chapters for the Source Book on Latin America, and also defined, as a new task, the preparation of a geographical vocabulary in Spanish and Portuguese. To the six languages into which the 1965 Unesco Source Book had been translated were added Hindi, Polish and Slovene.

Despite the widened terms of reference the emphasis in the Commission's work continued to be on teaching in schools, though it must be mentioned that in Bratislava in August 1971 the problems of innovation in geography at the university level were put under active review. The British sub-committee was the most active of the national sub-committees meeting twice a year with Norman Graves as convener.

The Commission, 1972-1980

These were the years of Norman Graves' Chairmanship. The Commission had been reappointed at the 22nd Congress in Montreal 1982 with much more specific terms of reference which, with one exception relating to the education of geographers as planners, were related to geographical education at school level and the continuation of studies in collaboration with Unesco. Brouillette, Ivanicka and Vilà Valentí were joined in membership by Clyde Kohn (Iowa) and Mrs S.E. Teo of Singapore. Seven working groups were quickly formed:

A to continue work on the Latin American Source Book;
B to start work on a bibliography of the geography of education;
C to continue studies on learning problems in geographical education at pre-university level;
D to develop work on objectives in geographical education;
E to initiate work on the contribution of geography to environmental education;
F to promote international collaboration on map work exercises;
G to undertake a comparative study of the education of geographers as planners. (IGU *Bulletin XXIV* (1/2) 1973, 33, 44-46)

Progress was made quickly in organizing discussion on the special problems of teaching geography in South-East Asia: a meeting in Singapore in September 1972, followed by a workshop in Sydney a year later, identified the tasks to be undertaken and set up plans for the production of teaching units. A third workshop was held in Delhi in

1974. The Source Book on the geography of Latin America was completed (Vilà Valentí, 1975) and progress made on the Vocabulario de Términos Geográficos (3000 terms). The bibliography of the geography of education was drafted by G. Hones, R. Ryba and others. J.P. Stoltman had initiated a programme of research on students' perceptions of geography teachers' teaching styles.

Significant for the future was a meeting at Aix-en-Provence in July/August 1973 to consider the preparation of a new edition of the *Unesco Source Book for Geography*. The question was again raised how geography teaching might help to foster international understanding. It was also thought that population problems, economic and social development and environmental education deserved more attention than had been given in the 1965 edition. How could the educational objectives of geographical education be redefined? Four points were agreed:

> (a) the demonstration that some of the common problems of mankind could find different solutions in different cultural contexts, leading to an appreciation and tolerance of different cultures;
> (b) that environmental considerations were important in all economic development and therefore that students should become aware of the problems of ecological equilibrium and of the social costs of economic development as well as of aesthetic considerations;
> (c) that the social and economic behaviour of man resulted in certain spatial patterns and arrangements which were dynamic and therefore evolving: that students should therefore be made aware of spatial distribution, spatial interaction, and spatial diffusion;
> (d) demonstration that the nature and solution of the spatial aspects of problems depended on the scale at which these were considered. (IGU *Bulletin XXV* (1) 1974, 14-15)

Clearly this was a more finely analysed treatment of the subject's contribution to international understanding than that with which the original commission had begun its work in 1952, reflecting both the changes that had taken place in the subject itself and the experience gained from the regional meetings. It was also agreed that the new edition should reflect developments in educational thought especially on children's mental development, curriculum development, classroom strategies, and evaluation of learning and teaching.

Graves remained as Chairman on the reappointment of the Commission at the 23rd Congress in Moscow in 1976. New members were Professor J.P. Stoltman (Western Michigan), Dr P.O. Okunrotifa

(Ibadan), Professor V. Maksakovsky (Moscow), Professor R. Geipel (Munich) and Professor Paul Claval (Paris). Vilà-Valentí remained a member. The name of Benoît Brouillette disappeared from the list. He had been involved, as consultant, member, secretary and chairman, since 1952 and his record of energy and initiative deserves special mention. From the reports published in IGU *Bulletins* some changes in emphasis in the Commission's work are to be detected. Certainly a closer interest developed in educational research and in its application to the field of geography. An example of this trend is offered by the conference in London in March/April 1978 on the geography curriculum for the 16-19 age group. There was greater interest in the Geography/Psychology interface (Stoltman), in perception problems (Slater) and in the use of models in the transmission of geographical information (Verduin-Muller). A further new development was a plan (with the IGU Population Geography Commission) for a project with Unesco on population education (Graves, 1975b).

Earlier activities continued with varying success. A successful regional meeting was held in Ibadan at the time of the IGU Regional Conference in 1978. Less happily, little progress was made on the *Vocabulario de Términos Geográficos* but Dr J. Barth (Federal Republic of Germany) had begun work on a *Multi-Lingual Dictionary of Terms used in Geographical Education*. There was also progress in elucidating the contribution of geography within social studies programmes (IGU *Bulletin XXX* (1/2) 1979, 97-98; *XXXI* (1/2) 1980, 7-9). Work on what was eventually published in 1982 as the *New Unesco Source Book for Geography Teaching* (Graves, 1982h) was completed. Comparison with its predecessor reveals many changes in attitudes and approaches and reflects the new attitudes of the Commission referred to above. As illustrations, the chapters on 'Mental development and the learning of geography' (Naish), 'Approaches to teaching and learning strategies' (Robert), 'Real problem-solving' (Kohn), 'Gathering and processing information' (Okunrotifa), and 'Evaluation of geographical education' (Graves) may be referred to, though there are others. What was displayed was a much closer relationship between developing thought in and about geography and the products of educational research.

Progress since 1980

Having completed two successful periods as Chairman, Norman Graves stood down at the 24th International Geographical Congress in Tokyo, 1980, while remaining a member. Joseph Stoltman (Western

Michigan) became Chairman and the new members were Mme. Lucile Marbeau (Paris), Dr Livia Oliveira (Brazil), Julio de Mesquito (São Paulo), Dr Anthony Milne (Sydney), Dr Henriette Verduin-Muller (Utrecht) and Dr Octavian Mandrut (Romania). Professor Masakovskiy (Moscow) remained from the previous Commission. Since that time work has continued actively and there have been a number of interesting developments. The Commission sponsored an international conference on computer assisted learning in London, in April 1983, a meeting of considerable practical value. Links with the Geographical Association have resulted in the growth of an international network of exchange on computer assisted learning. The Commission's interest in information and documentation was maintained through a meeting in Utrecht in August 1984. Work has also been carried out in collaboration with the Committee on the Teaching of Science of the International Council of Scientific Unions and Norman Graves served as Chairman of the team assigned to write prototype teaching units on land, water and mineral Resources (IGU *Bulletin, XXXIV* (1/2), 1984, 18-19).

The Commission was reappointed at the 25th International Congress in Paris, 1984, with Joseph Stoltman continuing in the Chair. New members included Dr Hartwig Haubrich (Freiburg), Dr Suresh Garsole (Pune, India), and Mr Michael Naish (thereby continuing the link with the Institute of Education, London, so firmly established by Professor Graves). In addition to its general purpose of 'enhancing the teaching of geography internationally at the elementary, secondary and tertiary levels', the Commission indicated certain special goals. It was concerned to make research information on the teaching of the subject widely available; to recommend new directions in the teaching, and the study of the teaching, of the subject; to ensure that practical ways were found of translating research developments in scientific geography to classroom levels; and to develop through workshops and other means effective use of textual, visual and electronic media for classroom use.

A vigorous symposium was held at Barcelona, August 1986. Translation of the *New Unesco Source Book* into Russian was reported. Commission members and associates have continued to publish widely, especially in the fields of computer assisted learning, teaching methods and the scientific content of geography instruction. A major new development has been the Global Geography Project carried out in affiliation with the Agency for Instructional Technology, Bloomington, Indiana. This video film project has completed the production of teaching materials on issues of geographical significance in ten countries with additional comparative material. The recordings allow for adaptation to different languages and technical systems. The Commission has also established an *ad hoc* committee on thematic maps, under the leadership of Professor J.T. Coppock (Edinburgh) which is enquiring into the production of a series of maps, in conjunction with the International Council of Scientific Unions, to disseminate widely essential geographical distributions (IGU *Bulletin XXXVI*, 1986; *XXVIII* (1/2), 1988, 7-9).

So the work of encouraging internationally the teaching of geography continues. At the 26th Congress in Sydney in 1988 the Commission was again re-established, now under the Chairmanship of Dr Haubrich (Germany). An ambitious programme is planned and we wish the Commission well in its future activities.

Concluding remarks

It will be seen that, over time, the aims and objectives of the Commission have changed. The early emphasis on the lowly place of the subject in education and on rectifying the obsolete nature of concepts and teaching methods has given place to an emphasis on the educational strength of the subject and to positive demonstrations, through the Source Books, of the vitality of the subject, of its value as an educational discipline and of its possible applications. Good teaching techniques have been devised and disseminated; advice has been given on the resources that are necessary and how they may best be used. Research has been carried out and the results made known widely. The results of relevant educational research have been brought to the attention of geographers and *vice versa*. The change in the Commission's attitudes is well indicated by a comparison of the *Source Books* of 1965 and 1982, the former more prescriptive and didactic, the latter better founded in educational research and more advisory and suggestive. It is also worth noting the ways in which the Commission has appreciated changes in geographical thought and translated these into teaching possibilities.

Emrys Jones, in an essay reviewing progress in human geography 1952-77, referred to the problems in geography of thinking and conducting research on the world scale while also continuing to study the diversity of regional, national and local conditions. 'Geographers', he remarked 'should try and distinguish carefully between what is universal in their thinking and what is culture-specific ' (Jones, 1979). Over time, the Commission has faced this problem, testing its general propositions against regional gatherings of geographers, and producing regional source books which, while maintaining the universal approach, reflect the differing characteristics and provide for the needs of schools in various regional settings.

This summary review of the Commission's work hides, perhaps, some of the problems and constraints under which IGU Commissions work. The Union, though in number of member countries the largest of the members of the International Council of Scientific Unions, is also probably the poorest. Only very small funds can be allocated to individual commissions. The Commission on Education has been successful in its liaison with other international organizations and has obtained funds particularly from Unesco, though often in return for contracted tasks. Time and energy must be given by a Chairman of a Commission to raising funds and to allocating them in the most fruitful way amongst competing activities. The success of international collaborative efforts such as we have been reviewing depends greatly upon the initiative and voluntary work of individual scholars willing to give time to the international organization of scientific efforts and to inspiring a commonality of purpose in colleagues from different lands and from varied traditions. The tasks of overcoming barriers of distance and language in pursuit of common aims require patience and diplomacy; the ability to appreciate points of view arising from traditions other than one's own. Such work brings meaning to the cause of international understanding. It requires vision and hard work. Well done, it brings great satisfaction.

The tasks of inspiring the best standards of geography teaching and disseminating them in suitable forms world-wide is a continuing one. It is relatively straightforward to teach those eager and willing to learn: a more difficult task to reach to those areas and teachers, both within countries and in many parts of the world, who for reasons sometimes beyond their own control (distance, inaccessibility, lack of resources) do not receive the messages and impulses. The Commission attracts to its meetings participants from a large number of countries but that number is still small in relation to the total membership of IGU. Much of the material published or circulated stems from centres in Western Europe and North America together with a limited number of institutions elsewhere. In many countries of the developing world communications are imperfect and it is not always easy to obtain books and papers published elsewhere or to get to know about them. The Commission has used Unesco's distributive system; its regional conferences and Source Books have been another answer to this problem. It has recently brought technology to its aid but there are large areas of the world without the technical facilities to employ visual aids, as they are thought of in the developed world.

The world changes quickly: problems of the environment, resource availability, population growth, urbanization, poverty, famine and flood increase in severity and achieve greater international awareness. It is a hundred years since Kropotkin (1885) argued the case for the study of geography as a key to international understanding; half a century since Fairgrieve's call. There is lost time to be made up: it is a race to keep up with the pace of change both in scientific knowledge and in changing geographical conditions; millions of minds have to be reached. There are signs of progress, especially in public awareness of environmental issues.

In this cause the Commission has done outstanding work and deserves the fullest possible support from geographers everywhere. This can be given not merely in terms of the increased resources which it deserves but in interest, in reading and thinking about its publications, in attending its meetings, in spreading discussion of its ideas. All those who have taken part in its work deserve our best thanks: more especially, on this occasion, we can rejoice in having had in our midst in Britain a man such as Norman Graves who has, over so many years, freely given his time, organizing skill, linguistic ability, research endeavour and personal qualities of leadership to the task of building international geographical understanding in the field of education.

Chapter Sixteen
An Australian Example: a case study of curriculum change
D.S. Biddle

The purpose of this chapter is to describe and analyse the changes which have occurred in the development and implementation of three senior secondary school geography syllabuses in New South Wales, Australia; the first syllabus being implemented in 1955 and the third in 1988. These three syllabuses illustrate the considerable changes which have occurred, over a period of 33 years, in the decision-making process and in the curriculum process.

There have been frequent changes in the decision making process, between the 1950s and the 1980s, for the development and implementation of senior secondary school geography syllabuses in New South Wales. Some of these changes have been politically motivated while others have been a reflection of the improvement, among teachers, in their educational qualifications, paticularly their knowledge of the curriculum process, which led them to demand representation on syllabus committees and boards of studies.

In investigating the curriculum process attention has been directed to changes in the organization of syllabus documents; in the conceptual frameworks used to provide structures for geography courses; and in the methods of assessing student performance.

The syllabuses selected for this study were geography courses taught in the senior secondary schools for more than thirty years. The first *Syllabus in Geography* was promulgated by the Board of Secondary School Studies in 1954 and introduced into schools in New South Wales in 1955. This syllabus was replaced by *Geography Syllabus, Forms 5 and 6, First, Second and Third Levels*, promulgated by the Board of Senior School Studies in 1965 and implemented in 1966. The third, *Geography*

Syllabus Years 11-12, was promulgated by the Board of Secondary Education in 1987 and implemented in 1988. There have been radical changes in the decision making process and in the curriculum process used to formulate these three syllabuses.

Syllabus in geography, 1954

Decision making process

This *Syllabus in Geography* was formulated by the Chief Examiner for the Leaving Certificate Examination assisted by the Chief Examiner for the Intermediate Certificate Examination and an Inspector of Schools who was the Assessor for the examination papers set by the chief examiners. At this time there were no teacher representatives, or other representatives, to assist the chief examiners in the preparation of the syllabus, or the setting of examination papers, apart from the education department representative, who was secondary school inspector with little or no tertiary qualification in geography.

The Chief Examiner for the Leaving Certificate Examination was responsible to the Board of Secondary School Studies for the formulation of the syllabus; the setting and marking of the examination papers; and advice about instructional resources, such as reference books.

During the planning of this syllabus the chief examiner contacted many teachers in the State to obtain their views on the types of topics that would interest their students. He was at a disadvantage, however, since syllabus construction was done under strict security regulations. When the syllabus was completed it was submitted for approval to the Board of Secondary Studies. The nature and content of the syllabus remained confidential until it was forwarded to teachers for implementation.

The system appears to have been developed so that the Head of the Geography Department at the University of Sydney had complete control of the geography courses taught in secondary schools. This also applied to all other academic subject syllabuses in the secondary school curriculum. The reason for confidentiality given by the Minister of Education was that the government did not want publishers to produce school textbooks on the course until it was finalized and approved by the Board. There was a lucrative market for publishers at this time because it was possible to cover the whole of each year of the course with one textbook (e.g. Ford and Rowe, 1956, 1958). The second major reason given was that the Department of Education did not want radical minority groups creating controversy about the syllabus content, because it could cause costly delays in the implementation of the course and might produce stress and uncertainty among the majority of teachers, whose principal concern was to obtain the highest marks possible for their students at the external examination.

Curriculum process

This was the first secondary school geography syllabus in Australia to contain a preface with stated aims and a suggested methodology for teaching the course effectively. To quote from the Preface:

> The courses has been formulated on the assumption that the purpose of teaching geography in the secondary school is to give the student:
> (a) an appreciation of the varied aspects of the face of the earth;
> (b) some understanding of the interrelationships between natural conditions and human activities;
> (c) a recognition of a world pattern of geographical environments;
> (d) a knowledge of the regional geography of his own country; and
> (e) a knowledge of the geography of other countries which occupy significant places in the present international scene. (Board of Secondary School Studies, New South Wales, 1954, 1).

The next section of the Preface referred to the development of informed attitudes; to the value of the course in educating students to enjoy their environment and in encouraging them to visit other environments; and the development of understanding of people's problems in a variety of environments.

The final section contained some suggestions on teaching strategies to assist teachers to retain the interest of students. Briefly, the strategies described in detail were the study of the local area; the use of sample studies; the use of active methods such as field work and practical work; the discussion of the geographical background to current events; and developing the reading and interpretation of various types of maps (Board of Secondary School Studies, 1954, 2).

The conceptual frameworks used to structure the syllabus were based on Herbertson's natural regions, particularly in the first semester of Year 4 (Herbertson, 1905) and Unstead's geographical regions in the second semester of Year 4 and in Year 5 (Unstead, 1916). The concept of natural regions is clearly stated in the introduction to the syllabus:

> This course is concerned with the regional geography of the continents, particularly with the ways in which man has utilized the physical and biotic

environment for winning a livelihood. It is suggested that attention should first be given to Africa and South America in both of which the regional pattern and the human response are comparatively simple.
(Board of Secondary School Studies, 1954, 7)

In the second semester of Year 4 more emphasis was placed on mineral and energy resources and the factors affecting the location of manufacturing industries in North America. In Year 5 urbanization and the functions of towns and cities were emphasized in Eurasia and the study of Australia was intended to co-ordinate the systematic studies completed for the other continents into a synthesis of regions using Herbertson's natural regions approach, where physical and biotic elements were considered dominant, and Unstead's geographical regions, where sociocultural elements, of 'man's' impact on the landscape, were prominent. Figure 16.1 shows the structure of the syllabus in geography for Fourth and Fifth Years in 1954.

REGIONAL GEOGRAPHY OF CONTINENTS

Aims of syllabus stated in Preface.

FOURTH YEAR:	1. Africa 2. South America	Semester 1
	3. North America	Semester 2
FIFTH YEAR:	4. Eurasia	Semester 3
	5. Australasia	Semester 4

General systematic geography, local area studies, current affairs, map reading and interpretation to be studied, when appropriate, with each of the continents.

LEAVING CERTIFICATE EXAMINATION

Figure 16.1: Syllabus in Geography 1954, Leaving Certificate
(source: Board of Secondary School Studies, New South Wales, 1954).

The major influences on the chief examiners when selecting the conceptual framework for this syllabus, were the Unesco publication, *A*

Handbook of Suggestions on the Teaching of Geography (Scarfe, 1951), *Geography in Secondary Schools* (Scottish Education Department, 1951), and world regional textbooks published in the United Kingdom.

The only assistance given to teachers in interpreting this syllabus was provided by the chief examiner who prepared a four page pamphlet (Andrews, 1959). Each year this was supplemented by brief examiner's comments which were made available to geography teachers six or more months after the annual examination results were published in January.

The method used for assessing student performance was the traditional essay-type examination with no recognition of school assessments during the year. The examination papers were marked by the chief examiner and a team of university specialists in geography who were required to plot the marks they awarded on graph paper so that the chief examiner could check their distribution of marks against other examiners and make adjustments to the final results obtained by the students. Papers were collected from the chief examiner and usually marked by the examiners in their university studies. The marked responses plus a record of results were returned to the chief examiner who corrected and collated them before forwarding them to the Board of Secondary School Studies.

The reason that this syllabus was changed in 1965 was not because teachers were discontented with the regional approach but because of the political pressures to change the rationale and structure of secondary education in New South Wales.

Geography syllabus, Forms 5 and 6, first, second and third levels, 1965.

Decision making process

This syllabus was formulated by a Geography Syllabus Committee consisting of nine university and teachers' college lecturers, eight secondary geography teachers from government and private schools, two geography inspectors of schools, and one teacher from technical and further education. The Chairman of the Syllabus Committee and the Examining Panel had to be a professor of geography selected from one of the nine lecturers. The chairman was responsible to the Board of Senior School Studies, which with the Secondary Schools Board, replaced the Board of Secondary School Studies in 1965. This was a significant change in representation for teachers although, because of their numbers and status, university and teachers' college lecturers still dominated discussions in committee.

The Board of Senior School Studies was responsible for implementing the aims of secondary education accepted by the State Government with the adoption of the recommendations of the Wyndham Report (Wyndham, 1957). They achieved this by forwarding instructions to syllabus committees requiring them to implement these aims through the topics in their particular syllabus (Board of Senior School Studies, 1963).

The Geography Syllabus Committee appointed a sub-committee for four university specialists in aspects of geography, one geography teacher educator and two senior geography teachers to prepare a draft syllabus. Before their first meeting the sub-committee carried out a sample survey of teachers inviting them to analyse critically the previous syllabus and suggest revisions for a new course. This information was collated and proved valuable to the committee.

The first meeting of the sub-committee was concerned with the selection of general aims and the more specific educational objectives. This was followed by a discussion on possible conceptual frameworks for structuring the syllabus, or syllabuses. After the conceptual framework was selected the university specialists were given the task of identifying the appropriate content topics.

At the following sub-committee meeting a syllabus document, containing content and suggested examination questions for each level, was prepared for consideration by the Geography Syllabus Committee. The meetings of the total committee were long and frequent heated discussions occurred because of the radical changes in the course proposed, but eventually three syllabuses were forwarded to the Board of Senior School Studies and these were adopted and implemented.

Curriculum process

This was the first time, since 1911, that members of syllabus committees in New South Wales were provided with a statement on the purposes of secondary education and directed to produce a syllabus to implement these purposes. As a result the Preface to the 1965 senior geography syllabus contained a preamble commenting on the contribution that the study of geography could make to the general education of students.

The second section consisted of educational objectives summarized under comprehension, attitudes and skills. The third section provided suggestions on the precentage of time required for each part of the course which was divided into physical, social and economic, and regional geography. Figure 16.2 shows the structure of the geography syllabus for Forms 5 and 6 in 1965.

PART A: PHYSICAL GEOGRAPHY

Section 1 The water cycle
Section 2 Water as an agent of weathering and sculpture
Section 3 Water and the world pattern of climate and vegetation
Section 4 Water and man

PART B: SOCIAL AND ECONOMIC GEOGRAPHY

Section 1 Agricultural geography
Section 2 The geography of manufacturing
Section 3 Urban geography

PART C: REGIONAL GEOGRAPHY

Combination of the characteristics discussed in Parts A and B to produce distinctive regional characteristics in Australia or New Zealand and one other area.

Figure 16.2: Geography Syllabus in Forms 5 and 6, 1965, First, Second and Third Levels, Higher School Certificate
(source: Board of Senior School Studies, New South Wales, 1965).

The conceptual framework in which the content of this syllabus was organized was influenced by the Madingley Lectures published in *Frontiers in Geography Teaching* (Chorley and Haggett, 1965). The Chairman of the Syllabus Committee, Professor George Dury, had attended these lectures in 1963. He was critical of the previous geography syllabus because it was based on archaic theories and outmoded concepts and methodologies to the extent that students completing the syllabus were at a disadvantage when they entered university because they had to unlearn many of the facts and concepts learned at school.

Dury proposed a systems model as the basis for developing a geography course because it provided a means of demonstrating linkages among features and places in geography and emphasized integration of process and product rather than fragmentation of physical and human processes in geographical studies.

These concepts, however, were not well known to many of the members of the syllabus committee, so a decision was made to develop a syllabus based on a conceptual model of the scope of geography which could be modified, over a period of five years, to fit into a systems approach when teachers learned more about systems theory through conferences and in-service courses.

The scope of geography model used emphasized systematic geography more than regional geography. This emphasis on systematic geography and the changes in theory and practice in geographical studies were radical changes from the content and methods used in the continental regional syllabus it replaced. Consequently, the members of the syllabus committee decided that, in order to ensure that the new course was implemented successfully, a number of approaches would have to be used for the diffusion of information about the course throughout the State education system. This was achieved through the co-operation of the geography departments in the universities, teachers' colleges, professional asssociations of geographers, a national newspaper and the publicity sections of the private and state school education systems.

A major change in the organization of the syllabus occurred in 1973. It was an outcome of changes required by the Board of Senior School Studies. The Board decided to change the organization of the school curriculum, based on three levels of difficulty for each subject, because teachers experienced problems when selecting the correct level for students. The new organization was based on a unit system: one unit in a course was equivalent to three forty minute lessons per week and was worth 50 marks in the external examination. Geography was given a two unit course with six lessons per week and a 3 Unit course with nine lessons per week.

The 1965 syllabus had emphasized integration although the course was divided, and examined in three parts, to ensure that students covered all parts. Many teachers were critical of this fragmentation because they had commenced using a systems approach to planning their programme. This provided the Syllabus Committee with the opportunity to introduce a systems model for the conceptual framework of the syllabus. The changes to the structure of the syllabus can be gauged by comparing Figure 16.2 with Figure 16.3 that shows the structure of the geography syllabus for Forms 5 and 6 in 1973. There were a number of minor revisions, mostly to reduce the study load for students, between 1973 and 1980.

THEME 1: THE WATER CYCLE

1. The water cycle as a system of water transfer
2. Systems associated with the water cycle with emphasis on
   either the wider system of weather and climate
   or the natural systems in terrestrial aspects of the water cycle.
3. The interaction of man and natural systems.

THEME 2: HUMAN ORGANISATION SYSTEMS

1. The operation of the workings and growth of human organisation systems.
2. Systems of production within the human ecosystem with emphasis on
   either agricultural systems
   or manufacturing systems
3. Urban systems

THEME 3: INTERACTING SYSTEMS

The synthesis of interacting systems in selected regions.

Figure 16.3: Geography Syllabus in Forms 5 and 6, 1973. 3 Unit Course and 2 Unit Course Higher School Certificate (source: Board of Senior School Studies, New South Wales, 1973)

Figure 16.4 shows the structure of the geography syllabus for Years 11 and 12 in 1980. Although there were few changes in the content in 1980 the organization of the syllabus document was quite different because the content was printed on the left-hand page and the explanatory notes were rewritten and included in the syllabus on the right-hand page. This syllabus operated with minor revisions and updating of content until 1988.

The changes which occurred in the assessment and evaluation of student's performance were more significant than the changes in content after 1973. The first external examination paper consisted of essay questions and a large choice was given to students. A major change was the introduction of the corporate marking system when 150 markers were congregated in the one room and all examination scripts were marked under supervision using a number of procedures to maintain reliability of marking (Biddle, 1971; Irwin 1982). An unexpected outcome of the corporate marking system was the annual evaluation of the course, types of assessment, and marking procedures

THEME 1: NATURAL SYSTEMS

1. *The Water Cycle*
   (a) General Study
   (b) Case Study

2. *Other Natural Systems*
   Emphasis on *either* (a) *or* (b)
   (a) Atmospheric systems and their effects
   (b) Terrestrial systems and their effects

3. *The Ecosystem*
   (a) The local region
   (b) Any other area(s)

THEME 2: HUMAN SYSTEMS

1. *Primary and Secondary Industry Systems*
   Emphasis on *either* (a) *or* (b)
   (a) Agricultural systems
   (b) Manufacturing systems

2. *Tertiary Industry Systems*

3. *Urban Systems*

THEME 3: THE SYNTHESIS OF HUMAN AND NATURAL SYSTEMS

1. *The Local Region*

2. *Other Regions*

Figure 16.4: Geography Syllabus in Years 11 and 12, 1980, 3 Unit and 2 Unit Courses Higher School Certificate (source: Board of Senior School Studies, New South Wales, 1980).

which occurred during discussions held at the end of the marking session.

It was during one of these discussions that teachers recommended the introduction of a broadsheet, in 1970, using various sources of data, including maps, to emphasize and assess the development of skill objectives to counter the effect of those teachers who were concentrating solely on the learning of content and essay-writing techniques. The introduction of the unit system in 1973 was much easier to implement than the levels system because students could study the two unit course for six periods per week or, if they were keen about geography, they could study the three unit course for nine periods per week. The two unit and three unit examination papers were separate papers with the latter being the more difficult. The maximum marks possible for the two unit was 100 and for the three unit examination 150.

The next change in the assessment procedures came in 1983 when a decision was made to require all students to sit for the two unit examination paper while those who wished to study at the three-unit level were required to sit for an additional three unit paper. Another major change was in the format of the examination papers which were: (a) the introduction of a compulsory question based on a wide range of skills used in geography; and (b) the reduction in the number of essay questions from 15 to 12. To assist teachers and reduce the concerns of students, specimen examination papers were distributed to secondary schools (Board of Senior School Studies, 1982).

The final change in assessment procedures for this syllabus occurred in 1986 when 50 per cent of the final marks awarded were internally assessed and 50 per cent were from the external examination. The internal assessment was moderated by the external results obtained by the students.

The decision to review Geography: Natural and Human Systems was taken in 1982 after the Board of Senior School Studies advised syllabus committees that the Year 12 course should be an entity in itself and that the external examination would be confined to this course rather than to the integrated Year 11 and 12 course.

The Geography Teachers' Association then organized meetings where teachers discussed alternative approaches to senior school geography courses. The general view was that it was time to introduce a more humanistic approach which was supported in the 1980s by the nationalistic focus of the bicentennial celebrations and the frequent media reports on politicians who wanted more emphasis on Australian studies, aboriginal studies, women's studies and multiculutral education, none of which fitted comfortably into the systems approach.

Geography syllabus years 11-12: two unit and three unit course

Decision making process

This syllabus was formulated by a Geography Syllabus Committee consisting of fourteen teachers from government, private schools and the Geography Teachers' Association of New South Wales, two representatives of the Department of Education and eight university and college of advanced education lecturers in geography. The obvious change was that teachers were in the majority on this committee for the first time.

The chairperson, on behalf of the committee, was responsible to the Board of Secondary Education, which combined the functions of the Secondary Schools Board (Years 7-10) with the Board of Senior School Studies (Years 11-12), to implement the aims of secondary education and the social engineering policies of the government through the geography syllabus; to provide a syllabus in which the Year 11 course was distinct from the Year 12 course; to prepare specimen examination questions for Year 12: and to cater for students of varying levels of ability.

Curriculum process

The curriculum process used by the Geography Syllabus Committee took five years to complete. The committee decided that it would follow a process of continual consultation. It organized a questionnaire survey of teachers, articles by syllabus committee members in the *Geography Bulletin*, liaison with various interest groups, and conferences (Codrington, 1987, 77).

By 1986 they had produced a curriculum document rather than a syllabus, which included a preamble describing the course structure; educational aims in terms of knowledge, research skills, social skills, and the development of attitudes, values and feelings towards people-environment issues; a methodology consisting of active inquiry methods, and practice of cognitive and manipulative skills, fieldwork, and the preparation of a geography project; topic structures; the course outline; student assessment; and evaluation of the teaching programme (Board of Secondary Education, 1987). Other documents, prepared by the members of the syllabus committee and co-opted teachers, were concerned with planning topic programmes in Year 11 and included suggestions on programme outlines, examples of approaches to topics, teaching/learning strategies, and assessment guidelines. Some of the documents published were *Australians and their Biophysical Environment, The Australian Experience: Population and Employment*, and *Specimen Papers, Course Requirements and an Assessment Guide* (Board of Secondary Education, 1987).

The Syllabus consists of a common core based on the theme,

Australia in its World Context, to be studied in Year 11, and a choice of one of two lobes, Global Environments and Australia's Neighbours to be studied in Year 12. Both Year 12 lobes consist of core topics and options. Two pages are devoted to each topic in the Syllabus. On each left hand side page there is a statement of topic objectives, a topic summary, and topic generalizations. On the right hand side page is the topic expansion which specifies in some detail the extent of the subject matter and the requirement to complete one or more sample studies, and/or a major study, or a comparative study (Ralph, 1988, 12-14). The conceptual framework selected was the environment, person-environment interactions at various levels of complexity, at different scales, and changing over time. The course structure was developed from this framework keeping in mind the constraints imposed by the Board of Studies. Figure 16.5 shows the structure of the geography syllabus for Years 11 and 12 in 1987.

When considering Year 12 members of the syllabus committee were influenced by the curriculum framework used in the Geography 16-19 Curriculum Development Project (Schools Council, 1979; Naish, 1985a). A comparison of the outline of this syllabus (Naish, 1985a, 111) with the Year 12 course outline (see Figure 16.5) illustrates the similarities in the approach although the Australian example has fewer choices.

The first external examination for this syllabus was held in 1989. The external examination paper for the two-unit course was divided into a skills section (25 marks), core lobe (50) and option (25); the three-unit paper contained two option topics (25 marks each). It was assessed internally 100 per cent and externally 100 per cent with the first mark moderated by the second and both marks were included on the Higher School Certificate. The corporate marking system was used to mark the examination scripts.

Conclusion

This investigation of the desicion making process and curriculum process of three syllabuses in New South Wales indicates that progress has been made and continues to be made because:

1. the development and implementation of secondary school geography courses have moved from control by tertiary education specialists to teachers in the schools;

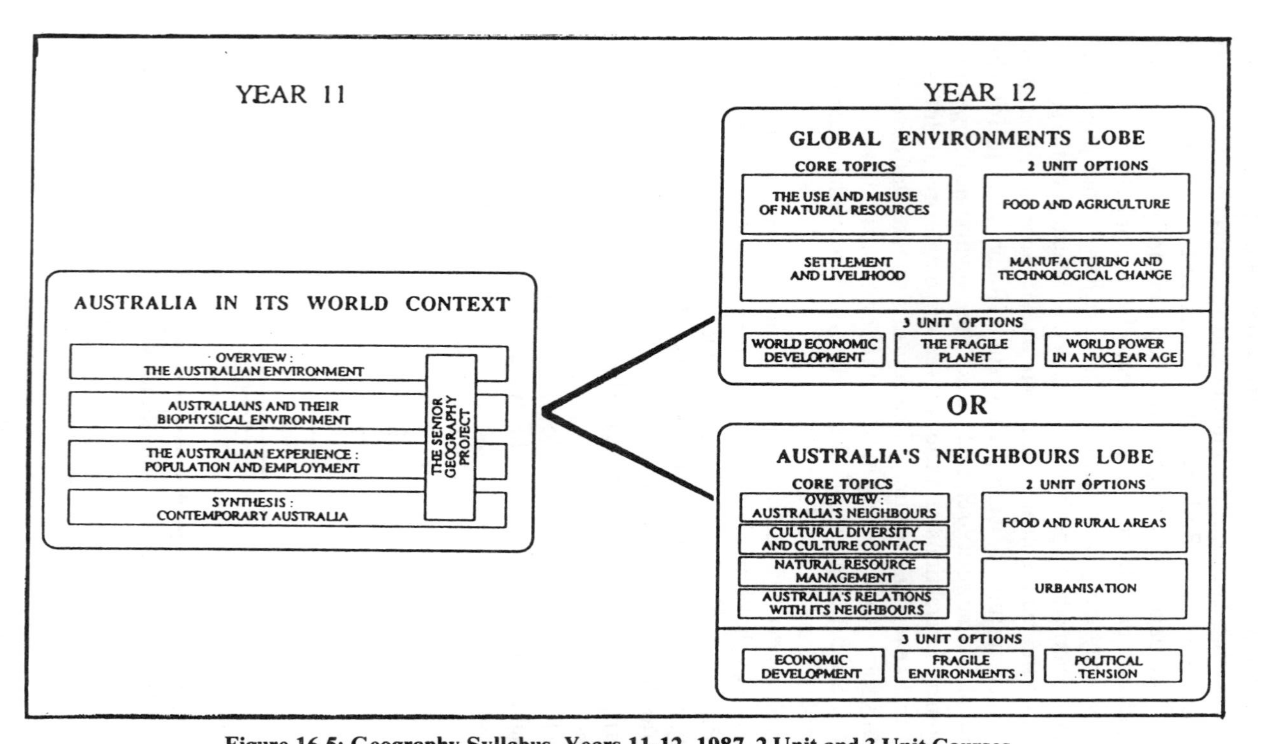

Figure 16.5: Geography Syllabus, Years 11-12, 1987, 2 Unit and 3 Unit Courses, Higher School Certificate (source: Board of Secondary Education, New South Wales, 1987)

2. the curriculum development process has become one of continual consultation with teachers, student specialists in geography, parents and other interested groups rather than one restricted to confidential decision making by university personnel and inspectors of schools.

3. the members of Boards of Studies are prepared to accept a syllabus document which is more in keeping with modern curriculum theory and practice;

4. syllabus topics are being selected which are suitable and relevant to students of varying levels of ability;

5. far more emphasis is being placed on development of attitudes, values and feelings towards community issues;

6. particular emphasis is being given to the development of research skills and social skills; and

7. techniques of assessing students' performance are being refined over time to provide more reliable results for students.

Geography teachers in New South Wales believe that the changes in curriculum development and implementation, which have occurred since the 1950s, have provided more interesting and relevant courses and more reliable assessment procedures for their students and have enhanced their professional status in the community.

Chapter Seventeen
Geographic Education in the United States: the renaissance of the 1980s
Joseph P. Stoltman

The United States is undergoing a renaissance in geographic education. Since 1983, political leaders, teachers, professional geographers, students and societies of geographers have become engaged in a major revitalization of the discipline within the curriculum. While somewhat spontaneous in its emergence, there were a number of underlying circumstances that presented compelling arguments for a renaissance of the discipline, as well as a number of developments that prompted its resurgence. Ten of the significant developments that either led to or which have contributed to a continuation of the renaissance in geographic education are presented in this chapter.

Outlook bright

At the end of the 1980s decade, geography in American schools has a brighter outlook and more promising future than at any time during the present century. It hasn't always been that way. Generally speaking, geography has occupied a surprisingly insignificant position in pre-collegiate education in the United States during the past fifty years (Natoli, 1986). While numerous factors attributed to the demise of geography in the schools, the absence of a proactive role by professional and academic societies of geographers was partly responsible. Curriculum movements in the United States through the 1970s, including the High School Geography Project, did little to restore geography to a prominent role in the schools of the nation. However, in the 1980s attention began to refocus upon geography and its role in the education of American youth. By 1983 there were a series of initiatives by professional and academic societies and individual geographers that focused attention upon the discipline. This chapter will present and briefly discuss what the author believes to be ten significant developments of the 1980s that have resulted in a renaissance in geography teaching at the school level.

Significant developments

First, it is necessary to explain the criteria used to determine a significant development. For the purposes of this chapter, it is a development that occurs either within or outside the parameters of geographic education, extends to a wide audience, has implications for school curricula across the country, and is important to the way geography is viewed in the larger educational context of society and presented in the schools. Those implications range from attracting the attention of policy makers in the educational arena to providing guidance and choices for curriculum planners, classroom teachers, and students.

Significant development 1.
In 1980, The Survey of Public Perceptions of Education, the twentieth annual survey using a scientifically selected, national sample of respondents, was completed by the Gallup Poll for Phi Delta Kappa. The survey contained a question directed toward the importance of a global geographic viewpoint. Approximately one-half of the respondents felt more time should be devoted to learning about other nations of the world and how people live (Gallup, 1980). The survey delivered a message from the American public. It clearly suggested that geography was recognized as an important element in a person's education.

Significant development 2.
The publication by the National Commission On Excellence in Education entitled *A Nation At Risk: the imperative for educational reform* (National Commission on Excellence in Education, 1983) sent shock waves through the ranks of public policy planners, whether politicians, civil servants, or educators, as well as the general citizenry of the country. In brief, the publication claimed that the educational attainments for a large proportion of citizens had regressed to a level where it presented serious threats to the basic fabric, including the

social, economic and participatory aspects of governance in the country. While the publication did not address geography specifically as a subject in the curriculum, inferences were made from collective data regarding the basic learning essential to the preparation of an educated citizenry. For example, more general recommendations were based on statistical data showing such trends as the following: during the period 1960-61, only 14 per cent of the students in grades 7 – 12 were enrolled in geography courses, a lower percentage than had been observed in previous periods during the century. However, by the mid-1970s the percentage had dropped to 9 per cent (Gardner, 1986). It should be noted that this steady decrease in attention to geography occurred during a period when enrolment in K – 12 schooling was increasing at a rapid rate. The result was that of the larger and larger numbers of students, fewer and fewer were studying geography.

Signficant Development 3.

While the inference regarding the lack of geographic knowledge among students in the United States was presented in *A Nation At Risk*, the actual documentation of the lack of geographic knowledge among the nation's school population began in earnest following publication of the volume. One popular approach to providing evidence regarding the low level of geographic knowledge was the administration of tests to students. Many of the tests were prepared without the benefit of scientific test development criteria, others had been developed and administered by different organizations in earlier decades, and still others had been prepared by organizations after a considerable investment in their design and development (Barrows, 1981; Pike and Barrows, 1979).

One observation from the large number of tests was clear. Regardless of the age levels of the students being tested, primary school through to university students, and despite the many weaknesses in the design of several of the testing instruments being used, the results obtained time and time again across the country were strikingly similar. Students in the United States, across the entire spectrum of education, were lacking in basic geographic knowledge, in the skills for interpretation of geographic information, and had little comprehension of the international aspects of the world and their place and role in that world (Hill, 1981).

The testing did two things. First, it verified the geographic illiteracy of the student segment of society, an illiteracy that has been frequently generalized to include older Americans as well. Second, the testing caught the interest of the media. For the remainder of the decade, newspapers, television, radio, and numerous magazines continued to feature reports and articles about how little knowledge Americans had about their country and the rest of the world. One of the unfortunate outcomes of the publicity was that, with few exceptions the media oriented reporting prior to 1987 did not address the questions, 'What can be done about the unsatisfactory state of geographic knowledge?' National and international comparative assessment studies continued through the 1980s, and provided additional information and data regarding geographical literacy. Those later studies, while adding insights to the problem in some instances, served a greater role as a media attraction and confirmation that little had changed since the assessment surveys of the earlier parts of the decade (Hill, 1981; National Geographic Society, 1988a; Rice, 1983). They did little to suggest how the problems of geographic illiteracy could be ameliorated other than by teaching more geography.

Significant development 4.
The United States educational system is reliant upon commercially published textbooks. Geography instruction is no exception, and the dependency upon textbooks is due in part of the manner in which the content is presented. Nearly all geography textbooks are four colour with a large selection of photo, map, and graphic visuals. Beginning in 1983, the publishers of social studies materials began to emphasize geography textbooks mainly for the first years of secondary school (junior high school or middle school) with students in those schools ranging from 12 to 14 years of age. By 1986 there were at least 11 geography textbooks designed specifically for that market. However, not all of them were newly written. Several carried 1976 copyright dates with subsequent reprintings, while others had been reprinted, but not seriously revised, for a considerable time. The trend continued and by 1988, there were 16 secondary textbooks available for consideration by teachers and book selection committees across the grade range seven to twelve (12 to 18 year olds). The *Journal of Geography* list of new or newly revised geography textbooks for the secondary school market confirmed the increased publishing activity (*Journal of Geography*, 1988a, 1988b).

Nearly all the secondary level geography textbooks published followed a regional format. World regional geography dominated the content design of secondary school textbooks, with the geography of a major segment of the world, such as the Eastern or Western Hemisphere, being used less often. While most texts employed a world regional approach, several incorporated issues analysis within the regions or important issues in geography with regional case studies.

While the importance of textbooks in geography teaching is always open to debate, the availability of newly published books gave two clear signals. First, the increased numbers of textbooks by publishers was a response to the information and media coverage regarding geographic illiteracy in the United States. Publishers predicted an increased demand for geography materials developing by the mid to late-1980s. This has been the case. Secondly, the marketing surveys that were carried out using curriculum guidelines from the various states suggested the demand would be in regional geography. It was widely recognized that state guidelines for curriculum and the availability of regional geography textbooks would greatly influence the renaissance in the discipline at the school level.

Significant development 5.

The publication of the *Guidelines for Geographic Education: Elementary and Secondary Schools* (Joint Committee on Geographic Education, 1984) presented clearly articulated themes and concepts to teachers and writers of instructional materials in geography and social studies. The *Guidelines* offered an essential focus for geography and suggested how the discipline could address the problems associated with the low level of geographic literacy. It was recognized that if gegoraphy within American education was to make progress, then it must present mainstream themes that the discipline could support with confidence, and that geographic educators in the schools and universities could pursue with imagination and vigour (Olmstead, 1987).

The fundamental themes presented in the *Guidelines* conceptualized content from geography that was of concern to teachers of geography and social studies at all levels. The concepts were presented in a fashion that made them workable in the curriculum. Furthermore, the *Guidelines* articulated many of the ideas embedded within instructional materials and developed those ideas explicitly for classroom teachers, curriculum developers, and school administrators. Many of those ideas had been incorporated within materials and used by classroom teachers, but had never been classified with the nomenclature of the discipline. While the five themes did not represent the only way to organize geography for instructional purposes, they did communicate the importance of organizing ideas that had application to the classroom. The themes were direct, comprehensible, and easy as well as interesting to apply. In short, the fundamental themes caught the attention of educators across the country. The themes represented a structure that was supported by professional geographers and teachers (Joint Committee on Geographic Education, 1984).

The five fundamental themes of geography proposed in the guidelines are as follows:

(i.) *Location: position on the earth's surface.* Absolute and relative location are two ways of describing the position of places on the earth's surface. In many situations it is important to identify absolute locations as precise points on the earth's surface. For instance, determining the precise position of fresh water supplies is critical to fulfilling the world's fresh water needs. Determining relative location – the position of one place with respect to other important places – is equally significant. If, for example, the position of fresh water supplies with respect to potential water users is too remote, then it will not be feasible to exploit these supplies.

(ii.) *Place: physical and human characteristics.* All places on earth have distinct physical and human characteristics that give them meaning and distinguish them from other places. The physical characteristics derive from the geological, hydrological, atmospheric, and biological processes that produce landforms, water bodies, climate, soils, natural vegetation, and animal life. Human ideas and actions also shape the character of places. Places vary in their population composition, as well as in their settlement patterns, architecture, kinds of economic and recreational activities, and transportation and communication networks. One place can be distinguished from another by the ideologies and philosophical or religious tenets of people who live there, by their languages, and by their forms of economic, social, and political organization. Taken together, the physical and human characteristics of places provide keys to identifying and interpreting both basic and complex interrelations between people and their environments.

(iii.) *Relationships within places: humans and environments.* All places on the earth have advantages and disadvantages for human settlement. High population densities have developed on flood plains, for example, where people could take advantage of level ground, fertile soils, water resources, and opportunities for river transportation. By comparion, population densities are ususally low in deserts. Yet floodplains are periodically subjected to severe damage, and some desert areas have been modified to support large populations.

People modify and adapt to natural settings in ways that reveal their cultural values, economic and political circumstances, and technological abilities. It is important to understand how such human-environment relationships develop and what the consequences are for people and for the environment. It helps people develop an appreciation for the natural environment they share with others on earth and their own cultural heritage as well as that of people in other places.

(iv.) *Movement: humans interacting on the earth.* Human beings are unevenly distributed across the face of the earth. Some live in rural areas and others live in towns, villages, or cities. People interact with each other through travel from one place to another, through communications, and they rely upon products, information, or ideas that come from beyond their immediate environment.

The most visible evidences of global interdependence and the interaction of places are the transportation and communication lines that link every part of the world. These demonstrate that most people interact with other places almost every day of their lives. Interaction continues to change as transportation and communication technologies change. The geographical and societal changes that come about are an important result of the movement of people, ideas, and products.

(v.) *Regions: how they form and change.* The basic unit of geographic study is the region. The region is any area that displays unity in terms of selected criteria. Regions may show the extent of political power, such as nations, provinces, countries, or cities. Some regions are defined by a single characteristic, such as their governmental unit, language group, or landform type, and others by the interplay of many complex features. Regions are used as tools to examine, define, describe, explain, and analyse the human and natural environment. There are almost countless ways to define meaningful regions, depending on the issues and problems being considered.

Regions perform numerous functions in geographic education. They define convenient and manageable units upon which to build our knowledge of the world. They provide a context for studying contemporary issues and current events. We may view regions as an intermediate step between our knowledge of local places and our knowledge of the entire planet.

The *Guidelines* have also focused attention on the cognitive skills that are all pervasive in geographic education. Prior emphasis upon skills in geography had presented little more than graphicacy, or reading maps and charts. Yet, it had long been recognized that geographic skills entail considerably more than reading maps and the *Guidelines* present five major skills categories related to geography. These are:

(i.) *Asking geographic questions.* Geography is distinguished by the kinds of questions it asks: the 'where?' and 'why there?' aspects of the issue or problem. It is important for students to develop and practice skills in asking such questions and searching answers or suggestions that offer an explanation to a question.

(ii.) *Acquiring geographic information.* These skills include being able to identify locations using grid systems, making observations and acquiring information in the field, and obtaining and organizing geographic information from different graphic modes, including maps, tables, and graphs.

(iii.) *Presenting geographic information.* These skills involve an ability to prepare maps, tables, and graphs, and make an organized, coherent written or oral presentation.

(iv.) *Interpreting geographic information.* Interpreting involves the ability to discover what a particular map, table, or graph says or implies about the question or issue being investigated. This includes describing trends portrayed on a line graph and recognizing the relationships between information on two or more maps.

(v.) *Developing and testing geographic generalizations.* Skills in this area require an ability to make inferences based on information presented on maps, tables, graphs and in narrative form.

Significant Development 6.

The concept of alliances between K – 12 teachers, school systems, geography faculty members in higher education, geography departments, private industry and public agencies had long been a part of the educational programme in the United States. The curricular areas that had fostered such collaborative efforts usually were business education, distributive education, and various types of technical and skills training. The fostering of alliances between schools, the private and public sectors and academic disciplines was relatively new, beginning in the early 1980s. In geography, such alliances first gained momentum in California, particularly in the geography department at the University of California at Los Angeles (Salter, 1986).

The California Geographic Alliance became a model for action, bringing to the discipline a proactive perspective on school geography that had been absent for most of the prior fifty years. Among the activities carried out by the California Geographic Alliance were:

lobbying of decision makers regarding curriculum matters; taking the case for geography to meetings of educators; gaining media coverage for geography; and establishing strong communications linkages between members of the alliance network.

The national organization of geographic alliances began in 1986 under the direction and funding of the National Geographic Society. Beginning with seven state geographic alliances in 1986, there were 27 states with alliances in 1989, with seven additional planning grant states awarded start-up funding in 1989. The alliance projects follow in-service training models for geography and social studies teachers that include summer institutes and follow up activities during the academic year. One summer institute or workshop has been held annually at the Headquarters of the National Geographic Society in Washington, D.C.

The most optimistic plan is that the alliance movement will continue until each of the fifty states has a geographic alliance. The funding is a combination of direct grants from the National Geographic Society, with the stipulation that matching funds be obtained from within the state. While the start-up funding represents an important commitment, the long term expectation is that college and university geographers, curriculum planners, and classroom teachers will forge close working partnerships toward the continued improvement of geographic education. The success of the alliance movement within the nation is an area of needed research within geographic education. Perhaps by 1995 research studies will have assessed the impact of the alliance movement from temporal, spatial and knowledge perspectives of geographic education.

The sponsoring of PLACE conferences in several regions of the United States has been an extension of the geography alliance movement. The PLACE conferences permit a wider participation from a state or region and focus upon a particular topic. The conferences have demonstrated considerable collaboration between university and school geographers in the preparation of instructional materials, the dissemination to the classroom of key ideas from the discipline, and a collegial commitment to increasing geography's role in the curriculum (Hill, 1988a).

Significant Development 7.

The Geographic Education National Implementation Project (GENIP) was established in 1985 by a consortium of professional societies in geography in order to implement the recommendations presented in the

Guidelines for Geographic Education. Consortium members included the following organizations: The Association of American Geographers, National Council for Geographic Education, National Geographic Society, and the American Geographical Society. The consortium represented a unified voice in the promotion and implementation of geographic education in the schools of the country. It represented the first time in this century that all the major geographic societies had organized officially in a common cause focusing upon geographical education.

The role of the consortium underpinning GENIP and its importance to geographic education had become clearly visible in two ways by 1988. First, the GENIP consortium was instrumental in having a National Geography Awareness Week proclaimed by the United States Congress and signed by the President. The first such week was in 1987. It is planned that after several years of successful implementation, Geography Awareness Week will become a widely recognized and nationally accepted annual celebration of geography.

Second, the volume *K - 6 Geography: themes, key ideas and learning opportunities* (GENIP, 1987) and *Geography in Grades 7 - 12: themes, key ideas and learning opportunities* (GENIP, 1989) were published by GENIP. The publications are an important step in the application of concepts presented by the *Guidelines for Geographic Education* at the interface between the teacher and students at the classroom level (Joint Committee on Geographic Education 1984). They are an important step in providing teachers and curriculum specialists with key ideas and learning opportunities from geography education and extending them to the classroom. The usefulness of the approach for social studies teachers with little or no formal preparation in geography was further highlighted in a subsequent publication by the National Council for the Social Studies (Stoltman and Libbee, 1988).

Significant development 8.

The Global Geography Project is being used in 44 states and the Canadian Provinces (Backler, 1988). The Global Geography project, a video project ready for classroom use, addresses the need for improved geography instruction in schools in an important way. The project's instructional design was shaped by the fundamental themes and skills for geographic education presented in the *Guidelines for Geographic Education* (Joint Committee on Geographic Education, 1984).

The project is important to the renaissance of geographic education in the United States for several reasons. First, over the period 1988 – 1993 the project will reach more students and teachers than any other single geography project developed in the United States. Second, it is entitled Global Geography, so students will receive the message that they are studying the discipline. Third, the video programmes are of high quality and educationally well designed. Fourth, as well as presenting content, each programme also examines an issue of geographic importance and implements a geographic skill. Fifth, the teacher's guide that accompanies the programmes includes the essential information for implementation in the classroom, including suggested objectives, black line masters of maps and models for duplication, and suggestions for extending the programme to consider issues of a similar nature in the local region.

Not since the High School Geography Project (White, 1970) has a United States Project earned such interest from geography teachers, curriculum planners, and media specialists in other countries. Under the title *Geographie in Beispielen*, the programme is translated into German (Agency for Instructional Technology, 1988), with plans for several additional languages. The international interest in the Global Geography Project, with its philosophical foundation being the five fundamental themes of geography, suggests that the impact of the renaissance in teaching and learning geography within the United States may be spreading to other countries.

Significant Development 9.

The renaissance in geographic education must address the question of teacher preparation if it is indeed to have a long term effect within the curriculum. The lack of adequate preparation in geography for newly graduating teacher education students has been documented in numerous publications (Rutter, 1986; Winston, 1984).

Two projects are underway that are planned to address the question of pre-service teacher preparation in geography. One project has resulted in teacher certification standards being proposed by the professional societies of geographers and educators. This is a major task since, in most instances, basic teacher certification guidelines are established by individual states and organizations representing associations of states.

In 1985 a special committee was appointed by the Geographic Education National Implementation Project (GENIP) to suggest the minimum course preparation in geography for future teachers of the discipline within the social studies and earth sciences curricula (Spetz, 1988). By recommending minimum requirements to accrediting boards and organizations, geographers will influence the amount and perhaps the types of coursework that teachers receive during their pre-service teacher education training.

What form will the future changes in teacher certification take? The committee recommendations include two options. The first is a two-semester course covering basic principles of cultural and physical geography. The second would be devoted to a world regional approach, giving emphasis to the themes of location and place from the *Guidelines for Geographic Education.* An alternative would be to present the cultural and physical geography course as two separate courses, along with a world regional course. This would result in a three-course sequence. Those alternatives are being presented as the minimum requirements for certification of *all* teachers regardless of content specialization. The certification of social studies and geography specialist teachers would incorporate additional course work in geography. Science teachers and social science teachers in the high school would have more extensive certification requirements within geography.

The second major undertaking is a project awarded to the Association of American Geographers through the Fund for the Improvement of Post Secondary Education (FIPSE) from the United States Department of Education. The Project is funded to enable geographic educators at eight colleges and universities in the United States to develop new course syllabuses for the preparation of preservice teacher education students. The FIPSE Project will provide data about teacher preparation in geographical education and present model programmes from each of the eight institutions of higher education which may then be widely disseminated for implementation at other institutions.

The funding of the FIPSE Project provides the community of geographers and geography teachers in the United States with a unique opportunity. The development of geographical education programmes at each of the Centres allows faculty members and participating teachers and administrators an opportunity to address national, state, and local concerns. The programmes, when finalized, should contribute significantly to the improvement of the quality of geographical education in years to come.

Significant development 10.
This mission of

> the National Gegoraphic Society Education Foundation is to encourage and provide timely and needed support for efforts that improve geography education and increase geographic knowledge. (National Geographic Society, 1988b)

Established in 1988, the Foundation provides an important incentive for education, industry, business, and government to combine their efforts with those of the Foundation in striving for that all-important goal of geographic literacy among the population both in school and in later life.

The Foundation heralds an optimistic future for geographic education in the United States. There are few disciplines that have privately funded foundations specifically dedicated to their educational mission. The establishment of the Education Foundation by the National Geographic Society is not only a capstone to a decade of effort at providing a renaissance for geographic education in the United States, it is also a commitment to providing grass-roots support for the continued improvement of the discipline within the schools of the country into the future.

Summary

Of the ten significant events identified, several were significant because they were essential to document conditions that existed at a particular time. Those studies and the release of information through the media raised the public's perception of geography, and directed the attention of policy makers to geography in the school curriculum. In many ways, the early survey and test results provided an important launching pad from which geographic education initiatives could be considered and designed. Secondly, the reports of nationally appointed commissions and study groups were important in bringing the state of geographic literacy to the attention of policy makers. The philosophical underpinnings and rationales presented by those reports were important in the decision-making process that resulted in greater attention being focused upon geography. Third, the dissemination of ideas through the increased attention to textbook and other materials by publishers were examples of the increasing importance of geography via both printed and audio visual materials. Finally, the diffusion of information about geographic issues of concern in the classroom have been the result of commitments by GENIP, the National Geographic Society's Geographic Alliance Network, and the FIPSE Project for the development of model course syllabuses. The renaissance of geographic education in the United States in general is greatly enhanced by the financial commitment of the National Geographic Society's Education Foundation and other projects funded by private and governmental agencies. However, it will require a considerable professional commitment by classroom teachers and professional geographers to catch the imagination of students studying geography in order for the renaissance to become a reality (Hill, 1988b). That commitment and enthusiasm will, with time, effect changes in curriculum materials, increase the expectations by citizens regarding geographic literacy, and assure the long-term commitment by professional geographers to the renaissance in geography teaching underway in the United States.

Chapter Eighteen
Geography Education Beyond the Western World: a case study of Nigeria

Julie Okpala

In 1985 a new geography curriculum was introduced for Nigerian senior secondary schools. This curriculum contained innovations in content and methods which, it was hoped, would improve the teaching and learning of geography in schools. This chapter analyses the problems of geography teaching which involve the teacher, learner, materials and strategies and then considers how far the new curriculum will bring about improvements. Findings show that conditions in geographic education may not necessarily improve. The author then argues that, through an active geographical association, geographers could improve the teaching of the subject in schools. The activities of the British Geographical Association (GA) are used to exemplify how an active geographical association could contribute to improving both the teaching and perception of geography.

In 1976, Nigeria started the 6-3-3-4 educational system. This six year primary, three junior secondary, three senior secondary and four university system was to gradually replace the 6-5/7-4/3 (six year primary, five or seven secondary and four or three university) education. The new educational system was required because of the need for learning that would prepare Nigerians for self reliance and vocational orientation. Thus, the new educational system led to preparation of national curricula in various subject areas including geography. A new geography curriculum was introduced in 1985. There was no specified curriculum in the old 5-year secondary programme as the examination syllabuses prepared by the West African Examinations Council (WAEC) were used for teaching in schools.

Concerning geography, there are four areas in which significant changes occurred in the new educational system. The first was that the place of geography in the school curriculum was improved. In the old system, for the school certificate examination, geography belonged to a group of General Subjects with Economics, History, Government, Literature in English and Religious Knowledge. In the new system, it is a core subject within an elective group with History and Literature in English. Secondly, geography became a distinctive senior secondary subject while Social Studies became a compulsory subject in the junior secondary. Within the old system, although Social Studies had been introduced by 1972, some schools taught geography in the five classes. Thirdly, there was a change in orientation in geography. The old system was criticized for not teaching geography tailored to the needs of the Nigerian child; the new based its theoretical framework on problem solving, concept acquisition and activity-based learning. Fourthly, in the old system, all school learning was assessed externally by the WAEC, a regional examining body with five participating countries – Nigeria, Ghana, Sierra Leone, Liberia and the Gambia. The new system introduced continuous assessment. Thus, in 1988, 40 per cent of the final grade in the Senior Secondary Certificate Examination was based on internal assessment by classroom teachers. From 1989 the proportion would be 30 per cent. With specific reference to geography, the major change in assessment was the place given to fieldwork. In the old system, an optional question was set on fieldwork in physical geography. Within the new system, fieldwork became a separate compulsory section. It is internally assessed and carries 25 per cent of the internal assessment grade.

Although changes have been introduced into geographic education in Nigeria, and some geographers (Abegunde, et al., 1987) perceive the future for geography as bright, the basic question which should be addressed is 'How far will the changes contribute to minimizing the problems facing geography teaching in Nigerian secondary schools?'

Problems of geography teaching in Nigerian secondary schools

Geographers from the 1960s into the 1980s have identified major problems of geographical education in Nigeria. These problems concern personnel, learners, teaching materials and strategies.

Personnel problems

The problem of personnel concerns quantity and quality. Nigeria had realized from the 1960s that no educational system can be stronger than its teachers. Hence, there was an attempt in the 1970s to encourage training of professional teachers including geographers by awarding teachers' bursaries. At present graduate professional geography teachers are being produced in the thirteen conventional federal universities, a Federal University of Technology, eight state universities and five colleges of education. One might have expected that the problem of scarcity of qualified teachers which Okpalanma (1978) reported, would have been minimized, but recent reports (Akorede, 1987) show that there are not enough graduate geography teachers in schools. Hence teachers possessing the higher diploma certificate, the Nigerian Certificate in Education, who were expected to teach in the junior secondary classes, in fact teach geography in senior secondary classes. It is hoped that these teachers will gradually have their knowledge updated and their skills developed through sandwich degree programmes organized by various institutions in the country.

While the lack of qualified teachers is being gradually overcome, the author is particularly concerned about the competences of the teachers. Okpala (1987) involved geography teachers in teaching for the development of problem-solving abilities and found that within this open-ended, pupil-oriented interactive teaching situation teachers exhibited misconceptions of content. A recent conversation with 20 graduate teachers on the meaning of problem-solving emphasized in the 1985 national curiculum which they are currently teaching, showed that the concept was not understood. This problem of quality is further supported by Adegoke (1987) who found that one of the major constraints on implementation of the 1985 geography curriculum is scarcity of competent up-to-date teachers with appropriate knowledge of new ideas and skills of imparting the new trends. Without going further into displaying the deficiencies of some teachers in handling certain content areas like elementary surveying, atmospheric resources and the concepts exemplified in problem-solving, it could be argued that the problem of teacher quality, which is covert, is more critical than the overt problem (insufficient numbers) which is gradually being tackled.

Learner problems

The number, quality and attitudes of students are important aspects of learner problems facing school geography in Nigeria. Research (Ndu, 1973; Achufusi, 1984; Pope, 1984) shows that students dislike geography because it is wide in scope and not regarded as a science subject in the Nigerian educational system. Previous results in school certificate geography were poor, geography is not related to the future career of the students and the teaching is poor.

Concerning performance in senior secondary geography, it is most likely that there could be better overall results for two reasons. Firstly, geography is compulsory in most science schools. As there are only three subjects in the group, geography might attract science-inclined students who have been found to perform better than the non-science-inclined students in school certificate geography examinations (Okpala, 1981). Secondly, the internal assessment grade might boost the overall grade, particularly as there is no form of external moderation. After all, no teacher would like this or her students to fail.

It could be argued that the situation on the other problems concerning broad scope remains unchanged. The 1985 curriculum did not make much improvement with regard to the scope of the subject. The scope could have been reduced if the recommended concept-centred approach (Federal Ministry of Education, 1986) had been adopted. Rather, the curriculum structure selected was a combination of a regional and a topical structure. The curriculum was overloaded in an attempt to expose students to basic geographical facts as well as accommodate the local environment and current environmental issues. The lack of conceptual structure can be deciphered from the nature of the themes specified. Examples of the themes are: local geography; the solar system; the outer zones of the earth; the nature of the earth's interior; rocks; major landform features; weather and climate; soil and vegetation; environmental resources; Nigeria; internal processes; effects of climate elements; vegetation; world population/settlement; regional geography in Africa with particular reference to West Africa; external processes of landform development; classification of climate (Greek system and Koppen's classification); major climate types; aspects of environmental interaction; environmental hazards; world vegetation types, transportation, industry, trade; geographical regions of Nigeria; map work; map interpretation; elementary land surveying; field project.

Biddle (1982), in arguing for a conceptual structure in geography pointed out the need to move from memorization of facts in the discipline and too much emphasis on end-products, towards the process of thinking. Thus, in the conceptual approach, the discipline should not be defined by the object studied, but rather by the kinds of questions asked and the conceptual structures used through which students learn the skills of thinking and the ways of ordering reality so that they can learn more efficiently in the future. In a conceptually based curriculum, the objectives are made specific and then selection of content and skills start with selection of organized learning centres based on themes. The themes are then divided into topics. Biddle exemplified a theme for school geography in a region such as Nigeria. The theme and the units are shown below.

Theme: Human responses to resources.
Units:
1. the nature and distribution of resources in Nigeria;
2. environmental impact of agricultural activities in Nigeria:
3. industrial activities and natural resources in Nigeria;
4. human responses to urban systems in Nigeria;
5. the individual, the environment and the future. (ibid. 287)

The themes and the units specified above relate to certain major organizing concepts in geography, viz., spatial location, distribution, association, interaction, analysis and synthesis. This type of curricular organization would encourage a multidisciplinary or interdisciplinary approach which would facilitate consideration of environmental problems. On the contrary, the theme and units on Nigeria in the National Geography Curriculum for senior secondary schools maintained a regional structure as indicated below.

Theme: Geographical regions of Nigeria.
Units: Eastern highlands, Sokota plains, Niger basin, Niger-Benue trough, Cross River basin, southern coastlands.
Content of each unit: Physical setting, people, population, settlement pattern, economic products, transport, industries and problems of development (Federal Ministry of Education, 1986, 31-34)

The regional approach involved in the 1985 geography curriculum was a universally accepted organizational framework in Europe up to the 1960s. Though still found frequently in schools, it has been criticized for encouraging memorization of considerable quantities of factual information rather than facilitating critical thinking. Where a systematic approach has been attempted in the new Nigerian curriculum as in 'the world population/settlement', 'transportation', and 'industry', there are no operational words to direct learning towards the solution of environmental problems. Biddle demonstrated specification of a systematic curriculum. An example is 'Population densities and standards of living' (Biddle, 1982, 283).

From the discussion above, it could be argued that the conceptual structure proposed for the new curriculum is not fulfilled. Therefore the problem of scope and other problems resulting from the structure of the old curriculum will persist. With regard to status, geography is still neither a science subject nor a professional area. It could thus be inferred that the perception of students about the discipline even within the new geography will remain unchanged. Despite the recommendations made in the new curriculum for pupil-oriented and activity-based methods such as guided discussion, group work, games and simulation, it might be inferred that teaching of geography will not improve.

In the old programme, the teaching of geography was dominated by talk-chalk and note copying (Okpala, 1987). For the new curriculum, it is likely that teachers will not make use of these recommended strategies as the pattern of examination questions does not at all encourage problem-solving to be emphasized in the teaching. Both the sample questions published by the WAEC (Okpala, 1988a) and the first senior secondary school certificate geography questions (WAEC, 1988) maintained the pattern of questioning which has for nearly two decades been criticized by geographers (Bakare, 1971; Okpala, 1974; Nwagu, 1985; Mkpa, 1988; Okpala, 1988b) as inadequate since it lacks practical application to environmental issues and also over-emphasizes memory. Such questions, which predominated in the 1988 Senior Secondary Certificate Geography examination, are exemplified below:

Map Reading and Interpretation of Survey Map

With reference to the map extract provided, Nigeria Sheet 299 N.W., on a scale 1:50,000, answer the following questions:

(a) (i) Write clearly over an example of each of the following features: spur, meander, knoll, uniform slope.
(ii) Shade clearly one area below 150 feet and one area above 900 feet.

(b) (i) Draw an annotated cross-section from OGADA MARKET to the Rest House at the confluence of the Rivers Ebah and Ossimo.
(ii) Is OGADA MARKET visible from the Rest House? Give reasons.

(c) What is the angular bearing of UMULUA-OBIOGBA school from OGBAHU school?

(d) Comment on the drainage pattern in the area covered by the map.

Elements of physical Geography

(a) List any three major groups in the Köppen's climatic classification.

(b) Describe any one of the major groups listed in (a) above under the following headings:
(i) temperature (ii) precipitation (iii) vegetation.

Human Geography
(i) Describe the effects of rail transportation on the economic development of any one country of your choice.
(ii) (a) Explain five factors that influence the location of industries.
(b) With reference to relevant examples, describe the characteristics of heavy industries.

Nigeria
Write short notes on any three of the following:
(a) Pastoral nomadism on the Jos Plateau.
(b) Fishing in the Chad Basin.
(c) Market gardening in the Lagos area.
(d) Yam cultivation in the middle belt.
(e) Rice growing in the Cross River plains.

West Africa and Africa
Write short notes on any three of the following:
(a) Lumbering in Zaire.
(b) Plantation agriculture in East Africa.
(c) Irrigation agriculture in the inland delta of the Niger Basin.
(d) Pastoral farming in West Africa. (WAEC, 1988, 1 - 2)

Educationists (Morris, 1972; Marsden, 1976; Lewy, 1977) have insisted that examinations should be carefully planned as the demands made in external examinations determine the teaching strategies involved in classrooms. Okpala (1987) used mapwork to show that when conventional questions, as perpetuated by the WAEC, are set in the external examination, the teaching is dominated by talk and chalk and note copying. It could be inferred that, as the conventional examining pattern is still maintained, conventional teaching strategies will still persist.

Materials
Recent researchers (Makanjuola, 1987; Awaritefe and Omogbai, 1987) have shown that essential materials for teaching geography are lacking in schools. Makanjuola's (1987) study in 43 schools in Ondo state showed that the basic facilities for geography teaching and the percentage of schools possessing them are: laboratory, 59.3; geography

garden, 53.5; wet and dry bulb thermometer 55.8; maximum and minimum thermometer, 51.2; Stevenson's screen, 69.8; wind vane, 62.8; rain gauge, 62.8; topographical maps, 62.8; wall maps 48.8; globe, 37.2; thermograph, 93; and anemometer, 90.7. In another study Awaritefe and Omogbai (1987) found, in a field survey involving 36 secondary schools in Bendel state in 1985, that 83.5 of the schools had neither weather stations nor instruments.

It is likely that geography taught without relevant equipment will be too theoretical for meaningful understanding. Therefore, however lofty a curriculum specification may be, students' interest cannot be stimulated in a situation that is devoid of relevant materials. It could be argued also that in such a situation learning will not be maximized.

Concerning fieldwork, although this has been given an important place in the new curriculum, it is doubtful whether there will be improvement in its involvement in schools. A study of participation in fieldwork (Awaritefe and Omogbai, 1987), referred to earlier, showed that only 16.66 per cent of the schools had participated in fieldwork between 1976 and 1985. For those who have never participated in fieldwork, 15.28 per cent had no future plans of participating while 68.06 per cent hoped to participate in future (ibid., 266). Among reasons given for non-participation are: lack of funds, transport difficulties and lack of qualified teachers. Other reasons are that teachers are not sufficiently keen or interested in fieldwork because questions directed at evaluating students' participation in fieldwork are not yet making significant impact in geography external examinations. Fieldwork is also perceived as having a disruptive effect on the normal school timetable. Consequently, school headteachers and other subject-unit teachers are not prepared to tolerate any time encroachment on their subject time allocation resulting from geography teaching or fieldwork participation. Although the report above is from one state only, the situation in other states will not be very different.

The possibility of using examinations to facilitate active fieldwork in geography is remote. The old geography programme contained an optional question on fieldwork in the WAEC examination. The new programme does not, as fieldwork is internally assessed. It could be argued that if the question on fieldwork in the old programme could not induce teachers and schools to provide opportunities for fieldwork for their students, the situation in the new programme is likely to worsen as fieldwork is internally assessed but not externally moderated.

From the discussion above it could be argued that the new curriculum may not necessarily lead to improving the teaching and learning of geography. The author therefore proposes that an active geographical association can be used as a hub for improving school geography in Nigeria.

An active Geographical Association: a hub for improving teaching of geography

The Nigerian Geographical Association was founded in 1957 with the aim of promoting geography at all levels. It has a national executive and zonal representatives (North East, South East, North West and North South). There are also four specialized committees namely: High School Geography, Rural Development, Environmental Planning, Regional Planning. The Association holds an annual conference and publishes *The Nigerian Geographical Journal.*

The zones and the specialized committees are semi-independent and are expected to organize activities for the progress of the discipline. The zonal representatives are charged with the responsibility of reaching out to the members. In the past, some zones have organized workshops for teachers. The High School Geography Group is particularly expected to reach out to geography teachers and involve them in activities that will improve teaching and learning especially in secondary classrooms.

Lieberman (1960) in discussing the significance of professional bodies to the growth of disciplines stressed that it is the responsibility of a comprehensive self-governing organization of practitioners to set high standards of practice and to raise the social and economic status of the group. The primary purpose of a professional organization was stressed as promotion of the organization rather than advancement of the self-interest of members. Thus on occasions when it is necessary for the public or government agencies to get to know the thinking of a profession on a particular issue, it is the responsibility of the practitioners to choose persons to represent them in various capacities. Otherwise it would be very difficult, if not impossible, to know when a particular professional person was giving private preferences or really expressing the weight of collective professional opinion on the issue. For this reason, the organization must be as comprehensive as possible, otherwise, there is a danger that the thinking of an active minority will be accepted instead of the thinking of an inactive majority. On improving the occupational status within professions, Lieberman (ibid., 476) emphasized that 'one of the major determinants of occupational status is the extent to which an occupational group is believed to have a body of knowledge and skills which is not shared by other groups'. It could therefore be argued that the Nigerian Geographical Association should spearhead promotion of geography as a discipline. The issue which will be addressed is how far the Nigerian Geographical Association is playing this role by contributing to solving the problems of teacher quality, learner attitude, poor teaching and lack of teaching materials.

With regard to helping in improving teacher quality, it could be argued that the Nigerian Geographical Association is not currently fulfilling the type of role specified by Lieberman. After initial training, teachers need to update themselves continuously on the new trends and methods of the discipline. Because of the large number of disciplines and teachers involved in any educational system, it is impossible for the government to provide regular in-service training for all teachers. It is therefore necessary for the Nigerian Geographical Association to take on responsibility for improving the quality of geography teachers in order to ensure continued growth of the discipline. High teacher quality is important to ensure effective teaching in schools. Also, quite often teachers are called upon to participate in planning geography curricula and setting external examination questions. If such teachers are well informed about the discipline through the activities of the professional association, the views of the few individuals involved would more properly represent the views of the association. There are instances which show that the activities of the NGA do not at present sufficiently facilitate high teacher quality. The first is the passive participation of classroom teachers in both NGA and High School Geography Group conferences. For example at the 1988 NGA annual conference, less than 10 per cent of the papers represented were by classroom teachers. During High School Geography conferences, presentations by classroom teachers are rare. Examples are the 1980 and 1987 conferences (Ola and Abioye, 1980; Abegunde et al., 1987) in which 13 and 26 papers were presented respectively and none was by a classroom teacher. Most of the papers presented are also too theoretical and lack practical relevance for classroom teachers. For example in the 1987 conference only one paper ('Making geography lively through improvisation and modelling: the Ikere experiment' (Dadare, 1987) had direct examplars for classroom experience.

The second instance is lack of involvement in the preparation and dissemination of the 1985 geography curriculum. New curricula are often prepared by geographers, some of whom may not be active members of the association. Hence, the views of the association may not be represented. The 1985 curriculum was structured without due consideration by the NGA. Thus the executors of the curriculum (the classroom teachers) came into contact with the ideas in the new curriculum only when it was sent to schools for implementation, except for the few teachers who were involved in writing the curriculum.

Although it could be claimed that the planning of the curriuclum was democratic as clientele of school geography (geographers, serving geography teachers, geography teacher educators and qualified individuals from the Ministry of Education) were involved, such involvement lacked collective input to represent the views of the NGA. In the structuring of the curriculum, which involved planning of the theoretical framework, 9-12 January 1985; a writing workshop, 13-19 January 1985; a critique workshop, 16-22 March 1985; approval by Joint Consultative Reference Committee, April 1985; and final approval, 27 June 1985, some geographers, geography-educators and classroom teachers were involved in their personal capacities and not as members of the NGA except for the chairman of the High School Geography Group. The NGA could have been involved through probably a curriculum committee, and papers presented for deliberation during the NGA conference. Information on the new curriculum could have been further disseminated to teachers before implementation through publications and workshops.

The activities of the (British) Geographical Association (GA) in educating members on new trends through circulation of papers and workshops are worth emulating. For example, before the General Certificate of Secondary Education which replaced the General Certificate of Education and the Certificate of Secondary Education was introduced, teachers were kept informed in workshops in over 60 local branches of the GA set up throughout the United Kingdom and through numerous publications (books, occasional publications, journals, pamphlets, bibliographic notes, newsletters and teaching suggestions for the non-specialist teachers) (Geographical Association, undated). The annual conference of the Geographical Association also includes workshops for teachers and this is so task oriented that it is accepted as an in-service training programme by some local education authorites. During GA conferences, members involved in innovatory and curriculum projects present papers and interim reports and call for reaction from members which are useful for restructuring the framework. Thus the association is directly involved in the innovative process. As teachers are actively involved in GA activities, when an innovation is eventually documented and sent to schools, many teachers are already aware of the broad ideas.

Concerning learners' problems, it is the responsibility of the NGA to stimulate learners' interest and awareness of the importance of geography. At present, geography holds little attraction to the young Nigerian as it is neither a profession nor a science. Most high school geography students, therefore hold the opinion that there are no job prospects for geographers except teaching. To date, the NGA does not publicize the importance of geography as a discipline. Contributions have been made by individuals. Ologe (1978, 1980, 1982, 1984) reported careers of graduates of his department during NGA conferences. Ofomata (1971) discussed *Jobs for Geographers* in his department's Occasional Publication. These have limited publicity, and limited generalizability. An active geographical association should embark on a coordinated national survey which would be published by the association. This has been acheived by the Association of American Geographers (Natoli, 1974, 1976, 1980) and the Geographical Association (Hebden, undated; Randle, 1983; Bailey and Binns, 1987). Ologe (1984) pointed out that the NGA is aware of the need for promoting professional interests of geographers hence it established a Career Committee (which has yet to start work, however).

With regard to the improvement of teaching and teaching materials, while the association should not take over the government's responsibility of equipping schools, it can improve the situation and set a standard which will influence the government into appreciating the importance of the subject and into providing necessary materials for teaching as in the sciences and technology. An active high school geography group should acquaint teachers with use of materials including improvisation and strategies for teaching. It should attract active participation by its members through various working groups such as those of the GA. The GA has over 60 branches throughout Britain and still calls for interested members to set up new GA branches in under-represented areas (Geographical Association, 1987a). There are also various working groups such as those for further education, environmental education, secondary – tertiary interface, educational computing. More groups are formed as the need arises. The annual conference is full of activities which include a book exhibition, lectures, symposia, excursions, working group meetings and a publishers' forum which is an opportunity to meet and discuss with authors of current texts (Geographical Association 1987b). In contrast, the activities of the NGA annual conference consist mainly of symposia, fieldwork and group meetings.

An active geographical association will constantly be aware of the needs of the discipline at any point in time, and with members well informed, would be able to infuse the necessary concepts and content into the curriculum and examination questions. An example is the case of fieldwork which is at present internally assessed. Such a mode of assessment cannot spur teachers into involving students in fieldwork experience as there is no external moderation. It is the responsibility of the association to work out the modalities for assessment of fieldwork and incorporate these into the WAEC policy through WAEC examiners in geography. This would also apply to general improvements in teaching.

Discussion

The NGA, through the high school geography group, has the potential to facilitate effective teaching of geography in Nigerian secondary schools. It could play the role which the GA and various geography teachers association are playing in other countries such as in Australia and New Zealand. In February 1987 the Nigerian Geographical Teachers Association (NGTA) was formed to cater for the needs of classroom teachers. This new association has organized conferences for teachers, especially in the South West Zones. Activities in the other zones have not yet taken off. It is not certain whether the new association will in future replace the high school geography group to avoid duplication of functions. Whatever happens in future, the points made in this chapter about an active geographical association, as exemplified by the GA, as a means to improving the teaching of geography in schools are valid. In a country as large as Nigeria, with an area of 923, 800 square kilometres and with a population in 1990 of 100 million, one centralized high school geography group cannot facilitate active involvement of classroom teachers. There should be at least one smaller high school geography group in each state in Nigeria and in the captial territory. Through such decentralization, more teachers will be involved.

As with the GA, there should be working groups which could be expanded as the need arises. There is a need for working groups on curriculum and examinations, teaching materials, fieldwork, computers, enviornmental education and linkage groups (with higher education, the government and the public). The activities of the association will create awareness in the government and the general public of the new geography and the special value of geography. Active participation in relevant activities geared to classroom needs would lead to active publication by the association. The latest issue of the Nigerian Geographical Association Journal was published in 1984. The NGA often rationalizes the dormancy of the journal by reference to lack of funds, but with increased membership funds would be available. If the NGA, like the GA, through decentralization of group activities and meaningful activities involves more geographers and geography teachers throughout Nigeria, more money will be generated. Also, if the High School conference is active and task oriented it could, like the GA annual conference, be recognized for expenses purposes as an approved course for teachers by both the federal and state governments.

The NGA should emulate the GA and associations in other countries (for example Australia and New Zealand) with regard to publishing as a means of improving teaching and generating funds. A call by the NGA in 1980 through the late Professor P.O. Okunrotifa to initiate publication of school textbooks for the association with full involvement of the classroom teachers met with no response. If members publish for the membership there will be greater circulation and hence greater turnover.

High school geography conferences should cease being primarily a medium for academics to publish papers. When one reads some of the papers presented during such conferences one cannot help asking: 'who are they writing for ... themselves?' If classroom teachers are actively involved through working groups and state branches, they will obviously participate actively during conferences.

Conclusion

The Geographical Association, used as a model association in this chapter, is primarily a teachers' association, while the NGA is a corporate body. Nevertheless, the working groups of the NGA are semi-autonomous and the NGA does not restrict their activities in as much as they contribute to the progress of the discipline. It could therefore be argued that the onus of improving the situation of school geography in Nigeria lies with the High School Geography Group. The group should decentralize its activities along the lines suggested in this chapter by creating branches in various states and by forming working sub-groups within the main group. The step which the late Professor Okunrotifa tried to initiate should be taken to encourage publication by the group for the association, as means of improving teaching and the financial situation.

In this chapter, the problems of geographic education in Nigeria have been exhaustively treated and the inactivity of the Nigerian Geographical Association in several areas exposed. The example of the Geographical Association has been cited to show how an active geographical association could facilitate improvement of teaching and learning of the subject. The critical and comparative approach used is deliberate; Nigeria is intended to serve as a case study from which generalizations have to be made not only about the instance but also from it.

Thus, the suggestions made in this chapter should be considered for implementation by geography groups in nations both within and beyond the Western world. Geographical education in various countries experiences diverse problems. Such problems include: securing a place for geography in secondary school programmes in United States of America (Wilms, 1988); low perception of jobs for geographers in the Netherlands (Veen, 1987); lack of reading materials at the secondary and conceptual conflict at the tertiary level in Uganda (Kyagulanyi, 1987); need to improve teaching and reduce the over-emphasis on examinations, in India (Pande, 1987); and predominance of expository methods, and poor resource materials in Jamaica (Webb, 1987). It is obvious that in many countries, geographical education is not making the required impact on learners and society. Such nations should try activating their geographical associations as a recipe for improving the teaching of the subject.

Part Five
Conclusion

Chapter Nineteen
Conclusion: The Graves Years in Geographical Education
W.M. Marsden

This chapter discusses the writings of Norman Graves over the last thirty years almost as the litmus paper by means of which developments in geographical education, curriculum study and, latterly, educational policy making, can be tested. It pays special attention to Graves' skills as a connecter of important developments in geography and education, as a promoter of research in geographical education, as above all a catalyst in creating co-operative international networks in the field and, finally, as forceful critic of trends in central policy making in education.

The Graves' years span one of the most interesting quarter of a century periods in the growth of geography as an academic discipline, and in geographical education. They run from the dying throes of the dominating influence of the regional framework in the late 1950s and early 1960s (Biddle, 1980), to the birth pangs and unhealthily rapid growth of a tighter degree of central control over the curriculum in the 1980s. Graves himself has catalogued earlier periods in the growth of geographical education in England and Wales as follows:

1. To 1800 : the period of 'isolated initiatives'
2. 1800-1880: the 'facts about the world' period
3. 1880-1920: the 'early break-through period', a previous 'new geography'
4. 1920-1945: the 'take off period' of this new regional approach
5. 1945-1965: the consolidation period (Graves, 1974, 147-148)

The appointment of Norman Graves in 1963 to head geographical education at the London Institute of Education, in a post previously held in turn by Fairgrieve, Scarfe and Honeybone, coincided with the time of the Madingley conferences which fuelled a 'new geography'. This was also a seminal period in educational theory in that the sixty-year old curriculum planning movement in the United States was about to gain a footing in this country. British texts such as Wheeler's *Curriculum Process* (1967) and Kerr's *Changing the Curriculum* (1968) drew attention to the richness and relevance of the ideas of such writers as Bloom and Bruner, Taba and Tyler, and Ausubel and Gagné.

These two major components of change fortunately proved to be on converging tracks. As Graves saw it, the need was for geographers and educationists to engage in 'a process of cross-fertilization', to 'become aware of each other's contribution to the continuing problem of defining objectives in education' (1972c, 1046), and for a shift from 'learning content to using content for the purpose of implementing certain educational aims and objectives' (Graves, 1981b, 85). But the convergence was a confused and testing one for teachers to accommodate to, embroiled as they were in devising syllabuses for comprehensive schooling and the new CSE examinations. But these too provided constructive challenges. As Graves put it, it was a time of 'crisis and opportunity' (Graves, 1974).

The task of the geographical educator in these circumstances was surely to help to make the connections: between old and new paradigms in the subject, as relevant to the school situation; between the discipline and the new curriculum thinking; between innovators in the field at home and abroad; and the placing of the whole in a broad cultural context of time and place. What was not needed was the proneness to polarization of issues, the ring-fence attitudes within subjects, and the curricular chauvinism that had been all too common previously.

Norman Graves manifestly saw his function as a facilitator, and brought a range of skills to the endeavour. Unusual among academic colleagues in the field in being bilingual, his early publications testified to the breadth of his interests. His MA thesis (1957) was a study of historical and comparative aspects of geography teaching in nineteenth and twentieth-century French schools. His important methodological text *(Geography in Education* (1975a) contained two substantial chapters of historical context, reflecting Goodlad's advice: 'the wise explorer studies the maps of those who went before' (Goodlad, 1966, 91). Many of his later surveys of the state of the art contain an historical introduction, but more specific contributions have been a paper on the impact of Vidal de la Blache on geographical education in France

(1980e, 8-17), and co-authorship of an extraordinarily useful bibliography of British sources on the history of geographical education from 1870 to 1970 (Graves and Lukehurst, 1972a). This, characteristically for Graves, was a joint production, in this case between the Geographical Association and the International Geographical Union.

It is evident that Graves' major strength is the classic geographical one of synthesis. The first element in the synthesis lay in linking and reconciling earlier approaches with the new, in a situation in which the earlier could have been too easily dismissed. During his years of school-teaching in the 1950s Graves had clearly kept up with developments which might reasonably be termed 'enlightened traditionalist', including grasp of the need to bring direct observation into the classroom in the form of what were then called sample studies, and of course direct observation through local field work. Such ideas emerge in useful advice on the examples of case study material (1965c, 1969, and 1971a), on field work techniques (1964b and 1965b), and in his co-authorship with R.C. Honeybone of *North America and Asia* (Honeybone and Graves, 1966) in the Heinemann *Geography for Schools* series which pioneered the infusion of case studies into the geography course book literature. While not a major innovator in nor implementer of the so-called quantitative revolution, which was spear-headed from elsewhere (see Everson and Fitzgerald, 1969; Tidswell, 1973; Walford, 1973; Fitzgerald, 1974; and, in the textbook field, for example, Cole and Beynon, 1968 and Grenyer et al., 1979), Graves infiltrated the new ideas, skilfully integrating them with more conventional materials, as in his co-authored *Geography of the British Isles* (Graves and White, 1971b).

Complexity was compounded in the 1970s by a series of mini-revolutions in the subject, a reaction against the dehumanization seen to be brought in its train by the positivisim and the abstractions of the scientific revolution. While certainly no rejecter of quantification, Graves seemed more in tune with trends towards behavioural approaches, social welfare and a geography of environmental concern, if published output is anything to go by. This interest is demonstrated in an early paper on the neglect of the teaching of Asia in schools in England and Wales (1968a), but more substantially in work on principles and materials for promoting international understanding (1975b, 1984d (with Torney and Dunlop), and 1985a) and environmental concern (1986a and 1987b), characteristically integrated in a co-authored school text (Graves, Lidstone and Naish, 1987a). At the same time Graves has been quick to sponsor, if indirectly, interest in computer-assisted learning in geography (1984a). A second element in the synthesis is arguably more difficult to achieve, namely the attainment of a balance between geography and education, a signal failure of the pre-Graves period, in which the orientation for grammar school pupils was arguably too much discipline dominated, and that for less able and younger children too little.

Graves was one of the earliest geographical educationists to take on board the importance of the developments in curriculum theory. Thus he worked on the implications of Hirst's influential, albeit dubious, dichotomization of the 'forms and fields of knowledge' for geographical education (Graves and Simons, 1966b; Graves and Moore, 1972b); explored objectives hierarchies in the secondary geography context (1972c); and returned later to the issue of the implications of paradigm theory for geography as potential background for curriculum planning in the subject (1981c).

The comprehensivization of secondary schooling generated new moves towards subject integration as headteachers, faced with the need for fresh syllabuses and different modes of timetabling, did not necessarily adopt separate subject frameworks, particularly in the first three years of the secondary school phase. A 'new social studies' movement emerged (Lawton and Dufour, 1974), keen to avoid the mistakes of the earlier civics-centred social studies, seeking a higher level of academic respectability through structuring material on the basis of concepts drawn from social science disciplines. While Graves' 1968 statement on geography and integration for the Royal Geographical Society (1968b) would hardly be regarded as progressive by social scientists, and was concordant with prevailing views at the time of separating syllabuses for the less able (integrated studies) and more able (single subjects), it was years in advance, in terms of logic, intellectual grasp and conceptual refinement, of a notorious earlier RGS memorandum on the issue (Royal Geographical Society, 1950).

Graves' work in meshing the conceptual revolutions in geography and education can be seen as critical in several ways. In the first place, the 1970-1980 decade witnessed the appearance of his influential quartet of methodological texts: a more theoretical *Geography in Education* (1975a), an intermediate *Curriculum Planning in Geography* (1979a), and the more practical Geographical Association publications, *Geography in Secondary Education* (1971a), and *Geographical Education in Secondary School* (1980a), the latter major revision testimony to a determination to keep up to date.

A second vital piece of integration has been Graves' support of curriculum development projects, which without exception have incorporated thought about educational frameworks as well as subject content. Despite the low esteem of geography as a school subject in the United States, the earliest such innovation was the American High School Geography Project (AHSGP). The first intimation many British geography teachers had of the importance of this project was in an article by Graves (1968b). The AHSGP deeply influenced the first two Schools Council geography ventures in this country, the Avery Hill and Bristol projects. The fact that the latter confined itself to the 14-16 rather than 14-18 age range, left the way open for a 16-19 project, directed by Michael Naish, in Graves' own department (Graves, 1980d).

A third, easily neglected, component has been in the promotion of a wide range of research in geographical education (1982d and 1984b), having maintained and reinforced the tradition of the London Institute of Education, through its MA and PhD provision, as a leading world centre in this area. It is perhaps significant that the main historical surveys of research in geographical education have come from members of the Institute (Scarfe, 1949; Long, 1964; Naish, 1972).

Fourthly, Graves' commitments to the promotion of a balance of geography and education in teacher education courses is evidenced in a series of statements written for an international audience (1976a, 1978b, 1984e and f).

A more specific area of geographical education with which Norman Graves' name is much associated is that of evaluation and assessment. All his methodological texts have important sections on this theme and there are in addition more concentrated studies of objective testing and school examinations (1972d), external examinations (1977 and 1982f), graded tests (1984c) and, with Naish, on profiling (1986b).

For all the scope of this achievement, it would have had to be attested as more limited had it not been disseminated so widely. It may in the future be judged Graves' most important contribution that he has been so sensitive and energetic a generator of international contacts in his field. One of the most debilitating aspects of the pre-1960 period had been isolationism. Graves is a born comparativist and internationalist. Apart from the personal commitment, it is a stroke of good fortune that he was one of the first in the generation succeeding those geographical educators who, however progressive their views, were too encumbered with imperial thinking to have been credible as effectively internationalist in their sympathies. While Scarfe worked with Unesco and, like Honeybone, moved from the Institute to an overseas post, it was their successor Graves who opened up the field.

In fostering the global expansion of geographical education, Graves' main outlets have been through two agencies, Unesco and the International Geographical Union. He was engaged in consulting work with Unesco from 1961 to 1984, out of which a number of important publications resulted, including a short statement on teaching geography in Africa (1966a), a joint enterprise between the two organizations in the Unesco *Source Book for Geography Teaching* (1965b and c) designed particularly to promote good geography teaching in countries of the developing world, and followed by a later more sophisticated production, the *New Unesco Source Book for Geography Teaching* (1982h). In addition, there are important contributions on developing international understanding through geography (1975b and 1985a), and a Handbook for *African Geography for Schools* (1975c).

As a long-serving member of the Commission for Geographical Education of the International Geographical Union, Norman Graves has produced papers for all the four-yearly meetings from London (1964a), to Delhi (1968a), Montreal (1972c), Moscow (1976a), Tokyo (1980e), Paris (1984b) and Sydney (1988), as well as many intermediate regional meetings between. He was Chair of the Geographical Education Commission from 1972 to 1980, and has played a major role in enlarging its publications programme, both as editor (1978a, 1984a and b) as author (1976a, 1980e, 1984f) and through squeezing resources from the various bodies with which he has had influence to underwrite this programme.

His distinctive academic contribution has been recognized by the London Institute of Education which promoted him to Reader in 1974, to a Personal Chair in 1978, and the R.O. Buchanan Chair of Geographical Education in 1981. The Geographical Association made him its President in 1978-9, and he has received a number of overseas honours. His eminence has properly and regularly generated commissions to provide authoritative overviews of the state of the art of geographical education in England and Wales, all of which have testified to his breadth of interest and unrivalled general knowledge of the field (1974, 1979b, 1980b, 1980c, 1981a, 1982a, 1982b, 1982c). In edited contributions he has drawn on his exceptional range of international friends and contacts, as in IGU Geographical Education Commission surveys of the problems of teaching the 16-19 age group (1978a) and research methods in geographical education (1984b).

The substantial progress in geographical education in England and Wales of the 1970s, demonstrated in Schools Council publications, methodological texts and new styles of textbooks, have continued into the 1980s, but it can be argued that the 1980s have heralded a new stage of development about which Graves' earlier counter-pointing of the poles of 'crisis and opportunity' can be re-applied. On the crisis side, growing central control of education is viewed with anxiety perhaps less because of the intrinsic substance of the National Curriculum, but rather because of the externally imposed backlash of relentless change, an uncritical faith in industrial management models, cumulative financial constraints, and an unappetising moral prescriptiveness which threatens schools, colleges and universities with endemic unrest: often a kind of change without innovation.

In this situation, it is perhaps symptomatic that Norman Graves has been elevated into high-level administration, the chief function of his pre-retirement years at the London Institute of Education. Here, too, he has not lost the opportunity to bring this new range of experience into the arena of public debate, as in his statement on *Teacher Education in Adversity* (1985b), the identification of a political ideology which 'misconceives the relationship between education and economic life' (1982d) and an important collection on the crisis in teacher education (1990).

On the side of opportunity, from a fraught scenario in the late 1970s when geography's place in the school curriculum was under threat, an effective Geographical Association lobby (Bailey and Binns, 1987) has helped to secure the subject's position as a foundation subject in the National Curriculum. The statements of the Geographical Association and the official HMI document *Geography from 5 to 16* (Department of Education and Science, 1986) display a considerable degree of unanimity about what geography has to offer. These forces would appear to define the subject's offering not in narrow control, but in broader cultural terms. These include giving priority to developing the skills of graphicacy, to fostering a curiosity about and a sensitivity to places, to reinforcing the value of observation through field work, and to providing a major contribution to cross-curricular, global elements in school, incuding environmental and human rights education. Recent writings (Graves, 1982g; Graves, Torney and Dunlop, 1984d; Graves,

1986a, 1987b) have shown him not only in tune with this kind of thinking but, as ever during the last quarter of a century, among the leading protagonists in the field.

The culmination of Graves' latter-day writing, which has continued to flow notwithstanding administrative responsibilities, is a rounded study of the current crisis in education (Graves, 1988). Emphasis is on crisis rather than, as in an earlier paper, 'crisis and opportunity'. As usual, the work is timely, attentive to detail, sensitive to context, and balanced in contemplation of the complex conflicting ideologies embroiled in the crisis, specifically the retreat from consensus and the threat of a centralization process embodied in the so-called Education Reform Act of 1988. In assessing the pH value of this book, what is concerning is that so sane and liberal a commentator on the world education scene should be making judgements more acid than any he has penned before. As Norman Graves concludes, any sensible way ahead must involve a restoration of the value placed on education and its teachers, raising status and morale, rather than destabilizing the system and demoralizing the profession.

Norman J. Graves: a Bibliography, 1959-1990

ARTICLES

(1959) 'Over Vormende Waarde in France Middelbare Scholen', *Persoon en Gemeenschap*, XIII:2, Antwerp
(1960) 'The development of teacher training for public secondary schools in France', *Higher Education Journal* Vol 12 No 5
(1961) '"Comprehensive schools" in Engeland', *Persoon en Gemeenschap*, XIV:1, Antwerp
(1961) 'Hoe een comprehensive school Werkt', *Persoon en Gemeenschap*, XIV:3, Antwerp
(1963) 'De Democratisering Van Het Onderwys in Engeland', *Persoon en Gemeenschap*, XV:8-9, Antwerp
(1964) 'Technical education in France in the nineteenth century I: The first eighty years', *Vocational Aspects of Education*, XVI: 34
(1964) 'Technical education in France in the nineteenth century II: The last twenty years', *Vocational Aspects Of Education*, XVI: 35
(1964) 'Geography and Europe in secondary schools', *The European Teacher* Vol 1 No 2
(1964) 'The XXth International Geographical Congress London July 1964', *Geography* Vol XLIV Part 4
(1964) 'Geographical fieldwork in school', *The New Era* Vol 45 No 9
(1965) 'Une Californie Française, The Languedoc and Lower Rhone Irrigation Project', *Geography* Vol L Part 1
(1965) 'The "Grandes Ecoles" in France', *Vocational Aspects of Education*, XVII:36
(1966) 'Geography and philosophy' (with Simons, M.), *Bulletin of The University of London Institute of Education* New Series No 9
(1966) 'Exams: time for reappraisal', *The Teacher*, Vol 7 No 23
(1966) 'Drafting a geography programme', *The Teacher*, Vol 8, No 16
(1966) 'Fewer facts and more techniques', *The Teacher*, Vol 8 No 22

(1966) 'Meeting of geographers on the teaching of geography in Africa' *Geography* Vol 51 Part 2
(1967) 'Textbook test: 8 – geography to O-level', *New Education*, Vol 3 No 5
(1968) 'Geography, social science and interdisciplinary inquiry', *The Geographical Journal* Vol 134 Part 3
(1968) 'The High School Geography Project of The Association of American Geographers', *Geography* Vol 53 Part 1
(1969) 'New developments in geography in the UK and their relevance to teaching in schools', *The Geography Teacher*, The Association of Geography Teachers of India, Madras
(1970) 'Développements récents dans l'organisation de l'enseignement de la géographie en Grande Bretagne', *Cahiers de Géographie de Québec* 14e Annee No 31, Québec
(1970) 'The problem of food surpluses: approaches for the classroom', *The World and the School* No 19
(1971) 'Objectives in teaching particular subjects with special reference to the teaching of geography', *Bulletin of The University of London Institute of Education* New Series No 23
(1972) 'Le problème de la hiérarchie des objectifs de l'enseignement, de la géographie', *Didactique Géographie*, Vol 1 No 3, Faculté des Sciences de l'Education, Université de Montréal
(1973) 'Problems in the specification of the objectives of geographical education', *Journal of the Grantham College of Education*, Grantham College, Hong Kong
(1974) 'Geographical education in Britain: crisis and opportunity', *Geographical Education*, 2:2, Sydney Australia
(1975) 'A geographer looks at environmental education', *Forum* Central Institute of Education University of Delhi, Delhi
(1976) 'The International Geographical Union's Commission on Geography in Education', *Geography* Vol 61 Part 2
(1977) 'Geography and the 'N' and 'F' proposals', *Teaching Geography*, Vol 2 No 3
(1977) 'Geography in education at the 23rd International Geographical Congress, USSR, 1976', *Journal of Geography in Higher Education*, Vol 1 No 1
(1978) 'Ausbildung und Fortbildung der Geographielehrer für Sekundarschulen in England und Wales: gegenwärtige Probleme und künftige Möglichenkeiten', *Der Erdkundeunterricht* Heft 27, Ernst Klett Stuttgart

(1978) 'Changes of attitudes towards the training of teachers of Geography', *Geography* Vol 62 Part 2
(1978) 'Geographical education for the 16-19 age group. A British problem', in Okunrotifa, P.O. and Ola, D.K., *Commission on Geography in Education* University of Ibadan, Ibadan, Nigeria
(1978) 'Aims and objectives in degree curriculum design', *Journal of Geography in Higher Education* Vol 2 No 2
(1979) 'Contrasts and contradictions in geographical education', *Geography* Vol 64 No 4
(1980) 'Geographical education in Britain', *Progress in Human Geography* Vol 4 No 4
(1981) 'Spot on the EEC: France', *Geo* Series 3 Issue 2
(1981) 'Geographical education', *Progress in Human Geography* Vol 5 No 4
(1981) 'International aspects of geographical education', *Journal of Geography* Vol 80, USA
(1981) 'Can geographical studies be subsumed under one paradigm or are a plurality of paradigms inevitable?' *Terra* Vol 93, Helsinki
(1982) 'Geography: its relevance to education and life', *Conference and Workshop Papers* Geography Teachers' Association, Singapore
(1982) 'Geographical education', *Progress in Human Geography* Vol 6 No 4
(1982) 'The examination jungle: CEE and after', *Teaching Geography* Vol 7 No 3
(1983) 'Issues in geographical education', *Asian Culture* No 2, Singapore
(1983) 'Finalità e Strategie Didàttiche della Moderna Geografia', *La Geografia Nelle Scuole* , Vol 28:3, Rome
(1983) 'The Falklands or Las Malvinas: an issue in political geography', *Journal of Geography* Vol 82:3, USA
(1983) 'The case for higher education', *The Geographical Magazine* Vol LV No 8
(1985) 'Geography and recent trends in education for international understanding', *Terra* Vol 97 No 1, Helsinki
(1986) 'La géographie dans L'enseignement secondaire, l'expérience anglaise', *L'Espace Géographique* No 2, Paris
(1986) 'The environment under threat: a challenge to education', *The New Era* Vol 67 No 1
(1986) 'Education for human environmental values', *The New Era* Vol 67 No 4

(1987) 'Teacher quality and education', *The New Era* Vol 68 No 3
(1987) 'Research in geographical education', *New Zealand Journal o[f] Geography* No 84, Christchurch
(1988) 'Education for a caring community: retrospects and prospects' *The New Era in Education* Vol 68 No 2
(1990) 'First impressions' (with Kent, A., Lambert, D., Naish, M. an[d] Slater, F.) *Teaching Geography* Vol 15 No 1

Books and contributions to books

(1965) 'The teaching of regional geography to pupils aged 11-17 years' in *Final Report of Commission on Teaching of Geography*, The Geographical Institute/Denoyer Gippert, Chicago
(1965) Chapter 3 'Teaching techniques: direct observation', Chapter 4 'Teaching techniques: indirect observation', in Brouillette, B. (ed.) *Unesco Source Book For Geography Teaching*, Unesco/Longmans, London
(1966) *North America and Asia*, (with Honeybone, R.C.) Heinemann Educational Books, London
(1968) 'An investigation into the teaching of Asia in English and Welsh secondary schools', in Das Gupta, S. and Romanowska-Lakshmana, T. (Ed.) *IGU Abstract Of Papers*, Calcutta
(1969) 'A tropical peasant holding in Ceylon', in *Asian Sample Studies*, Geographical Association
(1971) *Geography in Secondary Education*, Geographical Association
(1971) *Geography of The British Isles*, (with White, J.T.) Heinemann Educational Books, London
(1972) Chapter 2 'The nature of geographical knowledge' (with Moore, T.) and Chapter 14. 'School examinations' in Graves, N., (Ed.) *New Movements in The Study and Teaching of Geography*, Maurice Temple Smith, London
(1972) 'The problem of hierarchy in the objectives of geography teaching at the pre-university level', in Adams, W.P. and Heillener, F.M., *International Geography 1972*, University of Toronto Press
(1972) *Geography in Education: a Bibliography of British Sources 1870-1970*, (with Lukehurst, C.) Geographical Association
(1973) 'A talk on modern geography', *Conference Report No 10*, University of London University Entrance and School Examinations Council

(1975) *Geography in Education*, Heinemann Educational Books, London
(1976) 'The education and training of teachers of geography for secondary schools in England and Wales', in *International Geography 1976: Section 10*, International Geographical Union.
(1979) *Curriculum Planning in Geography*, Heinemann Educational Books, London.
(1979) 'Marseilles – city, port and manufacturing', in Spicer, B., Achurch, M., Blatchford, K. and Stringer, W. (Eds.) *The Global System: Production and Space*, Jacaranda Press, Melbourne
(1980) *Geographical Education in Secondary Schools*, Geographical Association
(1980) 'Curriculum development in geography for the 14-19 age group: an overview' in Rawling, E. (Ed.) *Geography into the 1980s*, Geographical Association
(1980) 'Proposición de modelos en el planeamiento del curriculum de geografía' in Grenas, R. et al., *Informe Final: Reunión Regional sobre la Enseñanza de los Estudios Sociales*, Unión Geográfica Internacional y Ministerio de Educación, Costa Rica
(1980) 'Geography in education', in Brown, E.H. *Geography Yesterday and Tomorrow*, Oxford University Press
(1980) 'Paul Vidal De La Blache and geographical education in France' in Marsden, W.E. *Historical Perspectives on Geographical Education*, IGU and University of London Institute of Education
(1982) 'Schulgeographie in England und Wales', in Haubrich, H. (ed.) *Geographische Erziehung im Internationalen Blickfeld*, Westermann, Braunschweig
(1982) 'Research in geographical education' in Graves, N.J., Naish, M.C., Kent, W.A., Slater, F.A. and Hilton, K. *Geography in Education Now* Bedford Way Papers/Heinemann Educational Books, London
(1982) 'Emerging roles for geographic and social science curricula and instruction related to Latin America', in Horst, O. and Stoltman, J.P. (Ed.) *New Themes in Instruction of Latin American Geography*, Conference of Latin American Geographers, Muncie, Indiana, USA
(1982) *Geography and the Quality of Life*, International Council of Scientific Unions, Committee on the Teaching of Science
(1982) 'The evaluation of geographical education', in Graves, N.J., *New Unesco Source Book For Geography Teaching*, Unesco/Longman
(1982) 'The development of computer assisted learning in geography in

England and Wales' *Abstracts of The IGU Latin American Regional Conference*, International Geographical Union, Curitiba, Parana Brazil

(1984) 'Implications for teacher education: some examples', in Graves, N.J., Dunlop, O.J. and Torney-Purta, J.V. (Ed.) *Teaching for International Understanding, Peace and Human Rights,* Unesco, Paris

(1984) 'Educating geography teachers: the experience of England and Wales', in Marsden, W.E. (Ed.) *Teacher Education Models in Geography: An International Comparison*, Commission on Geographical Education, IGU and Department of Geography Western Michigan University, Kalamazoo, Michigan, USA

(1984) 'Graded tests in geography: an initial examination of the problems of their construction', in Haubrich, H. (Ed.) *Perception of People and Places Through Media*, Vol 2 Pädagogische Hochschule, Freiburg

(1985) *Teacher Education in Adversity*, University of London Institute of Education

(1987) *People and Environment*, (with Lidstone, J.G. and Naish, M.C.) Heinemann Educational Books

(1988) 'Curriculum development in the 1990s', in Gerber, R. and Lidstone, J.G., *Developing Skills in Geographical Education,* Jacaranda, Brisbane

(1988) *The Education Crisis: Which Way Now*? Christopher Helm, London

(1988) 'The changing nature of research in geographical education', in Gerber, R. and Lidstone, J.G., *Skills in Geographical Education*, IGU Symposium on Geographical Education, Brisbane

(1988) 'La Educación Geográfica en El Reino Unido', in Grupo Cronos *Reflexiones sobre la Enseñanza de la Geografia y la Historia en El Reino Unido y España*, Instituto Universitario De Ciencias De La Educación, Ediciones Universidad De Salamanca, Salamanca, Spain

(1988) 'Problemas De Contenido y Estrategias De Enseñanza En La Educación Geográfica', in Grupo Cronos, *Reflexiones sobre la Ensenañza de la Geográfia y la Historia en El Reino Unido y España*, Instituto Universitario De Ciencias De La Educación, Ediciones Universidad De Salamanca, Salamanca, Spain

(1989) 'Research in geographical education', in Graves, N., Kent, A., Naish, M., Slater, F., *Research in Geographical Education: MA Dissertations 1968-1988* Geography Section Institute of Education University of London

(1990) 'La Enseñanza Mediante La Actividad En Geografia', in Alminana, E.G., Ortiz, A.Z., Gonzales Munoz, M. del C., Fabregat, C.H., and San José, G.S. (Ed.) *Primeras Jornadas de Didáctica de la Geográfia,* Asociacion de Geográfos Españoles, Grupo de Didáctica, Madrid, Spain

(1990) 'Thinking and research on teacher education ', in Graves, N.J. (Ed.) *Initial Teacher Education: Policies and Progress* Kogan Page, London.

Report

(1990) *Geographical Information and Documentation on European Countries* Council for Cultural Co-operation, Council of Europe. DECS/EGT(90)

Translation

(1984) *La Géographie Dans Le Royaume Uni 1980-1984*, The Royal Society, London.

Editorships

(1968-1972) *Teaching Geography Series*, Geographical Association

(1972) *New Movements in the Study and Teaching of Geography*, Maurice Temple Smith, London

(1973) *Perspectives on Geographical Education* (with Bale, J. and Walford, R.), Oliver and Boyd, London.

(1974) *African Geography for Schools: a Handbook for Teachers* (with Brouillette, B. and Last, G.), Longman/Unesco, London

(1975) *Teaching Materials on Population, International Understanding and Environmental Education*, Unesco, Paris

(1976) *Geography in Education*, Abstracts and Papers, International Geographical Union, Commission on Geography in Education, Leningrad.

(1979) *Geographical Education: Curriculum Problems in Certain European Countries with Special Reference to the 16-19 Age Group*, Commission on Geographical Education, IGU and University of London Institute of Education

(1982) *New Unesco Source Book for Geography Teaching*, Longman/The Unesco Press, London

(1984) *Computer Assisted Learning in Geography*, Commission on Geographical Education, IGU and University of London Institute of Education

(1984) *Research and Research Methods in Geographical Education*, Commission on Geographical Education, IGU and University of London Institute of Education

(1984) *Teaching for International Understanding, Peace and Human Rights* (with Dunlop, O.J. and Torney-Purta, J.V.), Unesco, Paris

(1986) *Profiling In Geography* (with Naish, M.C.), Geographical Association, Sheffield

(1987) *Land, Water and Mineral Resources in Science Education*, Pergamon, Oxford.

(1990) *Initial Teacher Education: Policies and Progress*, Kogan Page, London.

Bibliography

ABEGUNDE, M.A.A. et al (eds.) (1987), *Perspectives on Senior Secondary Geography* (Proceedings of the conference on Senior Secondary Geography, Ahmadu Bello, University of Zaria). Lagos: the High School Geography Committee of the Nigerian Geographical Association.

ACHEBE, C. (1958), *Things Fall Apart*. London: Heinemann.

ACHUFUSI, U.D. (1984), 'Factors influencing students' choice of geography in West African School Certificate examination: a survey study in Njikoka local government area of Anambra State', unpublished BEd dissertation. Benin: University of Benin.

ADEGOKE, K.A. (1987), 'Constraints on the changing Nigerian High School geography curriculum: an expository study', in Abegunde et al (eds.).

AGENCY FOR INSTRUCTIONAL TECHNOLOGY (1988), 'Global geography use spans continents, cultures', *AIT Newsletter*, *19* (4), 2 - 3.

AKOREDE, V.E.A. (1987), 'Major implementation challenges of the senior secondary school geography curriculum', in Abegunde, et al (eds.).

ALLEN, R. (1988a), 'A survey of computer usage and views on CAL among secondary geography teachers', unpublished.

——— (1988b), 'Delphi study on new technology in the teaching of secondary school geography by the year 2000. The Final Consensus Predictions', unpublished.

AMBIO (1982), Special issue on 'Nuclear war: the aftermath', *Ambio*, *11* (2 - 3).

——— (1989), Special issue on 'Nuclear war and the environment', *Ambio*, *18* (7).

ANDREWS, J. (1959), *Comments: Geography Syllabus, Fourth and Fifth Years*. Sydney: Board of Secondary School Studies.

AWARITEFE, O.D. and OMOGBAI, B.E. (1987), 'The Local weather station and the new senior secondary school geography curriculum: a dimension of practical approach', in Abegunde et al.

BACKLER, A. (1988), *Teacher's Guide: global geography*. Bloomington, IN: Agency for Instructional Technology.

BAILEY, P. (1974), *Teaching Geography*. Newton Abbott: David and Charles.

——— (1987), 'What are the geographer's contributions? Geography in the curriculum from 5 to 19', in Bailey and Binns, (eds.).

——— and BINNS, T. (eds.) (1987), *A Case for Geography: a response to the Secretary of State for Education from members of the Geographical Association*. Sheffield: Geographical Association.

BAKARE, C.M. (1971), 'Levels of cognitive functioning tested by past School Certificate geography examinations', in J.A. Majasan, (ed.), *New Dimensions in Nigerian High School Geography*. Ibadan: University of Ibadan.

BAKER, J. and DRUMMOND, J. (1984), 'Environmental monitoring and map revision using integrated Landsat and digital cartographic data', *ITC Journal*, *1*, 10 - 19.

BAKER, S. (1988), 'A personal survey into the state of information technology in geography', unpublished.

BALCHIN, W.G.V. (1965), *The Times Educational Supplement*, 2633, 5 November, 947.

BALE, J. (1976), *The Location of Manufacturing Industry*. London: Longman.

——— (1982), *Patterns of Underdevelopment*. Walton-on-Thames: Nelson.

——— (1983), 'Welfare geography', in Huckle (ed.). (1983a), 64-73.

———(1987), *Geography in the Primary School*. London: Routledge & Kegan Paul.

BALLEY, C. (1972), 'L'enseignement de la géographie à travers l'activité d'une section des congrès', in International Geographical Union, *Geography through a Century of International Congresses*, 161 - 173.

BARROWS, T.S. (1981), *College Students' Knowledge and Beliefs: a survey of global understanding*. New Rochelle, NY: Change Magazine Press.

BARTLETT, D.B. (1948), 'An investigation into the attitudes of boys and girls towards the content of, and the methods of teaching geography in grammar schools', unpublished MA dissertation. London: Institute of Education, University of London.

BARTZ, B. (1965), *Map Design for Children*. Field Enterprises Educational Corporation, mimeo. Chicago ILL: University of Chicago.

BEDDIS, R.A. (1982), *A Sense of Place*, 3 volumes and *Teacher's Guide*. Oxford: Oxford University Press.

BENFIELD, E. (1987), *Industry and Primary Schools*. Cambridge: Hobsons.

BERRY, R. (1985), 'Beyond all reasonable doubt: an enquiry-based unit using evidence from geography textbooks', *Geographical Education*, *5*(1), 8 - 10.

BERTIN, J. (1981), *Graphics and Graphic Information Processing*. Berlin: de Gruyter.

——— (1983), *Semiology of Graphics*. Wisconsin: University of Wisconsin Press.

BIDDLE, D.S. (1971), 'The quest for reliability in marking responses to essay questions in geography', *Geographical Education*, *1*(3), 286 - 295.

——— (1980), 'Paradigms and geography curricula in England and Wales, 1882-1972', *Geographical Education*, *3*, 577 - 98.

——— (1982), 'Course planning in geography', in N.J. Graves, ed., *New Unesco Source Book for Geography Teaching*. Harlow: Longman/The Unesco Press.

——— and SHORTLE, D. (1969), *Programme Planning in Geography*. Australia: Martindale Press.

BLAIR, C.L. and SIMPSON, R. (1984), *The Canadian Landscape*. Toronto: Copp Clark Pitman.

BLENKIN, G.M. and KELLY, A.V. (eds.), (1983), *The Primary Curriculum in Action. A process approach to educational practice*. London: Harper & Row.

——— (1987), *Early Childhood Education: a development curriculum*. London: Paul Chapman Publishing.

BLOOM, B.S. et al (1956), *Taxonomy of Educational Objectives, The Cognitive Domain*. London: Longman.

BLYTH, A., COOPER, K., DERRICOT, R., ELLIOTT, G., SUMNER, H. and WAPLINGTON, A. (1976), *Place, Time and Society 8-13: Curriculum Planning in History, Geography and Social Science*. Bristol: Collins-ESL for the Schools Council.

BLYTH, J. (1985), *Place and Time with Children Five to Nine*. Beckenham: Croom Helm.

BLYTH, W.A.L. (1984), *Development, Experience and Curriculum in Primary Education*. Beckenham: Croom Helm.

BOARD OF SECONDARY EDUCATION (1987), *Geography Syllabus, Years 11-12, 2 Unit and 3 Unit Course*. Sydney: Government Printer.

BOARD OF SECONDARY SCHOOL STUDIES, NEW SOUTH WALES (1954), *Syllabus in Geography*, Sydney: Government Printer.

BOARD OF SECONDARY SCHOOL STUDIES, QUEENSLAND (1977), *Introduction to Syllabus in Geography Years 11-12*. Brisbane.

BOARD OF SENIOR SCHOOL STUDIES (1963), Cyclostyled information forwarded to members of Syllabus Committees. Sydney: Government Printer.

——— (1965), *Geography Syllabus, Forms 5 and 6, First, Second and Third Levels*. Sydney: Government Printer.

——— (1973), *Geography Syllabus and Notes on the Syllabus, Forms 5 and 6, 3 Unit and 2 Unit Course*. Sydney: Government Printer.

——— (1980), *Geography: Natural and Human Systems, Syllabus and Notes on the Syllabus, 2 Unit and 3 Unit Course*. Sydney: Government Printer.

——— (1982), *Specimen Examination Questions: 2 Unit course: Natural and Human Systems, 3 Unit Course: Natural and Human Systems*. Sydney: Government Printer.

BOARDMAN, D. (1983), *Graphicacy and Geography Teaching*. Beckenham: Croom Helm.

——— (ed.) (1985), *New Directions in Geographical Education*. Lewes: Falmer Press.

——— (ed.) (1986), *Handbook for Geography Teachers*. Sheffield: Geographical Association.

——— (1988), *The Impact of a Curriculum Project: geography for the young school leaver*. Birmingham: University of Birmingham, *Educational Review*, Occasional Publications.

BODEN, P.K. (1976), *Developments in Geography Teaching*, London, Open Books.

——— (1977), *Promoting International Understanding Through School Textbooks: a case study*. Braunschweig: Georg Eckert Institut für Internationale Schulbuchforschung.

BOS, E. (1984), 'Systematic symbol design in cartographic education', *ITC Journal*, *1*, 20 - 28.

BRISCALL, J.R. (1980), 'From space to place in school geography teaching', unpublished MA dissertation. London: Institute of Education, University of London.

BROUILLETTE, B. (1961), 'La place de la géographie dans un enseignement adapté à l'époque moderne', *Revue analytique de l'education*, Paris, Unesco, *XIII*(1), 5 - 10.

——— GRAVES, N.J., LAST, G.C. (1974), *African Geography for Schools: a handbook for teachers*, London, Longman/Unesco.

BROUGH, E. (1983), 'Geography through art' in J. Huckle, (ed.) (1983a).

BROWN, E.H. (ed.) (1980), *Geography, Yesterday and Tomorrow*. Oxford: Oxford University Press.

BROWN, T.W. (1967), 'Commission on the Teaching of Geography', in J.W. Watson, (ed.) *20th International Congress: Congress Proceedings*, London, Nelson, 271 - 274.

BRUNER, J.S. (1960), *The Process of Education*. New York: Vintage Books.

——— (1967), *Towards a Theory of Instruction*. Cambridge, Mass: Belknap Press.

BUNGE, W. (1986), 'Epilogue: Our planet is big enough for peace but too small for war', in Johnson and Taylor (eds.), 289 - 291.

——— (1987), *Nuclear War Atlas*, 2nd edition. Oxford: Basil Blackwell.

BURNLEY, J. (1983), *Peace Education in NSW Schools*. Sydney: Government Printer.

———(1988), 'Teaching for human rights in geography', in Fien and Gerber (eds.), 61 - 79.

BURNS, R. (1986) 'The contemporary world and the classroom', *Ethos*, 10 - 14.

BURROUGH, P. (1986), *Principles of Geographical Information Systems for Land Resources Assessment*. Oxford: Clarendon Press.

BUTLER, J., CLOUGH, R., GERBER, R., SENIOR, C., SMITH, S., and WILSON, W. (1983-1985), *Jacaranda Atlas Programme*, Brisbane, Jacaranda.

——— et al. (1985), *Skills Book for Secondary Schools*, Jacaranda Atlas Programme. Brisbane: Jacaranda.

CARTER, D. (1986), *The Remote Sensing Sourcebook*, London: McCarta/ Kogan Page.

CASTELLS, M. (1978), *City, Class and Power*. London: Macmillan.

CATLING, S. (1985), *Mapstart*, Collins-Longman Atlas Programme, Glasgow/Harlow: Collins/Longman.

——— (1987), 'The child is a geographer: criteria for geographical content in the primary school curriculum', in Bailey and Binns (eds.).

——— (1988), 'Children and geography', in Mills (ed.).

——— (1989), 'Sound directions?', *The Times Educational Supplement*, 8 December, 43-44.

——— (1990a), *Issues in Mapping the Future of School Geography 5-16: The Response of the Geographical Association to the Interim Report of the National Curriculum Geography Working Group*. Sheffield: Geographical Association.

——— (1990b), 'Subjecting geography to the National Curriculum', *The Curriculum Journal*, *1*(1), 77-90.

——— (1990c), 'A primary perspective: the views of primary teachers on the Geography Working Group's Interim Report', *Primary Geographer*, 4 (Summer)

CHAMBERS, W. (1990), 'Gran loves it!', *Primary Geographer*, 3 (Spring)

CHORLEY, R.J., and HAGGETT, P. (1965), *Frontiers in Geographical Teaching: The Madingley Lectures in 1963*. London: Methuen.

CODRINGTON, D. (1987), 'An analysis of the process of curriculum development: a case study of the evolution of a new senior geography syllabus in New South Wales, 1982-1986', unpublished MA thesis. New South Wales: Macquarie University..

COHEN, A. and COHEN, L. (eds.) (1986), *Primary Education: a sourcebook for teachers*. London: Harper & Row.

COLE, J.P., and BEYNON, N.J. (1968-72), *New Ways in Geography Series*. Oxford: Basil Blackwell.

COLLIS, K., and BIGGS, J. (1979), *Classroom Examples of Cognitive Development: the solo taxonomy*. Hobart: University of Tasmania.

CONNER, C. (1974), 'Geography in middle schools', *Teaching Geography*, *1* (4), 178- 182.

CONTEMPORARY ISSUES (1987), 'War and Peace', Special Issue, *Contemporary Issues in Geography and Education*, *2* (3).

COOKE, D. et al. (1985), *Teaching Development Issues* (a set of seven books for teachers and pupils). Manchester: Manchester Polytechnic Development Education Project.

COOPER, D. (1988), 'Mapping skills required by geography students taking the General Certificate of Education at Advanced level', *Proceedings*, Volume 2, Symposium on Skills in Geographical Education, International Geographical Union, Brisbane, 609 - 613.

CORNEY, G. (1981), *Teacher Education and Geography 16-19*. London: University of London, Geography 16-19 Project.

COX, B. (1971), 'Curriculum process in the development of geography courses in secondary schools', paper read at ANZAAS Conference, 43rd Congress, Brisbane and reprinted in D.S. Biddle and C.E. Deer (eds.), *Readings in Geographical Education*, Vol. 1. Sydney: Whitcombe & Tombs.

COX, C., and SCRUTON, R. (1985), *Peace Studies: A Critical Survey*. London: Institute for European Defence and Strategic Studies.

CRACKNELL, G. (1985), 'The setting up and evaluation of an inservice course for computer assisted learning in geography', unpublished MA dissertation. London: Institute of Education, University of London.

CRACKNELL, J.R. (1976), 'Geography in junior schools', *Geography*, *61* (3), 150 - 156.

CUMMINGS, R. (1984), 'Pupil-talk in groups during a CAL simulation game', unpublished MA dissertation. London: Institute of Education, University of London.

CURRAN, P. (1985), *Principals of Remote Sensing*. Harlow: Longman.

——— and WARDLEY, N. (1985), 'Remote sensing in secondary school geography: the place of Landsat MSS', *Geography*, *70*, 237 - 247.

DADARE, J.A. (1987), 'Making Geography lively through improvisation and modelling: the Ikere experiment', in Abegunde et al.

DAUGHERTY, R. (ed.) (1989), *Geography in the National Curriculum. A Viewpoint from the Geographical Association*. Sheffield: Geographical Association.

DAVIDSON, G. (1984) 'Geography and the challenge of TVEI', *Teaching Geography*, *10*(1) 3 - 5.

DAVIES, W.K. (1972), *The Conceptual Revolution in Geography*. London: University of London Press.

DEPARTMENT OF EDUCATION AND SCIENCE (1978), *Primary Education in England*. London: HMSO.

——— (1981), *The School Curriculum*. London. HMSO.

——— (1982a), *Education 5 to 9*. London: HMSO.

——— (1982b) *The New Teacher in School*, London: HMSO.

——— (1983), *9 to 13 Middle Schools*. London: HMSO.

——— (1985a), *Education 8 to 12 in Combined and Middle Schools*. London: HMSO.

——— (1985b), *Better Schools*. London: HMSO.

——— (1985c) *The Educational System of England and Wales*. London: HMSO.

——— (1986), *Geography from 5 to 16*. London: HMSO.

——— (1987a), *The National Curriculum 5 to 16: A Consultative Document*. London: DES.

——— (1987b), *Primary Schools: Some Aspects of Good Practice*. London: HMSO.

——— (1988a), *The New Teacher in School*, London, HMSO.

——— (1988b), *National Curriculum Design and Technology Working Group*. Interim Report, unpublished.

——— (1988c), *Science for Ages 5 to 16*. London: HMSO.

——— (1989a), *National Curriculum. From Policy to Practice*. London: DES.

——— (1989b), *Aspects of Primary Education: the teaching and learning of history and geography*. London: HMSO.

——— (1989c), *National Curriculum Geography Working Group Interim Report*. London: DES.

——— (1989d), Department of Education and Science News, 139/89, *National Curriculum Geography Working Group, Terms of Reference and Supplementary Guidance to the Chairman of the Geography Working Group*. London: DES.

———(1990a), *Geography for Ages 5 to 16*, London, DES.

——— (1990b), *Draft Statutory Orders for Geography in the National Curriculum*, London: HMSO.

——— (1991), *Geography in the National Curriculum*, London, HMSO.

DIAMOND, N. (1976), *Signs, Beautiful Noise*, CBS Records, USA.

DONALDSON, O.F. (1971), 'Geography and the Black American: the white papers and the invisible man', *Journal of Geography*, *70*, 138 - 149.

DOTTO, L. (1986), *Planet Earth in Jeopardy: environmental consequences of nuclear war*. Chichester: John Wiley & Sons.

DOVE, M.J. (1987), 'Opportunities and obstacles: the adoption of computer-assisted learning by geography teachers in Victoria, Australia', unpublished MA dissertation. London: Institute of Education, University of London.

DOWLING, M. (1980), *Early Projects*. London: Longman.

ECONOMIC AND SOCIAL RESEARCH COUNCIL (1988), 'Geographical Information Systems', *Newsletter 63*, October.

EDUCATION REFORM ACT (1988), London: HMSO.

EHRLICH, P., SAGAN, C., KENNEDY, D., and ROBERTS, W.O. (1983), *The Cold and the Dark: the world after nuclear war*. London: Sedgwick & Jackson.

EISNER, E. (1979), *The Educational Imagination*. Basingstoke: Macmillan.

ELLUL, J. (1981), *Perspectives on Our Age*. New York: Salisbury Press.

——— (1988), *Le bluff technologique*. Paris: Hachette.

ELSOM, D. (1985), 'Climatological effects of a large scale nuclear exchange: a review', in Pepper and Jenkins, (eds.), 126 - 147.

ENVIRONMENT (1988), Special issue on 'The environmental consequences of nuclear war', *Environment*, *30*(5).

EOSAT (1988), *Landsat Data User Notes*, *3* (2). Maryland: Eosat, Lanham.

EVERSON, J., and FITZGERALD, B.P. (1969), *Settlement Patterns*. London: Longman.

FAIRBROTHER, R. (ed.) (1985), *Primary Contact* Special Issue No. 3: Microcomputers. Manchester: Manchester Polytechnic.

FAIRGRIEVE, J. (1926), *Geography in School*. London: University of London Press.

FALCONER, A. and GERBER, R. (1978), *Landsat Satellite Images for the Classroom*. Melbourne: Jacaranda.

FEDERAL MINISTRY OF EDUCATION (1986), *Geography Curriculum for Senior Secondary Schools*. Lagos: Federal Ministry of Education.

FIEN, J. (1983), 'Humanistic geography', in J. Huckle (ed.) (1983a).

——— et al. (1984), *The Geography Teacher's Guide to the Classroom*. Melbourne: Macmillan.

——— (1988), 'Skills for living: A geographical perspective', in R. Gerber and J. Lidstone, (eds.), *Skills in Geographical Education*, Brisbane: International Geographical Union with The Jacaranda Press, Ch. 18.

——— , and GERBER, R., (eds.) (1988), *Teaching Geography for a Better World*. Edinburgh: Oliver and Boyd.

——— , and SLATER, F. (1981), 'Exploring values and attitudes through group discussion and evaluation', *Classroom Geographer*, April, 22 - 25.

FISHER, S., and HICKS, D. (1985), *World Studies 8-13: A Teacher's Handbook*, Edinburgh, Oliver & Boyd.

FITZGERALD, B.P. (1974), *Science in Geography Series*. Oxford: Oxford University Press.

FORD, E., and ROWE, B. (1956), *Africa and the Americas*. Sydney: Angus & Robertson.

——— (1958), *Eurasia and Australasia*. Sydney: Angus & Robertson.

FOX, P. (1984), *List of Geography Microcomputer Software*. Sheffield: The Geographical Association.

——— , and TAPSFIELD, A. (1986), *The Role and Value of New Technology in Geography: some practical suggestions*. Sheffield: The Geographical Association.

FREEMAN, D. (1981), 'Computer assisted learning in geography – a case study of Hertfordshire secondary schools', unpublished MA dissertation. London: Institute of Education, University of London.

——— (1988), 'Computers and geography', in J. Burden (ed.), *Geography 'Coming of Age'*. Hertfordshire Geography Teachers Association.

GALLUP, G. (1980), 'The twelfth annual Gallup poll of the public's attitudes towards the public schools', *Phi Delta Kappan*, *61* (1), 45.

GALTUNG, J. (1976), 'Peace Education: problems and conflicts', in M. Haavelsrud (ed.), *Education for Peace*. Guildford: Science and Technology Press, 80 - 87.

——— (1980), *The True Worlds: a transnational perspective*. New York: The Free Press.

GARDNER, D.P. (1986), 'Geography in the school curriculum', *Annals of the Association of American Geographers*, *76* (1), 2.

GAUTHIER, A., and VAUZELLE, M. (1986), *La Télédétection Spatiale: Un Nouvelle Visage de la Corse*. Ajaccio: CNES-CDRP.

GCE BOARDS (1983), *Common Cores at A Level*, Prepared by the GCE Boards of England, Wales and Northern Ireland.

GENIP (1987), *K – 6 Geography: themes, key ideas, and learning opportunities*. Indiana, PA: National Council for Geographic Education.

——— (1989), *Geography in Grades 7 - 12: themes, key ideas and learning opportunities*. Indiana, PA: National Council for Geographic Education.

GEOGRAPHICAL ASSOCIATION (1987a), *GA News*. Sheffield: Geographical Association, October.

——— (1987b), *Programme of the (1987) Annual Conference* 21-23 April. Sheffield: Geographical Association.

——— (undated), *The Geographical Association*, Sheffield, The Geographical Association.

GERASIMOV, I.P. (1985), 'Geography of peace and war: a Soviet view', in Pepper and Jenkins, (eds.), 192 - 201.

GERBER, R. (1980), 'Development of competence and performance in cartographic language by children at the concrete level of map-reasoning', unpublished PhD thesis. Brisbane: University of Queensland.

——— (1982), 'An international study of children's perception and understanding of type used on atlas maps', *The Cartographic Journal*, *19*(2), 115 - 121.

——— (1984a), 'What should maps do to be effective?' Paper presented to the 26th Australian Surveying Congress, Brisbane.

——— (1984b), 'A form-function analysis of school atlases', in Haubrich (ed.), (1984), *2*, 657 - 689.

——— (1985), 'Competence and performance in cartographic language', in Boardman (ed.), 153 - 170.

——— (1987), 'Gifted children and their development of understanding maps', in R. Gerber (ed.), *Research in Geographical Education*, *3*, 115 - 136.

——— , and LYONS, K. (1984a), 'The cartographic communication project: a process for developing more appropriate maps', Paper presented to the 25th Congress of the International Geographical Union, Paris.

——— , and LYONS, K. (1984b), 'Caring for the map user', paper presented to the 12th International Conference of the International Cartographic Association, Perth, Western Australia.

——— , LIDSTONE, J., and MEAD, S. (1989), *Living in Our World, 1*. Brisbane: The Jacaranda Press.

GHAYE, A.L. (1989), 'A teacher, an adult, or a friend?' in F.A. Slater, (ed.) (1989).

GHAYE, T., and GHAYE, L. (1983), *Discovering Geography Series*. London: Macmillan.

GILBERT, R. (1984), *The Impotent Image: reflections of ideology in the secondary school curriculum*. Lewes: The Falmer Press.

——— (1986), 'That's where they have to go: the challenge of ideology in geography', *Geographical Education*, *5*, (2), 43 - 46.

GILLIGAN, C. (1982), *In a Different Voice*. Harvard: Harvard University Press.

GOODLAD, J. (1966), *The Changing School Curriculum*. New York: Fund for the Advancement of Education.

GRAHAM, W.S. (1981), 'The readability of textual materials in biology', unpublished MPhil thesis. Birmingham: University of Aston at Birmingham.

GRAVES, N.J. (1957), 'Some historical and comparative aspects of the teaching of geography in French public secondary schools during the nineteenth and twentieth centuries', unpublished MA thesis. London: University of London.

——— (1964a), 'Technical education in France in the nineteenth century, Parts I and II', *The Vocational Aspect*, *16*(34), 148 - 160; *16*(35), 163 - 175.

——— (1964b), 'Geography field work in schools', *New Era*, *45*(11), 251 - 256.

——— (1965a), 'The "grand écoles" in France', *The Vocational Aspect*, *17*(36), 40 - 49.

——— (1965b), 'Teaching techniques: direct observation', in *Source Book for Geography Teaching*. London: Longmans/UNESCO, 36 - 74.

——— (1965c), 'Teaching techniques: indirect observation', in *Source Book for Geography Teaching*. London: Longmans/UNESCO, 75 - 141.

——— (1966a), 'Meeting of geographers on the teaching of geography in Africa: a joint Unesco/IGU seminar', *Geography*, *51*(2), 1966, 126 - 127.

———, and SIMONS, M. (1966b), 'Geography and philosophy', in J. Bale, N.J. Graves, and R. Walford (eds.) (1973), *Perspectives in Geographical Education*, 27 - 34.

——— (1968a), 'An investigation into the teaching of Asia in English and Welsh secondary schools', in S.D. Gupta, and T.R. Lakshaman (eds.), *Abstracts of Papers of 21st International Geographical Union Congress, Delhi, 1968*. Calcutta: National Committee for Geography, 393.

——— (1968b), 'Geography, social science and inter-disciplinary enquiry', *Geographical Journal*, *134*(3), 390 - 394.

——— (1968c), 'The High School Geography Project of the Association of American Geographers', *Geographical Journal 134* (3).

——— (1969), 'A tropical peasant holding in Ceylon', in *Asian Sample Studies*. Sheffield: Geographical Association, 14 - 22.

——— (1971a) *Geography in Secondary Education*. Sheffield: Geographical Association.

———, and WHITE, J.T. (1971b), *Geography of the British Isles*. London: Heinemann Educational Books.

———, and LUKEHURST, C.T. (1972a), *Geography in Education: a bibliography of British sources, 1870-1970*. Sheffield: Geographical Association.

———, and MOORE, T. (1972b), 'The nature of geographical knowledge', in N.J. Graves (ed.) *New Movements in the Study and Teaching of Geography*. London: Temple Smith, 17 - 28.

——— (1972c) 'The problem of hierarchy in the objectives of teaching at the pre-university level', in W.P. Adams and F.H. Helleiner (eds.) *International Geography 1972: the 22nd International Geographical Union Congress, Montreal*. Toronto: University of Toronto Press, 1045 - 1047.

——— (1972d), 'School examinations', in N.J. Graves (ed.), *New Movements in the Study and Teaching of Geography*. London: Temple Smith, 171 - 187.

——— (1974), 'Geographical education in Britain: crisis and opportunity', *Geographical Education*, *2*(2), 147 - 158.

——— (1975a), *Geography in Education*. London: Heinemann Educational Books.

——— (ed.) (1975b), *Teaching Materials on Population, International Understanding and Environmental Education*. Paris: Unesco.

——— , LAST, G., and BROUILETTE, B. (eds.) (1975c), *African Geography for Schools: a Handbook*. London: Unesco/Longman.

——— (1976a) 'The education and training of teachers of geography for secondary schools in England and Wales: present problems and future possibilities', in V.P. Maksakovsky and L.L. Abramov (eds.), *Geographical Education, Geographical Literature and Dissemination of Geographical Knowledge*. Moscow: International Geographical Union, 70 - 77.

——— (1976b), 'The International Geographical Union's Commission on Geography in Education', *Geography*, *61*, 95 - 96.

——— (1977), 'Geography and the N. and F. examination proposals', *Teaching Geography*, *2*(3), 131 - 132.

——— (ed.) (1978a), *Geographical Education: curriculum problems in certain European countries with special reference to the 16-19 age group*. London: International Geographical Union Commission on Geographical Education/Institute of Education, University of London.

——— (1978b), 'Changes in attitudes towards the training of teachers of geography', *Geography*, *63*(2), 259 - 267.

——— (1979a), *Curriculum Planning in Geography*. London: Heinemann Educational Books.

——— (1979b), 'Contrasts and contradictions in geographical education', *Geography*, *64*(1), 259 - 267.

——— (1980a) *Geographical Education in Secondary Schools*. Sheffield: Geographical Association.

——— (1980b), 'Geography in education' in Brown (ed.), 1980, 100 - 113.

——— (1980c), 'Geographical education in Britain', *Progress in Human Geography*, *4*(4), 560 - 567.

——— (1980d), 'Curriculum development in geography for the 14-19 age group: an overview', in E. Rawling (ed.) *Geography into the 1980s*. Sheffield: Geographical Association, 57 - 60.

——— (1980e) 'Paul Vidal de la Blache and Geographical Education in France', in W.E. Marsden, (ed.) *Historical Perspectives on Geographical Education*, London, International Geographical Union Commission on Geographical Education, Institute of Education, Univeristy of London, 8 - 17.

——— (1981a), 'Geographical education', in *Progress in Human Geography*, *6*(4), 562 - 571.

——— (1981b), 'International aspects of geographical education', *Journal of Geography*, *80*(3), 84 - 86.

——— (1981c), 'Can geographical studies be subsumed under one paradigm or are a plurality of paradigms inevitable?' *Terra*, *93*(3), 85 - 90.

——— (1982a), 'Geographical education', *Progress in Human Geography*, *6*(4), 563 - 575.

——— (1982b), 'School geography in England and Wales', in Haubrich (ed.), 1982, 92 - 99.

——— (1982c), 'Geography in education: a review', in A. Kent (ed.), *Perspectives on a Changing Geography*. Sheffield: Geographical Association, 15 - 22.

——— (1982d), 'Research in geographical education', in Graves et al., 1985c, 52 - 60.

——— (1982e), 'The evaluation of geographical education', in Graves (ed.), 1982h, 313 - 363.

——— (1982f), 'The examinations jungle: CEE and after', *Teaching Geography*, *7*(3), 133 - 135.

——— (1982g), *Geography, and Quality of Life*, International Council of Scientific Unions Committee on the Teaching of Science.

——— (ed.) (1982h), *New Unesco Source Book for Geography Teaching*. London: Longman/The Unesco Press.

——— (1983), 'The Falklands or Las Malvinas: an issue in political geography', *Journal of Geography*, 8(3), 123 - 125.

——— (ed.) (1984a), *Computer Assisted Learning in Geography*, London: International Geographical Union Commission on Geographical Education/University of London Institute of Education.

——— (ed.) (1984b), *Research and Research Methods in Geographical Education*. London: International Geographical Union Commission on Geographical Education/University of London Institute of Education.

——— (1984c), 'Graded tests in geography: an initial examination of problems of their construction', in H. Haubrich (ed.), *2*, 500 - 521.

——— , TORNEY, J., and DUNLOP, O.J. (eds.) (1984d), *Teaching for International Understanding, Peace and Human Rights*. Paris: Unesco.

——— (1984e), 'Implications for teacher education: some examples', in Graves, Torney and Dunlop, 1984d.

——— (1984f) 'Educating geography teachers: the experience of England', in W.E. Marsden (ed.), *Teacher Education Models in Geography: an International Comparison*. Kalamazoo: International Geographical Union Commission on Geographical Education/Western Michigan University, 35 - 43.

———(1985a), 'Geography and recent trends in education for international understanding', *Terra*, *97*(1), 45 - 49.

——— (1985b), *Teacher Education in Adversity*. London: Institute of Education, University of London.

______ , NAISH, M., SLATER, F., KENT, A. and HILTON, K. (1985c), *Geography in Education Now*, Bedford Way Papers, 13, revised edition. London: Institute of Education, University of London.

______ (1986a), 'Education for human environmental values', *New Era*, *67*(4), 3 - 5.

______ , and NAISH, M. (eds.) (1986b), *Profiling in Geography*. Sheffield: Geographical Association.

______, LIDSTONE, J., and NAISH, M.C. (1987a), *People and Environment: a world perspective*. London: Heinemann Educational Books.

______ (ed.) (1987b), *Land, Water and Mineral Resources in Science Education*. Oxford: Pergamon Press.

______ (1988a), *The Education Crisis: which way now?* London: Christopher Helm.

______ (1988b), 'The changing nature of research in geographical education' in R. Gerber and J.G. Lidstone (eds), *Studies in Geographical Education*. Brisbane: IGU Symposium on Geographical Education.

______ , KENT, W.A., LAMBERT, D., NAISH, M., and SLATER, F.A. (1989), *Research in Geography Education: MA dissertations 1968-88*. London: Institute of Education, University of London.

______ (ed.) (1990), *Initial Teacher Education: policies and progress*, London Education Studies. London: Kogan Page in association with the Institute of Education, University of London.

GREGORY, D. (1985), 'People, places and practices: the future of human geography' in R. King (ed.), *Geographical Futures*. Sheffield: Geographical Association.

GREIG, S., PIKE, G. and SELBY, D. (1987), *Earthrights: education as if the planet really mattered*, London: Kogan Page.

GRENYER, N. et al (1979), *Oxford Geography Project*, Oxford: Oxford University Press.

GRUMMITT, S. (1978), 'The computer in the classroom – computer assisted learning in geography at the secondary level ', unpublished MA dissertation. London: Institute of Education, University of London.

GUNNING, S., GUNNING D. and WILSON, J. (1980), *Topic Teaching in the Primary School*. Beckenham: Croom Helm.

HAILE, D.M. (1988), 'Thinking into another's environment – an investigation into learner response to pictures of village scenes in Africa', unpublished MA dissertation. London: Institute of Education, University of London.

HALL, D.B. (1976), *Geography and the Geography Teacher*. London: Allen and Unwin.

HALL, D., KENT, W.A., and WIEGAND, P. (1982), 'Geography teaching and computers', *Teaching Geography*, January.

______ (1985), 'CAL in geography: the state of the art', *Teaching Geography*, January.

HARRISON, C. (1979), 'Assessing the readability of school texts' in E.A. Lunzer and W.K. Gardner, *The Effective Use of Reading*. London: Heinemann.

HART, C. (ed.) (1985), *Worldwide Issues in Geography*. London: Collins.

HARVEY, D. (1969), *Explanation in Geography*. London: Edward Arnold.

——— (1973), *Social Justice and the City*. London: Edward Arnold.

HASSELL, D. (1982), 'Teacher style and computer assisted learning in geography', unpublished MA dissertation. London: Institute of Education, University of London.

HATT, T. (1987), 'Images de la terre, cartes et échelles', in *du Satellite a la classe: images de télédétection en physique, géographie, sciences naturelles, Recontres pédagogiques, 17*, Paris: INRP.

HAUBRICH, H. (ed.) (1982), *International Focus on Geographical Education*. Braunschweig: Westermann.

——— (ed.) (1984), *Perception of People and Places Through Media*. Freiburg: International Geographical Union Commission on Geographical Education, Pädagogische Hochschule.

——— (1986), 'Geography for international understanding - a world perspective', in Hernando, (ed.) *Geography, Education and Society*, Sitges.

——— (ed.) (1988a), 'How I see my country. Personal views on 15 year olds from 28 countries', Freiburg (to receive through the editor).

——— (ed.) (1988b) 'Where and how I live, 10 year olds write for the children in the world', Freiburg (to receive through the editor).

HAWKINS, G. (1989), *The Landsat Environmental Education Project*. World Wide Fund for Nature, *Lifelines*.

HEBDEN, R. (ed.) (undated), *Geography Graduate Careers*. Sheffield: Geographical Association.

HENLEY, R. (1986), 'Ideology in school geography: a consideration of methodology and language', unpublished MA disseration, Institute of Education, University of London, and also 'The ideology of geographical discourse', in F.A. Slater (ed.) (1989).

HERBERTSON, A.J. (1905), 'The major natural regions: an essay in systematic geography', *Geographical Journal*, *25*, 300 - 309.

HICKS, D.W. (1980a), 'Textbook imperialism: a study of ethnocentrism, education and geography', unpublished PhD thesis, Lancaster: University of Lancaster.

——— (1980b), *Images of the World: an introduction to bias in teaching materials*, Occasional Paper No.2. London: Institute of Education, University of London, Department of Education in Developing Countries and the Centre for Multicultural Education.

——— (1983), *Studying Peace: The Educational Rationale*, Occasional Paper No.4. Lancaster: Centre for Peace Studies.

——— (1986), *Teaching Nuclear Issues*, Occasional Paper 10. Lancaster: Centre for Peace Studies.

——— (1988a), 'Understanding the field', in D. Hicks, (ed.), *Education for Peace: issues, principles and practices in the classroom*. London: Routledge and Kegan Paul, Ch.1.

——— (ed.) (1988b), *Education for Peace: issues, principles and practices in the classroom*. London: Routledge & Kegan Paul.

——— and STEINER, D., (eds.) (1989), *A World Studies Workbook*. Edinburgh: Oliver & Boyd.

HILL, A.D. (1981), 'A survey of global understanding of American college students', *Professional Geographer*, *33* (2), 235 - 237.

——— (1988a), *Placing Geography in the Curriculum: ideas from the Western PLACE Conference*. Boulder, CO: Center for Geographic Education, University of Colorado.

——— (1988b) 'Teachers leading teachers in America's renaissance in geographic education', in R. Gerber and J. Lidstone (eds.), *Skills in Geographical Education Symposium '88: Volume 2*. Brisbane: Commission on Geographical Education of the International Geographical Union, 383 - 387.

HILTON, K. (1981), 'Landsat imagery and curriculum considerations in geography: an innovation at a turning point', in W. Kent (ed.), *Recent University Work in Geography and its relation to schools*. London: Institute of Education, University of London.

——— (1984), *Understanding Landforms*. Basingstoke: Macmillan.

——— (1989), *Cheshire From Space*. Chester: Cheshire County Council.

——— et al. (1987), 'Geography from space: Landsat Thematic Mapper Scenes in the classroom', *Teaching Geography*, *12* (2), 65 - 68.

——— and MORGAN, E. (1987) *The Earth Below*. London: Department of Trade and Industry/British National Space Centre.

———, STEWART, N., and McMORROW, J. (eds.) (1988), *Spaceview UK*. Nottingham: Remote Sensing Society.

HM INSPECTORATE (1986), *Geography from 5 to 6*. London: HMSO.

HOLT JENSEN A. (1980), *Geography, its History and Concepts*. London: Harper & Row.

HOLMES, B., WHITTINGTON, I., and FLETCHER, S. (1985), *The Child, The Teacher and the Micro-Using Simulations in the Classroom*. Cambridge: Cambridge Scholastic Services.

HOMEWOOD, T. (1987), 'An evaluation of the use of near natural colour and false colour Landsat imagery as a means of communication in the geography curriculum of secondary schools', unpublished MA dissertation. London: Institute of Education, University of London.

HONES, G.H. (1987), 'GeoBase: a curriculum development project', in W.A. Kent and R. Lewis, *Computer Assisted Learning in the Humanities and Social Sciences*. Oxford: Blackwell.

HONEYBONE, R.C., and GRAVES, N.J. (1966), *North America and Asia*. London: Heinemann.

HOST, V., MARBEAU, L. et al. (1971 and 1974), 'Les activités d'éveil à dominante intellectuelle au Cours préparatoire', Paris: INRP, collection *Recherches Pédagogiques*, no. 51.

HOUSE OF LORDS (1984), Select Committee on Science and Technology, *Remote Sensing and Digital Mapping*. London: HMSO.

HOWARTH, O.J.R. (1954), 'The Commonwealth in the geography syllabus', *Geography*, *39*, 5 - 10.

HOYLES, C. (ed.) (1988), *Girls and Computers*, Bedford Way Papers 34. London: Institute of Education, University of London.

HUCKLE, J. (1982), 'Values education through geography: a radical critique', in Boardman (ed.).

______ (ed.) (1983a), *Geographical Education Through Reflection and Action*. Oxford: Oxford University Press.

______ (1983b), 'The politics of school geography', In Huckle, (ed.) (1983a), 143 - 154.

______ (1983c), 'Environmental education', In Huckle (ed.) 1983a. 99 - 111.

______ (1986), 'Ten red questions to ask green teachers', *Green Teacher*, Issue 2.

______ (1988) 'The Daintree Rainforest: developing political literacy through an environmental issue', in Fien and Gerber (eds.), 45 - 60.

______ (1989), 'Lessons from political education', in Hicks and Steiner (eds.).

HUGON, M.A., and SEIBEL, C. (1988), *Recherches impliquées, recherches action: le cas de l'Education*, Pédagogies en développement, recueils. De Boeck Université, Editions universitaires.

HUTCHINSON, F. (1985), 'Report of the NSW Education Department', in *Education for Peace: Explorations and Proposals*. Canberra: Curriculum Development Centre, 117 - 266.

INCORPORATED ASSOCIATION OF ASSISTANT MASTERS IN SECONDARY SCHOOLS (1954), *The Teaching of Geography*. London: George Philip & Son.

INRP (Institut National de Recherche Pédagogique) (1969 - 1985), Les quatre séries de publication suivantes ont été réalisées sous la direction de L. Marbeau:

(i) *Bulletin de liaison du Cycle élémentaire*, Section des Sciences Humaines de l'INRP, Paris, no. 1 à 19, décembre 1969 à novembre 1983. Il s'y ajoute trois publications tirées à part en 1980.

(ii) *Bulletin de liaison, recherches dans le Premier cycle secondaire*, Section des Sciences Humaines de l'INRP, Paris, no. 1 à 48. octobre 1969 à juin 1982. Il s'y ajoute le dossier spécial de fin de recherche de juin 1981.

(iii) *Bulletin de liaison, recherches dans le Second cycle*, Section des Sciences Humaines de l'INRP, no. 1à 21, juillet 1971 à juin 1980. Il s'y ajoute le dossier spécial de juillet 1981.

(iv) Ministère de l'Education Nationale, Opération de la Direction des Ecoles (responsable de la recherche : Lucile Marbeau), Paris, *Expérimentation et évaluation d'un cursus d'activité d'éveil histoire, géographie, sciences sociales pour les enfants de 6 à 11 ans à l'Ecole élémentaire:* rapport de recherche au Cours préparatoire, juin 1983; rapport de recherche au Cours élémentaire, novembre 1984; rapport de fin de recherche, Cours moyen, novembre 1985.

INTERNATIONAL GEOGRAPHICAL UNION (1959), *Comptes Rendus du XVIIIe Congrès International de Géographie, Rio de Janeiro*, Comité National du Brésil, Rio de Janeiro, *1*, 236 - 240.

IRWIN, P.G. (1982), 'Examination reliability: geography and the New South Wales Higher School Certificate examination', unpublished paper. Newcastle: University of Newcastle.

JACOBS, P. (1985), *Operation Peace Studies: War in the Classroom*. Melbourne: Rosa Research and Publications.

JAMIESON, I. (ed.) (1984), *'We make Kettles': Studying Industry in the Primary School* York, SCDC/Longman.

JAY, L.J. (1965), 'A.J. Herbertson: his services to school geography', *Geography*, *50*, 350 - 361.

——— (1981), *Geography Teaching with a Little Latitude*. London: Allen and Unwin.

JEFFERYS, S.A. (1987), 'Children learning in the CAL classroom', unpublished MA dissertation. London: Institute of Education, University of London.

JENKINS, A. (1985), 'Peace education and the geography curriculum', in Pepper and Jenkins, (eds.), 202 - 213.

JOHNSON, R.J. (1983), *Geography and Geographers: Anglo-American Human Geography Since 1945*. London: Edward Arnold.

——— (1986), *On Human Geography*. Oxford: Basil Blackwell.

———, and TAYLOR, P.J. (eds.) (1986), *A World in Crisis? geographical perspectives*. Oxford: Basil Blackwell.

———, and TAYLOR, P.J. (1987), 'North : South – East : West : the two basic geographical divisions of the modern world', *Geographical Education*, *5*, (3), 5 - 11.

JOINT COMMITTEE ON GEOGRAPHIC EDUCATION (1984), *Guidelines for Geographic Education: elementary and secondary schools*. Washington, DC: Association of American Geographers and National Council for Geographic Education.

JONES, E. (1979), 'New perspectives on an old science', in S. Rokkan (ed.), *A Quarter Century of Social Science*. New Delhi.

——— and SINCLAIR, D.J. (1968-69), *Atlas of London and the London region*. Oxford: Pergamon.

JOURNAL OF GEOGRAPHY (1988a), Books and Materials Received, *Journal of Geography*, *87*(3), 117.

——— (1988b), Books and Materials Received, *Journal of Geography*, *87* (4), 152 - 159.
KELLY, A.V. (ed.) (1984), *Microcomputers and the Curriculum*, London: Harper & Row.
——— (1986), *Knowledge and Curriculum Planning*. London: Harper & Row.
KELLY, P.A. (1978), 'Values and attitudes in geographical education with special reference to environmental problems', unpublished MA dissertation. Institute of Education, University of London.
KELTIE, J.S. (1886), 'Geographical education: Report to the Council of the Royal Geographical Society', Supplementary Papers, *1*, Part 4, London, RGS.
KENDALL, D.N. (1946), 'Air photography in war and peace', *Geography*, *31*, 44 - 50.
KENNER, H. (1975), *A Handmade World: The American Modernist Writers*. New York: Alfred A. Knopf.
——— (1987) *The Mechanic Muse*. Oxford: Oxford University Press.
KENT, W.A. (ed.) (1983), *Geography Teaching and the Micro*. London: Longman.
——— (1984), 'Research in computer assisted learning', in Graves, (ed.), 1984a.
——— (1985) 'Humanities', in J. Wellington (ed.), *Children, Computers and the Curriculum*. London: Harper & Row.
——— (ed.) (1986a), *The Use of Computers in the Teaching of Geography*. London: International Geographical Union, Commission on Geographical Education, Institute of Education.
——— (ed.) (1986b), *Computers in Action in Geography Classrooms*, Teaching Geography Special. Sheffield: Geographical Association.
——— and LEWIS, R. (eds.) (1987), *Computer Assisted Learning in the Humanities and Social Sciences*. Oxford: Blackwell Scientific.
——— and RILEY, D. (eds.) (1988), *New Technology in Geography: Some Practical Suggestions*. Sheffield: Geographical Association.
KERR, J.F. (ed.) (1968), *Changing the Curriculum*. London: University of London Press.
KERRY, T., and EGGLESTON, J. (1988), *Topic Work in the Primary School*. London: Routledge.
KIDRON, M., and SEGAL, R. (1981), *The State of the World Atlas*. London: Pluto Press.
KIRBY, A.M. (1982), *The Politics of Location*. London: Methuen.
——— (1987), 'The great desert of the American mind', paper delivered to the American Historical Association, December.
KIRMAN, J. (1977), 'The use of infra-red false colour satellite images by grades 3, 4 and 5 pupils and teachers,' *Alberta Journal of Educational Research*, *23*, 52 - 64.

——— (1984), 'Landsat map teacher training', *Aviation Space*, *8*, (6), 14 - 15.

KRATHWOHL, D.R. et al. (1964), *Taxonomy of Educational Objectives*, the affective domain. London: Longman.

KROPOTKIN, P. (1885), 'What Geography ought to be', *The Nineteenth Century*, *18*, 940 - 956.

——— (1902), *Mutual Aid. A factor of evolution*. London: Heinemann.

KYAGULANYI, E.N.G. (1987), 'Geography teaching/methodology in Uganda', in H. Haubrich (ed.), *International Trends in Geographical Education*. Freiburg: IGU Commission on Geographical Education.

LARGE, P. (1988), 'Satellites: time the Government put its head in the clouds', *Guardian*, 8 October.

LAWLER, C.D. (1986), 'CAL and physical-based fieldwork in geography', unpublished MA dissertation. London: Institute of Education, University of London.

LAWTON, D. (1984), *The Tightening Grip. Growth of central control of the school curriculum*. London: Institute of Education, University of London.

——— and DUFOUR, B. (1974), *The New Social Studies: a Handbook for Teachers in Primary, Secondary, and Further Education*. London: Heinemann.

LEE, R. (1985), 'Teaching geography: The dialectic of structure and agency', *Journal of Geography*, *82*, 102 - 109; also in Boardman (1985).

LEONARD, P. (1984), 'The Process of learning with a micro – a game simulation observed', unpublished MA dissertation. London: Institute of Education, University of London.

LEWY, A. (ed.) (1977), *Handbook for Curriculum Evaluation*. Paris: UNESCO/ Longman.

LIDSTONE, J.G. (1985), 'A study of the use of geography textbooks by selected teachers in English secondary schools', unpublished PhD thesis. London: Institute of Education, University of London.

——— (1989), 'Using textbooks in geography' in J. Fien, R. Gerber, and P. Wilson (eds.), *The Geography Teacher's Guide to the Classroom*, 2nd edition. Melbourne: Macmillan.

LIEBERMAN, M. (1960), *Education as a Profession*. New Jersey: Prentice Hall, Inc.

LINTON, D.L. (1946a), 'Interpretation of air photographs', *Geography*, *31*, 89 - 97.

——— (1946b), 'The use of air photographs in the teaching of geography', *Geography*, *31*, 129 - 134.

LONG, M. (1964), 'The teaching of geography: a review of recent British research and investigations', *Geography*, *49* (224), 192 - 205.

LUNZER, E. and GARDNER, K. (eds.) (1979), *The Effective Use of Reading*. London: Heinemann Educational Books for the Schools Council.

LYON, D. (1988), *The Information Society: issues and illusions*. Cambridge: Polity Press.

MAHER, M. (1986), 'Environmental education: what are we fighting for?', *Geographical Education*, *5*(2), 21 - 25.
MAKANJUOLA, S.A. (1987), 'Geography laboratory and observatory centres: the missing vital infrastructures for effective geography teaching in schools', in Abegunde et al.
MARBEAU, L. (1979), 'Mise au point et expérimentation d'un schéma cohérent de sciences sociales adapté aux divers cycles d'enseignement du Cours préparatoire au baccalauréat', in 'les Sciences Humaines', *Les Amis de Sèvres*, 93, 41 - 58.
——— (1983), 'Méthodologie de la recherche action', *l'Information Géographique*, *47* (5). Paris: Masson, 199 - 205.
———, MARECHAL, J., PRESLE, M., et al. (1978), *Activités d'éveil – sciences sociales à l'Ecole élémentaire*. Paris: INRP, collection Recherches Pedagogiques, no. 93.
MARECHAL, J. (1986), 'Réflexion épistémologique et didactique de la géographie', *Actes du Colloque National sur la Didactique de l'Histoire et de la Géographie*. Paris: Institut National de Recherche Pedagogique, 45 - 64.
MARES, C., BLANCHARD, H., STEPHENSON, R., and REDHEAD, M. (1988), *Our Environment: teachers' guide*. Walton-on-Thames: Nelson.
MARSDEN, W.E. (1976), *Evaluating the Geography Curriculum*. Edinburgh: Oliver and Boyd.
——— (1988), 'Continuity and change in geography textbooks: perspectives from the 1930s to the 1960s', *Geography*, *73*(4) 327 - 343.
——— (1989), 'Balance in geography and education in the primary school', in J. Campbell, and V. Little (eds.), *The Humanities in the Primary School*. Lewes: Falmer.
MARSDEN, V. and MARSDEN, W. (1983), *World in Charge*. Edinburgh: Oliver & Boyd.
———(1987), *World Concerns*. Edinburgh: Oliver & Boyd.
MASSEY, D. (1986), 'Inside a textbook', *Journal of Geography*, *85*(3).
MASSEY, S. (1984), 'Geography matters' in D. Massey, and J. Allen (eds.) *Geography Matters*, Oxford: Oxford University Press.
MAYS, P. (1985), *Teaching Children Through the Environment*. Sevenoaks: Hodder & Stoughton.
McCARTY, H.H. (1963), 'The geographer in his intellectual environment', *New Zealand Geographer*, *19* (1), 1 - 6.
McELROY, B.I. (1980), 'School-based curriculum development – an investigation into teachers' perceptions of their role, the major constraints and the inservice education teacher education implications in this form of curriculum development', unpublished MA dissertation. London: Institute of Education, University of London.
——— (1988), 'Learning geography: a route to political literacy', in Fien, and Gerber, (eds.) 31 - 42.

MIDGLEY, H. and WALKER, D. (1985), *Microcomputers in Geography Teaching*. London: Hutchinson.

MILLS, D. (ed.) (1988), *Geographical Work in Primary and Middle Schools*. Sheffield: Geographical Association.

MILNE, A.K. (1979), 'Landsat imagery and teaching about the environment', *Geographical Education*, *3* (3), 319 - 330.

MILTON, M. (1984), 'A case study of mixed ability teaching in some geography and integrated studies classes at two comprehensive schools', unpublished MA dissertation. London: Institute of Education, University of London.

MKPA, D.N. (1988), 'Analysis of teacher-made geography test questions used in Imo State Secondary Schools', unpublished MEd dissertation. Nsukka: University of Nigeria.

MONK, J.J. (1983), 'Integrating women into the geography curriculum', *Journal of Geography*, *82*(6).

MORRIS, B. (1972), 'Examinations as instruments of educational reform', In B. Morris (ed.), *Objectives and Perspectives in Education*. London: Routledge & Kegan Paul.

MUELLER-EILLE, C. (1984), *Images of the World*. London: Collins, Longman.

MÜLLER, G. (1984), 'Die Inhaltsanalyse', in *Gegenwartskunde 4*, 457ff.

MYERS, N. (ed.) (1985), *The Gaia Atlas of Planet Management*. London and Sydney: Pan Books.

NAISH, M.C. (1972), 'Some aspects of the study and teaching of geography in Britain: a review of recent British research', *Teaching Geography*, 18. Sheffield: Geographical Association.

——— (1985a), 'Geography 16-19' in Boardman (ed.) (1985).

——— (1985b), 'Geography in the curriculum; beyond the "Great Debate"', in Graves et al. (1985c).

——— (1988), 'Postscript' in Fien and Gerber, (eds.), 188 - 189.

——— (ed.) (1990), *Experiences of Centralization, An International Study of the Impacts of Centralised Education Systems upon Geography Curricula*. The British Sub Commitee of the Commission for Geographical Education of the International Geographical Union.

———, RAWLING, E., and HART, C. (1987), *Geography 16-19. The contribution of a curriculum project to 16-19 education*. Harlow: Longman.

NATIONAL COMMISSION ON EXCELLENCE IN EDUCATION (1983), *A Nation at Risk: the imperative for educational reform*. Washington, DC: US Government Printing Office.

NATIONAL COUNCIL FOR EDUCATIONAL TECHNOLOGY (1989), *Learning Geography with Computers*, Rev. Edn. London: NCET.

NATIONAL CURRICULUM COUNCIL (1990), *NCC Consultation Report: Geography*. York: National Curriculum Council.

NATIONAL GEOGRAPHIC SOCIETY (1988a), *Geography: an international Gallup survey*. Princeton, NJ: The Gallup Organization.

——— (1988b), *National Geographic Society Education Foundation*, Washington, DC: National Geographic Society.

NATOLI, S.J. (1974, 1976), *Careers in Geography*. Washington, DC: Association of American Geographers.

——— (1980), *Geography: tomorrow's career*. Washington, DC: Association of American Geographers.

——— (1986), 'The evolving nature of geography', in S.P. Wronski, and D.H. Bragaw (eds.), *Social Studies and Social Science: a fifty year perspective*. Washington, DC: National Council for the Social Studies, 28 - 42.

NDU, A.N. (1973), 'Attitudes to geography', unpublished BSc dissertation. Nsukka: University of Nigeria.

NEWBY, H. (1988), *ESRC Newsletter* 63, 6 - 8 October. Swindon: Economic and Social Research Council.

NWAGU, E.K.N. (1985), 'Validity of teacher-made geography tests used in secondary schools in Anambra State', unpublished MEd dissertation. Nsukka: University of Nigeria.

OFOMATA, G.E.K. (1971), *Jobs for Geographers*, Occasional Publication (3). Nsukka: Department of Geography, University of Nigeria.

O'HARE, G. (1989), *Derbyshire from Space*. Nottingham: University of Nottingham.

OKOYE, I. (1984), *Men Without Ears*. Harlow: Longman.

OKPALA, J.I.N (1974), 'An evaluative study of teacher-made tests in geography', unpublished BSc dissertation. Nsukka: University of Nigeria.

——— (1981), 'Academic ability of School Certificate geography students', *Nigerian Geographical Journal*, *24*(1 and 2), 167 - 173.

——— (1987), 'The feasibility of reality oriented problem-solving questions in WAEC examinations as a means to improving the teaching and learning of mapwork in Nigerian secondary schools', unpublished PhD thesis. London: Institute of Education, University of London.

——— (1988a), 'The validity of the sample Senior Secondary School Certificate geography examination questions with regard to emphasis on problem-solving', Paper presented during the 31st Annual Conference of the Nigeria Geographical Association. Port Harcourt: University of Port Harcourt.

——— (1988b), 'Teaching styles in reading and interpreting topographical maps – the Nigerian experience', in R. Gerber, and J. Lidstone (eds.), *Developing Skills in Geographical Education*. Brisbane: Jacaranda Press.

OKPALANMA, L.O. (1978), 'Training teachers for geography in Nigeria', in P.O. Okunrotifa and D.K. Ola (eds.), *Geography in Education*. Ibadan: International Geographical Union.

OLA, D.K., and ABIOYE, P.A.F. et al (1980), 'Geography education in Nigeria in the 1980s', *Proceedings of the 5th Conference on High School Geography*. Ilorin: Kwara College of Technology.

OLMSTEAD, C. (1987), 'Knowing and being who we are', *Journal of Geography*, *86*(1), 3.

OLOGE, K.O. (1978), 'Career outlets of geography graduates from ABU', *Proceedings of the 21st Annual Conference of the Nigerian Geographical Association*. Jos: University of Jos.

——— (1980), 'Career consciousness and orientation of geography undergraduates at Ahmadu Bello University', *Proceedings of the 23rd Annual Conference of the Nigerian Geographical Association*. Calabar: University of Calabar.

——— (1982), 'Career outlets of geography graduates from Ahmadu Bello University 1976 - 1979', Paper presented at the 25th Annual Conference of the Nigerian Geographical Association. Ibadan: University of Ibadan.

——— (1984), 'Jobs for geographers. Careers outlets for geography graduates in Nigeria', Presidential Address presented at the 27th Annual Conference of the Nigerian Geographical Association. Nsukka: University of Nigeria.

OPENSHAW, S., STEADMAN, P. and GREENE, O., (1983), *Doomsday: Britain after nuclear attack*. Oxford: Blackwell.

OTTOSSON, T. (1987), *Map-reading and Way Finding*, Goteborg Studies in Educational Sciences 65. Goteborg: ACTA Universitatis Gothoburgenis.

PALFREY, R. (1986), 'Geography of social concern: an evening in the Capital Theatre' in W.A. Kent (ed.), *Alternative Teaching Strategies for Geography*. London: Institute of Education, University of London.

PANDE, S.N. (1987), 'Main currents, paradigms, theories, aims or trends in geography teaching in India', in H. Haubrich (ed.), *International Trends in Geographical Education*. Freiburg: IGU Commission on Geographical Education.

PAPERT, S. (1980), *Mindstorms: Children, Computers and Powerful Ideas*. Hemel Hempstead: Harvester Press.

PARTINGTON, G. (1986), 'The peace educators: The methodology of indoctrination', *Quadrant*, *30*, January-February, 58 - 66.

PEET, J.R. (1977), *Radical Geography: alternative viewpoints on contemporary social issues*. London: Methuen.

——— (1985), 'An introduction to Marxist Geography', *Journal of Geography*, *84*(1).

PEPPER, D. (1984), *The Roots of Modern Environmentalism*. Beckenham: Croom Helm.

——— (1987), 'The basis of a radical curriculum in environmental education' in C. Lacey and R. Williams, *Education, Ecology and Development; the case for an Education Network*. London: World Wildlife Fund and Kogan Page.

——— , and JENKINS, A. (eds.) (1985), *The Geography of Peace and War*. Oxford: Basil Blackwell.

PETERS, R.S. (1965), *Education as Initiation* Inaugural Lecture. London: Institute of Education, University of London.

PEUQUET, D. (1984), 'Data structures for a knowledge-based geographic information system', *Proceedings of the International Symposium on Spatial Data Handling*, Zurich, 372 - 391.

PIAGET, J. (1926), *The Language and Thought of the Child.* London: Routledge & Kegan Paul.

_______(1962), 'The stages of the intellectual development of the child', *Bulletin of the Menninger Clinic*, 26. Also in Wason, P.C., and Johnson-Laird, P.N. (eds.) (1968), *Thinking and Reasoning*. London: Penguin.

PIKE, L.W., and BARROWS, T.S. (1979), *Other Nations, Other Peoples.* Washington, DC: US Government Printing Office.

PINDER, R. (1987), *Why Don't Teachers Teach Like They Used to*? London: Hilary Shipman.

PLUCKROSE, H. (1979), *Children in their Primary Schools*. Harmondsworth: Penguin.

POPE, J.M. (1984), 'Some factors influencing students' choices of geography in WASC or GCE: a case study of selected secondary schools in Ilesha Local Government Area of Oyo State', unpublished BSc dissertation. Port Harcourt: University of Port Harcourt.

PROSSER, P. (1982), *The World on your Doorstep*. Maidenhead: McGraw-Hill.

RALPH, B. (1988), 'A walk through the new geography 11-12 syllabus', *Geography Bulletin*, *20*(1), 9 - 20.

RANDLE, T.W. (1983), *Geography and Careers: the school leavers*. Sheffield: Geographical Association.

RAWLING, E. (1987), 'Geography 11-16: criteria for geographical content in the secondary school curriculum' and 'The nature of geography as an educational medium' in Bailey and Binns (eds.).

RAWSON, R.R. and BEAVER, S.H. (1947), 'Aerial photography and geographical studies', *Geography*, *32*, 131 - 134.

REYNOLDS, R. (1982), *Satpack*. Bracknell, Berks.: Royal Meteorological Society.

RHYS, W. (1972), 'The development of logical thinking', in N. Graves (ed.) *New Movements in the Study and Teaching of Geography*. Melbourne: Cheshire, 93 - 106.

RICE, D. (1983), 'American education: The ABCs of failure', *Dallas-Times Herald*, Dallas, TX., 11 December, 1 - 34.

RICE, W.F. (1983), *The Fabric of Geography*. Harlow: Longman.

RILEY, D., and SPOLTON, L. (1974), *World Weather and Climate.* Cambridge: Cambridge University Press.

RITCHIE, A. (1987), 'An investigation into the use of false colour Landsat images of land use as a means of teaching selected geographical skills and concepts', unpublished MA dissertation. London: Institute of Education, University of London.

ROBBINS, F. (1933), 'Can geography contribute to an interest in and an understanding of, current magazine articles', *The Teaching of Geography*, Thirty-Second Yearbook of the National Society for the Study of Education. Chicago: The University of Chicago Press.

ROBERTS, M. (1989), 'Writing as reflection', in F.A. Slater (ed.) (1989).

ROBINSON, C. (1982), 'An evaluation of pupil attitudes towards computer assisted learning in geography', unpublished MA dissertation. London: Institute of Education, University of London.

ROBINSON, R. (1975), *Ways to Move*. Cambridge: Cambridge University Press.

——— (1985), 'Ten years of change: influences on school geography: 1972 - 1982', in Boardman.

——— (1987), 'Exploring students' images of the developing world', *Geographical Education*, *5*(3), 48 - 51.

——— and JACKSON, I. (1984), *People on Earth*. London: Longman.

ROGERS, S. (1987), 'The constraining and enabling influences on the take-up of CAL in geography in Essex secondary schools', unpublished MA dissertation. London: Institute of Education, University of London.

ROSS, A. (1984), *Making Connections: Developing the Primary School Curriculum using a Microcomputer for Information Retrieval*. London: Council for Educational Technology.

——— (1988), *Environmental Studies*. Leamington Spa: Scholastic Publications.

ROYAL GEOGRAPHICAL SOCIETY (1886), *Report of the Proceedings of the Society in Reference to the Improvement of Geographical Education (Keltie Report)*. London: John Murray.

——— (1950), 'Geography and "social studies" in schools'. *Geography 35* (169), 181 - 185.

RUTTER, R. (1986), 'Profile of the profession', *Social Education*, *50* (4), 252 - 255.

SALTER, C. (1986), 'Geography and California's educational reform: One approach to a common cause', *Annals of the Association of American Geographers*, *76*(1), 15 - 17.

SANDFORD, H. (1987), 'A comparison of published sources of guidance on atlas mapwork skills', in R. Gerber (ed.), *Research in Geographical Education*, *3*, 153 - 159.

SAYER, A. (1984), *Method in Social Science: A Realist View*. London: Hutchinson.

——— (1985a), 'Systematic mystification: the 16-19 Geography Project', *Contemporary Issues in Geography and Education*, *2*(2), Association for Curriculum Development.

——— (1985b), 'Realism and geography' in R.J. Johnson (ed.) (1985), *The Future of Geography*. London: Methuen.

SCARFE, N.V. (1949), 'The teaching of geography in schools: a review of British research' *Geography*, *34*(164), 57 - 65.

——— (1951) *A Handbook of Suggestions on the Teaching of Geography*. Paris: Unesco.

——— (1953) 'International Geographical Union Commission on the Teaching of Geography', *Geography*, *38*, 325-6: see also *Journal of Geography*, *52*, March 1953, 124.

——— (1956), *Report of the Commission on the Teaching of Geography in Schools*. New York: International Geographical Union.

SCHNEIDER, J. (1972), 'Les Commissions', in International Geographical Union, *Geography through a Century of International Congresses*, 64.

SCHOLNICK E. et al. (1987), 'Changing predictors of map use in wayfinding', Paper presented to the Biennial Meeting of the Society of Research in Child Development, Baltimore, USA.

SCHOOL EXAMINATIONS AND ASSESSMENT COUNCIL (SEAC) (1990), *A Guide to Teacher Assessment*. London: SEAC.

SCHOOLS COUNCIL (1979), 'What are we saying?', *Project News: Geography 16-19 Curriculum Development*, 8.

SCOTTISH EDUCATION DEPARTMENT (1951), *Geography in Secondary Schools*. Edinburgh: HMSO, 16 - 17.

SCOVILL, J. (ed.) (1966), *Atlas of Land forms*. New York: Wiley.

SELBY, D., and PIKE, G. (1988), *Global Teacher: Global Learner*. London: Hodder & Stoughton.

SHEPHERD, I.D.H., COOPER, Z.A., and WALKER, D.R.F. (1980), *Computer Assisted Learning in Geography*. London: Council for Educational Technology with the Geographical Association.

SIMMONS, A. (1984), 'War, peace and liberal education', *Bulletin of Atomic Scientists*, *40*(10).

SIMON, R. (1986), *Introducing Marxism*. London: Communist Party Publications.

SLATER, F.A. (1982), *Learning through Geography*. London: Heinemann Educational.

——— (ed.) (1986), *People and Environments* (Issues and enquiries). London: Collins Educational.

——— (1988), 'Teaching practice supervision – using a diary for reflection', *Proceedings of the Symposium of the IGU Commission for Geographical Education*, *1*. Brisbane.

——— (ed.) (1989), *Language and Learning in the Teaching of Geography*. London: Routledge.

———, and SPICER, B.J. (eds.) (1980), *Perception and Preference Studies at the International Level*. International Geographical Union, Commission for Geographical Education.

——— (1982), 'Studying relationships and building models through the analysis of maps and photographic evidence', in N.J. Graves (ed.), 1982h.

———, and WELLER, M. (1982), *Skills in geography*, 4 Volumes. London: Cassell.

SMITH, A. (1988), 'Smartening up textbooks: a dumb idea', *The Clearing House*, *61*, 256 - 259.

SMITH, D. (ed.) (1986), *Industry Education in the Primary School*. Coventry: Schools – Industry Partnership, Centre for Education and Industry, University of Warwick.

——— (1988), *Industry in the Primary School Curriculum*. Lewes: Falmer.

SMITH, D.M. (1977), *Human Geography: a welfare approach*. London: Arnold.

SOPER, S. (1987), *Primary First: a handbook for primary teachers*. Oxford: Oxford University Press.

SPETZ, D. (1988), 'The preparation of geography teachers', in S. Natoli (ed.), *Strengthening Geography in the Social Studies*. Washington, DC: National Council for the Social Studies, 51 - 58.

SPICER, B., ACHURCH, M., BLACHFORD, K. AND STRINGER, W. (1977), *The Global System*. Brisbane: Jacaranda.

STEELE, J. (1986), 'Remote sensing in secondary school education', unpublished MSc thesis. University of London.

STEFANOVIC, P., and SIJMONS (1984) 'Computer-assisted relief representation', *ITC Journal*, *1*, 40 - 47.

———, and VRIES-BAAYENS, A. (1984), 'Classification systems, choropleth maps and the computer', *ITC Journal*, *1*, 52 - 57.

STEPHENS, P. (1988), 'An enquiry into the extent to which the Geography 16-19 Project has fulfilled its objectives with regard to its enquiry approach to learning and its distinctive approach to geographical education', unpublished MA dissertation. London: Institute of Education, University of London.

STEWART, N. (ed.) (1987), *Proceedings of the Urchfont Manor Conference*. London: General Technology Systems.

STIMPSON, P., YEUNG PIU MING, S. (1987), 'An analysis of variations in the map-drawing ability of secondary school pupils', in R. Gerber (ed.) *Research in Geographical Education*, *3*, 137 - 152.

STOLTMAN, J.P., and LIBBEE, M. (1988), 'Geography in the social studies: scope and sequence', in S.J. Natoli (ed.), *Strengthening Geography in the Social Studies*. Washington, DC: National Council for the Social Studies, 42 - 50.

STORM, M. (1987), 'How far is geography to do with knowing where things are?', *ILEA Geography Bulletin*, 26, 19 - 21.

STOWELL, R., and BENTLEY, L. (1988), *New Wave Geography*. Brisbane: The Jacaranda Press.

STRADLING, R., BAINES, B. and PROCTOR, B. (1984), *Teaching Controversial Issues*. London: Edward Arnold.

STRINGER, W. (1976), 'Spatial cognition and geographical education', paper presented to the national conference of the Australian Geography Teachers' Association, Perth.

STUDDERT, A. (1985), 'Does it matter?', *Shared Experiences: Significant Issues*, February, 2 - 3.

SUTHERLAND, S., and WINN, W. (1987), 'The effect of the number and nature of features and of general ability on the simultaneous and successive processing of maps', Paper presented to the Annual Convention of the Association for Educational Communications and Technology, Atlanta, Georgia.

TABA, H. (1962), *Curriculum Development: Theory and Practice*. New York: Harcourt, Brace and World.

TANN, S. (ed.) (1988), *Developing Topic Work in the Primary School*. Lewes: Falmer.

TAYLOR, P.J. (1985), *Political Geography; World Economy, Nation – State and Locality*. Harlow: Longman.

THOMAS, K.M. (1985), 'CAL in geography: pupil-teacher perspectives on the problem of software evaluation', unpublished MA dissertation. London: Institute of Education, University of London.

THRALLS, Z.A. (1958), *The Teaching of Geography*. New York: Appleton-Century-Crofts.

TIDSWELL, V. (1973), *Pattern and Process in Human Geography*. London: University Tutorial Press.

TIMBERLAKE, L. (1987), *Only One Earth*. London: BBC.

TINDAL, M.A. (1978), *Educator's Guide for Mission to Earth: Landsat views the world*. Washington: NASA.

TOLLEY, H., and REYNOLDS, J.B. (1977), *Geography 14-18: A Handbook for School-based Curriculum Development*. Basingstoke: Macmillan.

TOMLINSON, R. (1984) 'Geographic information systems – a new frontier', *Proceedings of the International Symposium on Spatial Data Handling*, Zurich, 1 - 14.

TYLER, R.W. (1949), *Basic Principles of Curriculum and Instruction*. Chicago: University of Chicago Press.

UNESCO (1965), *Sourcebook for Geography Teaching*, London: Longman. Paris: Unesco.

UNSTEAD, J.F. (1916), 'A synthetic method of determining geographical regions', *Geographical Journal*, *48*, 240.

VAN NOORDEN, P. (1985), *Living Geography*. Richmond, Victoria: Heinemann.

VAUGHAN, J.E. (1972), 'Aspects of teaching geography in England in the early nineteenth century', *Paedagogica Historica*, *12*(1).

VEEN, W. (1987), 'Dutch educational politics and geography teaching in the 1980s', in H. Haubrich (ed.), *International Trends in Geographical Education*. Freiburg: IGU Commission on Geographical Education.

VERDUIN-MULLER, H.S. (1964), *Leren met Beelden*, Het gebruik van visuele hulpmiddelen bij het aardrijkskunde-onderwijs op de scholen voor het VHMO, enige aspecten van theorie en praktijk. Groningen: Wolters.

——— (1967), *Leren van Hospiteren*. Groningen: Walters.

——— (1982), *Geografie en Informatievoorziening*. Amsterdam: Meulenhoff Educatief.

VILÀ-VALENTÍ, J. (ed.) (1975), *Geografía de América Latina*. Barcelona: Editorial Teide.

VYGOTSKY, L.S. (1962), *Thought and Language*. New York: Wiley and Massachusetts Institute of Technology.

WALDEN, R., and WALKERDINE, V. (1985), *Girls and Mathematics from Primary to Secondary Schooling*, Bedford Way Paper 24. London: Institute of Education, University of London.

WALFORD, R. (ed.) (1973), *New Directions in Geography Teaching*. London: Longman.

——— (ed.) (1981a), *Signposts for Geography Teaching*. Harlow: Longman.

——— (1981b), 'Language, ideologies and geography teaching', in R. Walford (ed.) 1981a.

WALKER, D.R.F. (1981), 'Educational computing and geography', in Walford (ed.) (1981a).

WALKER, M.J. (1973), *Locations and Links*, Oxford, Blackwell.

WALLERSTEIN, I. (1974, 1980), *The Modern World-System*, Volumes I and II. New York: Academic Press.

——— (1984), *The Politics of the World-Economy*. Cambridge: Cambridge University Press.

WARD, G. (1988), *I've got a project on ... Rozelle*. New South Wales, Australia: Primary English Teaching Association.

WATERS, D. (1982), *Primary School Projects*. London: Heinemann.

WATSON, D. (ed.) (1984), *Exploring Geography with Microcomputers*. London: Council for Educational Technology.

——— (1987), *Developing CAL: computers in the curriculum*. London: Harper & Row.

WEBB, G. (1987), 'Structural constraints in the teaching and learning of geography in Jamaica', in H. Haubrich, *International Trends in Geographical Education*. Freiburg: IGU Commission on Geographical Education.

WEST AFRICAN EXAMINATIONS COUNCIL (WAEC) (1988), *Geography Paper 1 & 2 Senior Secondary School Certificate Examinations*. Lagos: West African Examinations Council.

WESTON, J. (ed.) (1986), *Red and Green: the new politics of the environment*. London: Pluto Press.

WHEELER, D.K. (1967), *Curriculum Process*. London, University of London Press.

WHITE, G.F. (1970), *Assessment in Midstream, Final Report of the High School Geography Project*. Washington, DC: Association of American Geographers, 1 - 2.

WHITEFORD, G.T. (1985) 'Tomorrow's perspective today: satellite geography', *Journal of Environmental Education*, *16*(3), 21 - 28.

WHITEMAN, P. (1982), 'The relative influence of false colour and Landsat imagery in classroom geography', unpublished MA dissertation. London: Institute of Education, University of London.

WIEGAND, P. (1987), 'Expectations in geography', in Bailey and Binns (eds).

——— and ORRELL, K. (1982), *New Leads in Geographical Education*. Sheffield: Geographical Association.

WILLIAM, T., and RICHARDS, C. (1980) 'What geography do juniors learn? An investigation in Lichfield', *Teaching Geography*, *6*(1), 18 - 20.

WILLIAMS, M. (1976), *Geography and the Integrated Curriculum*. London: Heinemann Educational.

——— (1988), 'Continuing education of geography teachers' in R. Gerber and J. Lidstone (eds.), *Developing Skills in Geographical Education*. Brisbane: International Geographical Union Commission on Geographical Education with the Jacaranda Press.

WILMS, D. (1988), *Alliance Geographers as Political Lobbyists, Skills in Geographical Education Symposium '88' Proceedings 2*, International Geographical Education Commission, Brisbane, August 14-20, 1988.

WINN, W. (1987), 'Communication, cognition and children's atlases', *Cartographica*, *24*(1), 61 - 81.

WINSTON, B. (1984), 'Teacher education in geography in the United States', in W. Marsden (ed.), *Teacher Education Models in Geography: An International Comparison*. Kalamazoo, MI: Western Michigan University, 133 - 149.

WISE, M.J. (1983) 'Education and Development', in Wise, M.J., and Squires, S. (eds.) *The Role of Geosciences in Development* Tokyo, United Nations University and Tokyo Geographical Society, 1.

WRIGHT, D.R. (1981), 'Distorting the picture', *The Times Educational Supplement*, 6 November, 20.

——— (1983), 'International textbook research: facts and issues', *Internationale Schulbuchforshung*, *5*(3).

——— (1985a), 'Are geography textbooks sexist?' *Teaching Geography*, *10*(2).

——— (1985b), 'In Black and White: racist bias in textbooks', *Geographical Education*, *5*(1) 8 - 10.

——— (1988), 'Applied textbook research in geography', in R. Gerber, and J. Lidstone (eds.), *Developing Skills in Geographical Education*. Brisbane: International Geographical Union Commission on Geographical Education with the Jacaranda Press.

——— and PARDEY (1982), 'Bias in statistics and statistical maps: the example of South Africa', in W.A. Kent (ed.) *Bias in Geographical Education*. London: Institute of Education, University of London, Geography Department.

WORLD WILDLIFE FUND (UK) (1988), *Only One Earth*, (Video and teaching pack). Godalming: WWF (UK).

WYNDHAM, H. (1957), *Report of the Committee appointed to Survey Secondary Education in New South Wales*. Sydney: Government Printer.

Index